A COMPENDIUM
OF
MATHEMATICS AND PHYSICS

A COMPENDIUM OF MATHEMATICS AND PHYSICS

By

DOROTHY S. MEYLER, M.Sc

Senior Lecturer in Pure Mathematics
University College of Wales, Aberystwyth

and

O. G. SUTTON, KT., C.B.E., D.Sc., F.R.S.

Director-General, Meteorological Office

D. VAN NOSTRAND COMPANY, INC.

PRINCETON, NEW JERSEY

TORONTO LONDON

NEW YORK

First Printed 1958.

Printed in Great Britain

EDITOR'S FOREWORD

PHYSICAL SCIENCE TEXTS

By

SIR GRAHAM SUTTON, C.B.E., D.Sc., F.R.S.
Director-General, Meteorological Office

Formerly Dean of the Royal Military College of Science, Shrivenham and Bashforth Professor of Mathematical Physics

THE present volume is one of a number planned to extend the Physical Science Texts beyond the Advanced or Scholarship levels of the General Certificate of Education. The earlier volumes in this series were prepared as texts for class teaching or self study in the upper forms at school, or in the first year at the university or technical college. In the next stage, the treatment necessarily assumes a greater degree of maturity in the student than did the earlier volumes, but the emphasis is still on a strongly realistic approach aimed at giving the sincere reader technical proficiency in his chosen subject. The material has been carefully selected on a broad and reasonably comprehensive basis, with the object of ensuring that the student acquires a proper grasp of the essentials before he begins to read more specialized texts. At the same time due regard has been paid to modern developments, and each volume is designed to give the reader an integrated account of a subject up to the level of an honours degree of any British or Commonwealth university, or the graduate membership of a professional institution.

A course of study in science may take one of two shapes. It may spread horizontally rather than vertically, with greater attention to the security of the foundations than to the level attained, or it may be deliberately designed to reach the heights by the quickest possible route. The tradition of scientific education in this country has been in favour of the former method, and despite the need to produce technologists quickly, I am convinced that the traditional policy is still the sounder. Experience shows that the student who has received a thorough unhurried training in the fundamentals reaches the stage of productive or original work very little, if at all, behind the man who has been persuaded to specialize at a much earlier stage, and in later life there is little doubt who is the better educated man. It is my hope that in these texts we have provided materials for a sound general education in the physical sciences, and that the student who works conscientiously through these books will face more specialized studies with complete confidence.

AUTHORS' PREFACE

In writing this book we have had in mind the needs of two classes of readers : research workers who require a reference book in which they can look up a theorem or a formula to find out in what conditions it holds, and how to apply it, and undergraduates or technical students who, as an aid in preparing for examinations, or for other reasons, want a summary of what is known in various branches of Mathematics and Physics. The account we have given stops short at a point a little beyond General Honours degree standard. No proofs have been included. The book, however, is more than a mere collection of formulae, in that explanations are given as far as space permits.

No attempt is made to define a number and the book does not include any Topology, but within these limits a standard of rigour at least as high as that required for a General Honours degree in Mathematics is maintained. Sufficient conditions for the validity of the results are given, but we have not attempted to give the best possible (i.e., the least stringent) conditions for all theorems.

In the section on Electricity we have quoted formulae in both the classical and the rationalized metre-kilogram-second systems of units, following closely, in the latter instance, the recommendations of the Science Masters Association.

We wish to express our thanks to Professor V. C. Morton who read most of the manuscript of Part I, to Dr. C. E. Easthope who read Chapter 21 in manuscript, and to Dr. G. T. Roberts who read Chapters 1-5 in manuscript and Part I in proof. Their suggestions led to many improvements. We also wish to thank Mr. D. Sullivan who read the page proofs of Part I.

For Part II our thanks go to Mr. J. M. R. Sutton, who read some of the manuscript, to the authors and publishers for permission to include diagrams and tables from *The Principles of Electrical Measurements* by H. Buckingham and E. M. Price (E.U.P.) and from *Electricity and Magnetism* by C. G. Wilson (E.U.P.) and to Mr. D. M. Houghton, who helped in the proof reading.

Dorothy S. Meyler

O. G. Sutton

PART I
PURE MATHEMATICS

CHAPTER 1

ARITHMETIC

1.1. Real numbers

A *rational* number is the quotient of two integers p, q. The integers are chosen so that p and q have no common factor and q is positive. A rational number can be expressed as a decimal which either terminates or recurs.

A *real* number, as defined by Dedekind, is a section of the rational numbers. It may be rational or irrational. An irrational real number can be expressed as a non-terminating non-recurring decimal.

If O and A, two fixed points, where A is to the right of O, are taken to represent 0 and 1, any real number x can be represented by a point P on the line OA where $x=OP/OA$. Every point P on the line corresponds to one real number. Points to the left of O represent negative numbers.

The set of real numbers obeys the following **Laws of Algebra.**

The *commutative* laws:
$$a+b=b+a, \tag{I}$$
$$ab=ba. \tag{II}$$
The *associative* laws:
$$(a+b)+c=a+(b+c), \tag{III}$$
$$(ab)c=a(bc). \tag{IV}$$
The *distributive* laws:
$$a(b+c)=ab+ac, \tag{V}$$
$$(b+c)a=ba+ca. \tag{VI}$$
Zero: An element 0 exists such that
$$a+0=a. \tag{VII}$$
Unity: An element 1 exists such that
$$a\,.\,1=a. \tag{VIII}$$
Additive inverse or *negative* element: The equation
$$a+x=0 \tag{IX}$$
has a solution for x which belongs to the set.

Division: For each $a \neq 0$, there is a b such that
$$ab=1. \tag{X}$$

1.2. Roots and powers with rational exponents

If n is a positive integer and a is real, $a^n=a\,.\,a\,.\,.\,.\,a$ (n factors), $a^{-n}=1/a^n$, $a^0=1$ (for $a\neq 0$); a is called the *base*, n or $-n$ the *exponent* or *index* of the power a^n or a^{-n} respectively.

An arithmetical nth root of a is a real number x satisfying $x^n = a$. If n is even, this root exists only if a is positive. In this section $a^{1/n}$ denotes the positive root. $a^{m/n}$ is defined as $(a^{1/n})^m$.

For rational numbers m, n,

$$a^m a^n = a^{m+n} \qquad a^m / a^n = a^{m-n}$$

$$(a \,.\, b)^m = a^m \,.\, b^m \qquad (a/b)^m = a^m / b^m$$

$$(a^m)^n = a^{mn} \, *$$

For definition of a^x for x irrational, see § **15.4.**

Definition. If a and b are positive numbers,

$$x = \log_b a \quad \text{if} \quad b^x = a.$$

b is called the *base* and x the *logarithm* of a to the base b.

$$\log_b 1 = 0.$$

$$\log_b x \to \pm\infty \text{ as } x \to \infty \text{ according as } b \gtrless 1.$$

$$\log_b x \to \mp\infty \text{ as } x \to +0 \text{ according as } b \gtrless 1.$$

$$\log_b (a \,.\, c) = \log_b a + \log_b c.$$

$$\log_b (a/c) = \log_b a - \log_b c.$$

$$\log_b a^n = n \log_b a.$$

$$\log_b a = \log_c a / \log_c b.$$

$$\log_b a = 1/\log_a b.$$

The base of common logarithms (or Briggs' logarithms) is 10. We denote common logarithms by log and natural or Naperian logarithms (see § **15.4**) by ln.

$$\ln a = \log a / \log e = 2{\cdot}30259 \log a.$$

$$\log a = \ln a / \ln 10 = 0{\cdot}43429 \ln a.$$

1.3. Binomial coefficients. The binomial theorem for a positive integral exponent

Definition. If n is a positive integer, factorial n is

$$n! = 1 \,.\, 2 \,.\, 3 \,.\,.\,.\, n.$$

$$0! = 1.$$

Stirling's formula (see Table I) gives a useful approximation to $n!$ If r is a positive integer and n is any real number, then

$$\binom{n}{r} = n(n-1)(n-2) \ldots (n-r+1)/r!$$

$$\binom{n}{0} = 1.$$

* The symbol a^{m^n} denotes $a^{(m^n)}$.

If n is a positive integer,

$$\binom{n}{r}=0, \text{ if } r>n; \quad \binom{n}{n}=1.$$

$$\binom{n}{r}=\binom{n}{n-r}=\frac{n!}{(n-r)!\,r!} \text{ if } r<n.$$

$$\binom{n+1}{r+1}=\binom{n}{r}+\binom{n-1}{r}+\binom{n-2}{r}+\ldots+\binom{r}{r}.$$

For any positive n and m

$$\binom{n+1}{r}=\binom{n}{r}+\binom{n}{r-1}.$$

$$\binom{m+n}{r}=\binom{m}{r}\binom{n}{0}+\binom{m}{r-1}\binom{n}{1}+\binom{m}{r-2}\binom{n}{2}+\ldots$$
$$+\binom{m}{1}\binom{n}{r-1}+\binom{m}{0}\binom{n}{r}.$$

Binomial theorem for a positive integral index n

$$(a\pm b)^n=\binom{n}{0}a^n\pm\binom{n}{1}a^{n-1}b+\binom{n}{2}a^{n-2}b^2\pm\ldots$$
$$+(\pm 1)^r\binom{n}{r}a^{n-r}b^r+\ldots+(\pm 1)^n\binom{n}{n}b^n,$$

where either the upper or the lower sign is taken throughout.

Multinomial theorem for a positive integral index n

$$(a_1+a_2+\ldots+a_k)^n=\Sigma\frac{n!}{n_1!n_2!\ldots n_k!}\,a_1^{n_1}a_2^{n_2}\ldots a_k^{n_k},$$

where $n_1, n_2, \ldots, n_k$ assume all positive integral and zero values such that $n_1+n_2+\ldots+n_k=n$.

1.4. Lagrange's identity

If $a_1, b_1, c_1;\; a_2, b_2, c_2$ are any numbers,

$$(a_1b_2-a_2b_1)^2+(b_1c_2-b_2c_1)^2+(c_1a_2-c_2a_1)^2$$
$$=(a_1^2+b_1^2+c_1^2)(a_2^2+b_2^2+c_2^2)-(a_1a_2+b_1b_2+c_1c_2)^2.$$

1.5. Inequalities.

All the numbers involved are real.

Definition of symbols $>$, $<$.

$a>b$, if a and b are real and $(a-b)$ is positive;

$a<b$, if a and b are real and $(a-b)$ is negative.

Rules of algebra for inequalities

If c is real and $a>b$, then $a+c>b+c$

$$a-c>b-c.$$

If $c>0$ and $a>b$, then $ac>bc$.

If $c<0$ and $a>b$, then $ac<bc$.

The absolute value of a, written $|a|$, is the positive numerical value of the real number a.

If a and b are real, $|a|>|b|$ if, and only if, $a^2>b^2$.

Bernoulli's inequality

If $x>0$ and $x\neq 1$, and $p\neq 0$ or 1,

then $$x^p-1>p(x-1),$$

unless $0<p<1$, when the inequality sign is reversed.

If $x>0$, $y>0$, $x\neq y$ and $p\neq 0$ or 1,

then $$px^{p-1}(x-y)>x^p-y^p>py^{p-1}(x-y).$$

unless $0<p<1$, when the inequality sign is reversed.

Inequalities of the arithmetic, geometric and harmonic means

Definition. Of n numbers $a_1, \ldots, a_n$, the

Arithmetic Mean $=(a_1+a_2+\ldots+a_n)/n \equiv A$, say.*

Geometric Mean $=(a_1a_2\ldots a_n)^{1/n} \equiv G$.

Harmonic Mean $=n\Big/\left(\dfrac{1}{a_1}+\dfrac{1}{a_2}+\ldots+\dfrac{1}{a_n}\right)\equiv H$.

If $a_1, a_2, \ldots, a_n$ are positive,

$$A\geqslant G\geqslant H.$$

Equality holds only if the a_i are all equal.

If a and b are positive,

$$a^2+b^2\geqslant 2ab,$$

$$(a+b)^2\geqslant 4ab.$$

If $a_r\geqslant 0$, $p_r>0$,

$$a_1^{p_1}a_2^{p_2}\ldots a_n^{p_n}\leqslant\left(\frac{p_1a_1+\ldots+p_na_n}{p_1+p_2+\ldots+p_n}\right)^{p_1+p_2+\ldots p_n}.$$

Equality holds only if $a_1=a_2=\ldots=a_n$.

* The symbol $\equiv$ means "is identically equal to".

Cauchy's inequality

If $a_r \geqslant 0$, $b_r \geqslant 0$, $r=1, \ldots, n$,

$$\left(\sum_{r=1}^{n} a_r^2\right)\left(\sum_{r=1}^{n} b_r^2\right) \geqslant \left(\sum_{r=1}^{n} a_r b_r\right)^2.$$

The equal sign holds only if

$$a_1/b_1 = a_2/b_2 = \ldots = a_n/b_n,$$

when the sets are said to be proportional.

Weierstrass' inequalities

If $0 < a_r < 1$, $r=1, \ldots, n$, $a_1 + a_2 + \ldots + a_n < 1$,

$$\frac{1}{1-\Sigma a_r} > \frac{1}{\Pi(1-a_r)} > \Pi(1+a_r) > 1 + \Sigma a_r.$$

1.6. Combinations and permutations

A *combination* of n elements r at a time is a selection of r of the elements; the order of the elements selected is not considered.

E.g. The combinations of the four elements a, b, c, d two at a time are
without repetition: *ab, ac, ad, bc, bd, cd.*
with repetition: *aa, ab, ac, ad, bb, bc, bd, cc, cd, dd.*

The number of combinations of n elements r at a time without repetition and with repetition are respectively

$$^nC_r = \binom{n}{r} \text{ and } {}^nC'_r = \binom{n+r-1}{r}.$$

A *permutation* of n elements is the operation of arranging the elements and yields a *derangement* or an *arrangement* of the elements.

The arrangements of the elements a, b, c are *abc, acb, bac, bca, cab, cba.* These have been arranged in *lexical* order, that is, the order in which they would appear in a dictionary.

The number of arrangements of n things is

$$P(n) = n!$$

If α_1 of the elements are equal to a_1, α_2 equal to a_2, ... α_r equal to a_r, the number of arrangements is

$$P_{\alpha_1, \alpha_2, \ldots, \alpha_r}(n) = \frac{n!}{\alpha_1!\alpha_2! \ldots \alpha_r!}.$$

In particular

$$P_{r, n-r}(n) = \frac{n!}{r!(n-r)!} = \binom{n}{r}.$$

The number of arrangements of n elements taken r at a time without repetition is

$$^nP_r = r!\binom{n}{r}.$$

The number of arrangements of n things taken r at a time with repetition is n^r.

Inversions and transpositions. In an arrangement of the numbers 1, 2, . . ., n two indices which are out of natural order, the greater index preceding the lesser, give rise to an *inversion*; e.g. 4 before 2 and 4 before 3 and 3 before 2 in (14325) are inversions. The number of inversions of natural order or of the original order in any arrangement can be counted systematically and is unique. An arrangement is said to be even or odd according as the number of inversions in it is even or odd. The number, $\frac{1}{2}(n!)$, of odd arrangements of n elements is equal to the number of even ones.

A *transposition* is the interchange of two indices in an arrangement without alteration of the others.

A single transposition changes an odd arrangement into an even one and vice versa.

Two arrangements A and B are said to be *reciprocal* or *inverse* if, when the index r occupies the sth place in A, then the index s occupies the rth place in B. The reciprocal of the reciprocal is the original arrangement. Reciprocal arrangements have the same number of inversions.

1.7. Complex numbers

The *complex number* z is defined as a number pair (x, y), where x and y are real.

Definition. If $z_1=(x_1, y_1)$, $z_2=(x_2, y_2)$,

$$z_1=z_2 \text{ if and only if } x_1=x_2,\ y_1=y_2.$$

$$z_1 \pm z_2=(x_1 \pm x_2,\ y_1 \pm y_2).$$

$$z_1z_2=(x_1x_2-y_1y_2,\ x_1y_2+x_2y_1).$$

$$\frac{1}{z_1}=\left(\frac{x_1}{x_1^2+y_1^2},\ \frac{-y_1}{x_1^2+y_1^2}\right), \text{ where } z_1 \neq (0, 0).$$

$$z_2/z_1=z_2(1/z_1).$$

Complex numbers obey the Laws of Algebra [§ 1.1 (I) – (X)].

The above definitions are consistent with the statement:

$z=x+iy$, where $i^2=-1$ and i obeys the Laws of Algebra (§ 1.1).

The *modulus* of z, written $|z|$, is given by $|z|=+\sqrt{(x^2+y^2)}$.

The *amplitude* or *argument* of z is the angle θ given by $\cos\theta = x/|z|$, $\sin\theta = y/|z|$, and is written amp z.

Amp z is many-valued. The *principal value* is that value of the argument which satisfies $-\pi < \theta \leqslant \pi$. The general value is $\theta + 2k\pi$, where k is an integer. If $|z| = r$, $z = x + iy = r(\cos\theta + i\sin\theta)$.

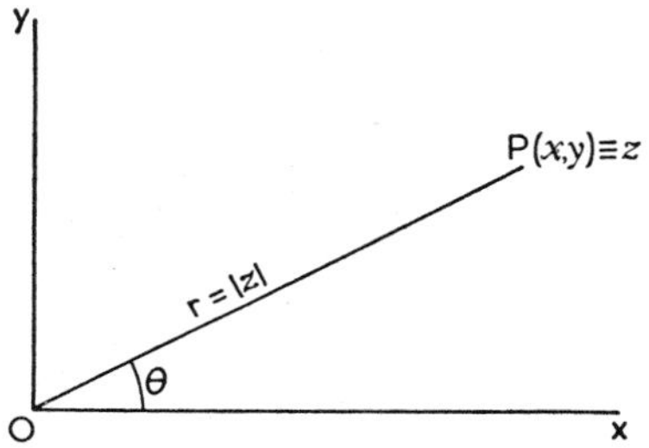

Fig. 1.1

Argand diagram. The complex number $z = (x, y) = x + iy$ may be represented in a plane by a point P whose Cartesian co-ordinates are (x, y) and polar co-ordinates are (r, θ), or by the vector $\overline{OP}$. See Fig. 1.1.

The *conjugate* of z, written $\bar{z}$, is $x - iy$ or $(x, -y)$.

$$z\bar{z} = |z|^2.$$

$$|z_1 z_2 \ldots z_n| = |z_1| \cdot |z_2| \ldots |z_n|.$$

One value of amp $(z_1 z_2 \ldots z_n)$ is amp z_1 + amp z_2 + ... + amp z_n.

$$|z_1/z_2| = |z_1|/|z_2|.$$

One value of amp z_1/z_2 is amp z_1 − amp z_2.

If a is complex, $z = a^{1/n}$ if $z^n = a$.

$$a^{m/n} = (a^{1/n})^m.$$

De Moivre's theorem

If r is real, one value of $(\cos\phi + i\sin\phi)^r$ is $\cos r\phi + i\sin r\phi$.

Inequalities

$$|z_1 \pm z_2| \leqslant |z_1| + |z_2|,$$
$$|z_1 \pm z_2| \geqslant |z_1| - |z_2|,$$
$$|z_1 \pm z_2| \geqslant |z_2| - |z_1|.$$

The complex numbers do not form an ordered set. The statement $z_1 > z_2$ is meaningless unless z_1 and z_2 are both real.

CHAPTER 2

THEORY OF EQUATIONS

2.1. An *algebraic equation* in one variable, of degree n (n a positive integer), is a relation

$$a_0x^n+a_1x^{n-1}+\ldots+a_rx^{n-r}+\ldots+a_{n-1}x+a_n=0,$$

where the *coefficients* a_r belong to a prescribed field or ring (q.v.) and $a_0\neq0$. The values of the variable x which satisfy the equation are called its *roots*.

An *algebraic number* is a real or complex number which satisfies an algebraic equation with integer coefficients. A number which satisfies an equation with algebraic coefficients also satisfies an equation with integer coefficients and is therefore algebraic. A number which does not satisfy an algebraic equation is said to be transcendental, e.g. π, e.

Equations in the field of complex numbers of degree less than or equal to four can be solved. There is no general method of solution for those of degree greater than or equal to five.

2.2. Solution of the quadratic, cubic and biquadratic

2.21. The *quadratic* or equation of the second degree is

$$ax^2+bx+c=0, \quad a\neq0.$$

Its roots are

$$\begin{matrix}x_1\\x_2\end{matrix}=\{-b\pm\sqrt{(b^2-4ac)}\}/(2a).$$

The number $\Delta=b^2-4ac$ is called the *discriminant* of the equation.

When a, b, c are real and

$\Delta>0$, the roots are real and distinct,

$\Delta=0$, the roots are real and equal,

$\Delta<0$, the roots are conjugate complex.

2.22. Binomial equation $x^n=a$

The equation $x^n=1=\cos 2k\pi+i\sin 2k\pi$ has the n distinct roots

$$x=\cos\frac{2k\pi}{n}+i\sin\frac{2k\pi}{n}, \quad (k=0, 1, \ldots, n-1).$$

If $\omega=\cos\dfrac{2\pi}{n}+i\sin\dfrac{2\pi}{n}$, the roots are $1, \omega, \omega^2, \ldots, \omega^{n-1}$.

The equation $x^n = a = |a|(\cos\phi + i\sin\phi)$ has the n roots

$$x = |a|^{1/n}\left\{\cos\frac{\phi+2k\pi}{n} + i\sin\frac{\phi+2k\pi}{n}\right\}, \quad (k=0, 1, \ldots, n-1),$$

where $|a|^{1/n}$ denotes the positive arithmetical root. The cube roots of unity are the roots of $x^3=1$, viz.:

$$x_0 = 1,$$

$$x_1 = \cos\frac{2\pi}{3} + i\sin\frac{2\pi}{3} = -\tfrac{1}{2} + \frac{\sqrt{3}}{2}i = \omega \text{ (say)},$$

$$x_2 = \cos\frac{4\pi}{3} + i\sin\frac{4\pi}{3} = -\tfrac{1}{2} - \frac{\sqrt{3}}{2}i = \omega^2.$$

2.23. The cubic equation

$$a_0x^3 + 3a_1x^2 + 3a_2x + a_3 = 0,$$

is reduced by the transformation $x = (y - a_1)/a_0$ to the form

$$y^3 + 3Hy + G = 0,$$

where $$H = a_0a_2 - a_1^2, \quad G = a_0^2a_3 - 3a_0a_1a_2 + 2a_1^3.$$

Cardan's solution can be used in every case, but it is simplest to use Cardan's solution if $G^2+4H^3>0$ and the trigonometrical solution if $G^2+4H^3<0$, in which case the roots are real if the coefficients are real. If $G^2+4H^3=0$, there is a repeated root of the equation in y of value either $+\sqrt{(-H)}$ or $-\sqrt{(-H)}$. Test which of these satisfies the equation.

Cardan's solution (due to Tartaglia)

Let p be any one of the values of $\left\{-\frac{G}{2} + \frac{1}{2}\sqrt{(G^2+4H^3)}\right\}^{1/3}$. Let $q = -H/p$. Then the roots of the equation in y are

$$p+q, \; p\omega + q\omega^2, \; p\omega^2 + q\omega,$$

where ω is a complex cube root of unity.

If $G^2+4H^3>0$, then the real positive value may be chosen for p, and the roots are

$$p+q, \; -\frac{1}{2}(p+q) + \frac{\sqrt{3}}{2}(p-q)i, \; -\frac{1}{2}(p+q) - \frac{\sqrt{3}}{2}(p-q)i.$$

Trigonometrical solution for the case $G^2+4H^3<0$

Let $\cos\phi = -\frac{1}{2}G(-H)^{-3/2}$, where the positive value of $(-H)^{3/2}$ is taken.

The roots of the equation in y are

$$2_+\sqrt{(-H)}\cos\tfrac{1}{3}\phi, \; 2_+\sqrt{(-H)}\cos(\tfrac{1}{3}\phi + \tfrac{2}{3}\pi), \; 2_+\sqrt{(-H)}\cos(\tfrac{1}{3}\phi + \tfrac{4}{3}\pi),$$

where $_+\sqrt{}$ indicates the positive root.

2.24. The quartic or biquadratic equation

$$ax^4+4bx^3+6cx^2+4dx+e=0.$$

By the transformation $x=y-b/a$ the equation is transformed to the form

$$y^4+py^2+qy+r=0.$$

Form the reducing cubic equation

$$z^3+\frac{p}{2}z^2+\frac{p^2-4r}{16}z-\frac{q^2}{64}=0.$$

Let u^2, v^2, w^2 be the roots of the latter equation. Choose u, v, w so that $uvw=-\dfrac{q}{8}$. Then the roots of the equation in y are

$$u+v+w,\ u-v-w,\ -u+v-w,\ -u-v+w.$$

Solution by factorization

$$a(ax^4+4bx^3+6cx^2+4dx+e)\equiv(ax^2+2bx+c+2a\theta)^2-(2Mx+N)^2,$$

where $$M^2=b^2-ac+a^2\theta,\quad N^2=(c+2a\theta)^2-ae,$$
$$MN=bc-ad+2ab\theta.$$

Hence θ is a root of

$$4a^3\theta^3-aI\theta+J=0, \qquad (1)$$

where $$I\equiv ae-4bd+3c^2$$

and $$J\equiv\begin{vmatrix} a & b & c \\ b & c & d \\ c & d & e \end{vmatrix}$$

are invariants of the binary quartic (see §§ 3.2, 4.6 and 4.7).

Let θ be one root of (1), $M=+(b^2-ac+a^2\theta)^{1/2}$,
$$N=(bc-ad+2ab\theta)/M.$$

Then the quartic equation is

$$\{ax^2+2(b+M)x+c+2a\theta+N\}\{ax^2+2(b-M)x+c+2a\theta-N\}=0$$

and its roots are found by factorizing the quadratics.

The discriminant of the quartic is $\Delta=256(I^3-27J^2)$. If $\Delta=0$, the quartic has two equal roots. If the coefficients are real and $\Delta<0$, there are two real and two non-real roots, whereas if the coefficients are real and $\Delta>0$, the roots are either all real or all non-real. If all are real, both b^2-ac and $3aJ+2(b^2-ac)I$ are positive, while if either of these is negative, the four roots are non-real, Δ being positive. (See also § 4.7.)

2.3. Theorems on algebraic equations

The general equation of degree n is

$$f(x) \equiv a_0x^n + a_1x^{n-1} + \ldots + a_rx^{n-r} + \ldots + a_n = 0, \quad a_0 \neq 0.$$

Remainder theorem. If $f(x)$ is divided by $(x-\alpha)$, the remainder is $f(\alpha)$.

Factor theorem. If α is a root of $f(x)=0$, $(x-\alpha)$ is a factor (see § 2.9) of $f(x)$.

If $(x-\alpha)^r$ is a factor of $f(x)$ and $(x-\alpha)^{r+1}$ is not, α is said to be a root of multiplicity r or an r-ple root of $f(x)=0$.

Fundamental theorem of algebra. An equation of degree n, whose coefficients are real or complex numbers, has n and only n roots in the field of complex numbers, each root being counted according to its multiplicity.

If $\alpha_1, \alpha_2, \ldots, \alpha_n$ are the (equal or distinct) roots of the equation $f(x)=0$, then

$$f(x) \equiv a_0(x-\alpha_1)(x-\alpha_2) \ldots (x-\alpha_n).$$

Symmetric functions of the roots

A function of n variables is said to be *symmetric* if it is unchanged by any permutation of the variables.

Let $\Sigma C_r(\alpha_1, \alpha_2, \ldots, \alpha_n)$ be the sum of the products of every combination, without repetition, of r of the roots. Then

$$\Sigma C_r(\alpha_1, \alpha_2, \ldots, \alpha_n) = (-1)^r a_r/a_0, \quad (r=1, 2, \ldots n).$$

Definition. The *weight* of the expression $a_0^{i_0} \ldots a_r^{i_r} \ldots a_n^{i_n}$ is defined to be $\sum_{r=1}^{n} ri_r$. A polynomial in a_r is *isobaric* if every term is of the same weight.

Every symmetric polynomial in the roots of an equation, of degree k in α_1 and of degree w in all the roots taken together, can be expressed as $(a_0)^{-k}$ multiplied by an isobaric polynomial of weight w and of degree k in the coefficients a_r.

Every rational symmetric function of the roots of an equation can be expressed as a rational function of the coefficients. The latter will be the quotient of two isobaric polynomials.

Newton's theorem on sums of powers of the roots

Let $s_k = \sum_{r=1}^{n} \alpha_r^k$, $s_{-k} = \sum_{r=1}^{n} \alpha_r^{-k}$, where k is a positive integer.

If $k>n$, $a_0s_k+a_1s_{k-1}+\ldots+a_rs_{k-r}+\ldots+a_ns_{k-n}=0$.

If $0<k\leqslant n$, $a_0s_k+a_1s_{k-1}+\ldots+a_{k-1}s_1+ka_k=0$.

If $a_n\neq0$ and $k>n$,

$$a_ns_{-k}+a_{n-1}s_{1-k}+\ldots+a_{n-r}s_{r-k}+\ldots+a_0s_{n-k}=0.$$

If $a_n\neq0$ and $0<k\leqslant n$,

$$a_ns_{-k}+a_{n-1}s_{1-k}+\ldots+a_{n-k+1}s_{-1}+ka_{n-k}=0.$$

2.4. Multiple roots

If α is an r-ple root of $f(x)=0$, it is an $(r-1)$-ple root of $f'(x)=0$.*

α is an r-ple root of $f(x)=0$ if, and only if,

$$f(\alpha)=f'(\alpha)=\ldots=f^{(r-1)}(\alpha)=0,\ f^{(r)}(\alpha)\neq0,\ \text{where } f^{(r)}(\alpha)\equiv\left(\frac{d^rf}{dx^r}\right)_{x=\alpha}.$$

The *discriminant* of an equation $f(x)=0$ is the expression

$$D\equiv\begin{vmatrix} s_0 & s_1 & \ldots & s_{n-1} \\ s_1 & s_2 & \ldots & s_n \\ \cdot & & & \\ \cdot & & & \\ \cdot & & & \\ \cdot & & & \\ \cdot & & & \\ s_{n-1} & s_n & \ldots & s_{2n-2} \end{vmatrix} \equiv \begin{array}{l}[(\alpha_1-\alpha_2)(\alpha_1-\alpha_3)\ldots(\alpha_1-\alpha_n)\\ \times(\alpha_2-\alpha_3)\ldots(\alpha_{n-1}-\alpha_n)]^2\end{array}$$

$$=\prod_{\substack{\lambda,\,\mu=1\\ \lambda<\mu}}^{n}(\alpha_\lambda-\alpha_\mu)^2$$

The necessary and sufficient condition that the equation $f(x)=0$ has a multiple root is $D=0$. D can be obtained in terms of the coefficients of the equation as the Sylvester eliminant of $f(x)=0$ and $f'(x)=0$ (see § 2.7).

2.5. Equations with real coefficients

Complex roots occur in conjugate imaginary pairs, $\alpha\pm i\beta$, where α and β are real.

Location of the real roots

The results are given for the equation

$$\phi(x)\equiv x^n+a_1x^{n-1}+\ldots+a_n=0,$$

in which the coefficient of x^n is unity and the a_i real.

* See definition of derivate (§ 12.3).

Between two real roots of the equation $\phi(x)=0$ lies at least one real root of the equation $\phi'(x)=0$.

An odd or an even number of real roots of $\phi(x)=0$ lie between two values a and b according as $\phi(a)$ and $\phi(b)$ differ in sign or have the same sign.

An equation of odd degree has at least one real root whose sign is different from that of a_n.

An equation of even degree, in which a_n is negative, has at least two real roots, one positive and one negative.

If a_m is the first negative coefficient and if a_p is the numerically greatest negative coefficient, then no positive root is greater than $1+(-a_p)^{1/m}$. By applying this theorem to the equation $\phi(-x)=0$ a lower bound for the real roots of $\phi(x)=0$ is obtained.

If no coefficient a_r is zero, the equation is said to be *complete*. A *continuation* or a *change* of sign is said to occur in $(1, a_1, \ldots, a_n)$ or in the polynomial $\phi(x)$ according as a_r and a_{r+1} have the same or opposite signs.

Descartes' rule of signs

In the equation $\phi(x)=0$ the number of positive roots cannot exceed the number of changes of sign in $(1, a_1, \ldots, a_n)$. The number of negative roots cannot exceed the number of changes of sign in the coefficients of the equation $\phi(-x)=0$.

In a complete equation the number of negative roots cannot exceed the number of continuations of sign in the coefficients.

Sturm's theorem gives the actual number of distinct roots of the equation between a and b thus:

Form the sequence of polynomials $\phi(x)$, $\phi'(x)$,* $\phi_2(x), \ldots, \phi_m(x)$ as follows: Divide $\phi(x)$ by $\phi'(x)$ and call the remainder $-\phi_2(x)$. Divide $\phi'(x)$ by $\phi_2(x)$ and call the remainder $-\phi_3(x)$, and so on. Then

$$\phi(x)=g_1(x)\phi'(x)-\phi_2(x),$$

$$\phi'(x)=g_2(x)\phi_2(x)-\phi_3(x),$$

$$\cdot \quad \cdot \quad \cdot \quad \cdot \quad \cdot \quad \cdot$$

$$\phi_{m-2}(x)=g_{m-1}(x)\phi_{m-1}(x)-\phi_m(x),$$

where the degrees of $\phi(x)$, $\phi'(x)$, $\phi_2(x), \ldots, \phi_m(x)$ steadily decrease and the last remainder $-\phi_m(x)$ is a constant which is not zero if $\phi(x)=0$ has no multiple root.

Sturm's theorem states that, if $\phi(a)\neq 0$, $\phi(b)\neq 0$, the number of

* See definition of derivate.

distinct real roots of $\phi(x)=0$ between a and b $(a<b)$ is equal to the excess of the number of changes of sign in the sequence

$$[\phi(a), \phi'(a), \phi_2(a), \ldots, \phi_m(a)]$$

over the number of changes of sign in the sequence

$$[\phi(b), \phi'(b), \phi_2(b), \ldots, \phi_m(b)].$$

2.6. Approximation methods

Newton's method

If α is an approximation to a root of an equation $f(x)=0$, then $\beta \equiv \alpha - f(\alpha)/f'(\alpha)$ is usually a closer approximation.

Newton's method can be applied to transcendental or algebraic equations. It is iterative and so is not vitiated by an error at an intermediate stage. If the equation $f(x)=0$ has two roots close together, care should be taken to obtain a sufficiently close approximation to the root required before beginning to apply Newton's method.

If $f(x)=0$ has a root between β and γ and if $f(\beta)$ and $f(\gamma)$ have opposite signs, an approximation to the root is given by

$$\alpha = \beta - (\beta-\gamma)f(\beta)/\{f(\beta)-f(\gamma)\}.$$

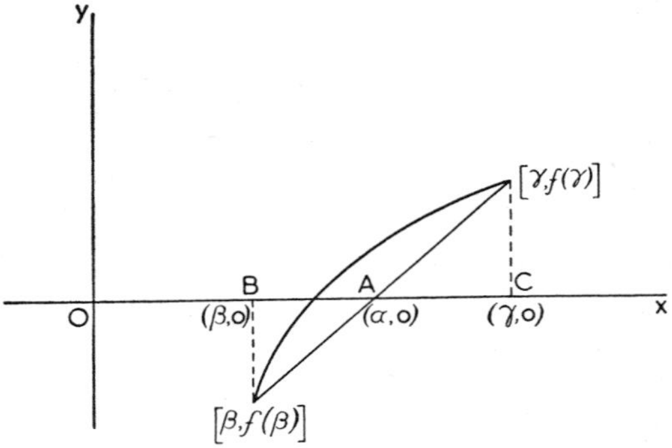

Fig. 2.1

This approximation may be obtained graphically. The distance OA (Fig. 2.1) is the value α.

Horner's method can be applied only to algebraic equations. It gives the answer correct to any decimal place required. To find an approximation to a real root of the equation $f(x)=0$, find two integers p and $p+1$ between which the root lies. Diminish the roots by p by writing $x=y+p$. Multiply the roots of the equation in y by 10 by writing $y=z/10$. Repeat the process; i.e. find two integers q, $q+1$ between which the root lies, where $0 \leqslant q < 9$. Diminish the roots by q and then multiply the roots by 10, and so on. The root is $p+\cdot q\ldots$

2.7. Sylvester's eliminant or resultant of two polynomials

$$f(x) \equiv a_0x^n + a_1x^{n-1} + \dots + a_n,$$

$$\phi(x) \equiv b_0x^k + b_1x^{k-1} + \dots + b_k,$$

is the determinant (q.v.) of order $n+k$

$$R \equiv \left|\begin{array}{cccccccc} a_0 & a_1 & \dots & a_{n-1} & a_n & 0 & \dots & 0 \\ 0 & a_0 & \dots & a_{n-2} & a_{n-1} & a_n & & 0 \\ \cdot & & & & & & & \\ \cdot & & & & & & & \\ \cdot & & & & & & & \\ 0 & 0 & 0 \; a_0 & a_1 & & \dots & \dots & a_n \\ b_0 & b_1 & \dots & b_k & 0 & & & 0 \\ 0 & b_0 & & b_{k-1} & b_k & & & 0 \\ \cdot & & & & & & & \\ \cdot & & & & & & & \\ \cdot & & & & & & & \\ 0 & & 0 & b_0 & & & & b_k \end{array}\right| \begin{array}{l} \left.\begin{array}{l} \\ \\ \\ \\ \\ \\ \end{array}\right\} k \text{ rows} \\ \left.\begin{array}{l} \\ \\ \\ \\ \\ \\ \end{array}\right\} n \text{ rows} \end{array}$$

$\underbrace{\qquad\qquad\qquad}_{\substack{n-1 \\ \text{columns}}}\;\underbrace{\qquad\qquad\qquad}_{\substack{k+1 \\ \text{columns}}}$

A common root of the equations $f(x)=0$ and $\phi(x)=0$ is a root of the equation obtained by equating to zero the greatest common factor (q.v.) of $f(x)$ and $\phi(x)$.

A necessary and sufficient condition for the existence of a common root of the equations $f(x)=0$ and $\phi(x)=0$ is that $R=0$. If $R=0$, the common root α is given by any one of the expressions (see § 12.5),

$$\alpha = \frac{\dfrac{\partial R}{\partial a_0}}{\dfrac{\partial R}{\partial a_1}} = \frac{\dfrac{\partial R}{\partial a_1}}{\dfrac{\partial R}{\partial a_2}} = \dots = \frac{\dfrac{\partial R}{\partial a_p}}{\dfrac{\partial R}{\partial a_{p+1}}} = \dots = \frac{\dfrac{\partial R}{\partial a_{n-1}}}{\dfrac{\partial R}{\partial a_n}} = \frac{\dfrac{\partial R}{\partial b_0}}{\dfrac{\partial R}{\partial b_1}} = \dots = \frac{\dfrac{\partial R}{\partial b_{k-1}}}{\dfrac{\partial R}{\partial b_k}}.$$

Elimination of one variable y between two equations in two variables x and y.

Arrange the equations $f(x, y)=0$ and $\phi(x, y)=0$ as polynomials in y with coefficients which are polynomials in x. Form the Sylvester eliminant $R(x)$ of the polynomials in y. This eliminant will in general be a polynomial in x of degree nk where n and k are the degrees of $f(x, y)$ and $\phi(x, y)$.

Corresponding to each root x_r of $R(x)=0$, there is one number y_r such that (x_r, y_r) satisfy both the equations $f(x, y)=0$ and $\phi(x, y)=0$.

2.8. Solution of linear equations

Non-homogeneous linear equations

The system of equations

$$\sum_{j=1}^{n} a_{ij}x_j = c_i \qquad (i=1, \ldots, m)$$

may be written

$$AX=C,$$

where (see Chapter 3)

$$A \equiv \begin{bmatrix} a_{11} & a_{12} & \cdots & a_{1n} \\ a_{21} & a_{22} & \cdots & a_{2n} \\ \cdot & & & \\ \cdot & & & \\ \cdot & & & \\ a_{m1} & a_{m2} & & a_{mn} \end{bmatrix}, \quad X \equiv \begin{bmatrix} x_1 \\ x_2 \\ \cdot \\ \cdot \\ \cdot \\ x_n \end{bmatrix}, \quad C \equiv \begin{bmatrix} c_1 \\ c_2 \\ \cdot \\ \cdot \\ \cdot \\ c_m \end{bmatrix}.$$

$$B \equiv \begin{bmatrix} a_{11} & a_{12} & \cdots & a_{1n} & c_1 \\ a_{21} & a_{22} & \cdots & a_{2n} & c_2 \\ \cdot & & & & \\ \cdot & & & & \\ \cdot & & & & \\ a_{m1} & a_{m2} & \cdots & a_{mn} & c_m \end{bmatrix} \equiv [A, C],$$

and B is called the augmented matrix of A.

Theorem. The equations are consistent, i.e. at least one set of values of X satisfies them, if $r=r'$, and inconsistent if $r<r'$, where r and r' are the ranks (see § 3.4) of A and B.

Methods of solution if $r=r'$

(i) Reduce the matrix B to reduced echelon form F by elementary *row* operations (see § 3.61). If $F=(H, K)$, where K is a single column, the equations are reduced to

$$HX=K.$$

Write these down. Keep on the left-hand side the variables x_j corresponding to the columns in which a leading row entry 1 occurs and take the remaining variables to the right-hand side. Those on the left are expressed explicitly in terms of those on the right and of the c_i. The values of the x_j now on the right may be chosen arbitrarily.

(ii) Renumber the equations and the variables so that the minor

$$D \equiv \begin{bmatrix} a_{11} & a_{12} & \cdots & a_{1r} \\ a_{21} & a_{22} & \cdots & a_{2r} \\ \cdot & & & \\ \cdot & & & \\ \cdot & & & \\ a_{r1} & a_{r2} & \cdots & a_{rr} \end{bmatrix}$$

is non-singular.

Rewrite the r equations involving the elements in D as

$$\sum_{j=1}^{r} a_{ij}x_j = c_i - \sum_{j=r+1}^{n} a_{ij}x_j \qquad (i=1, 2, \ldots, r).$$

Let $Y' = [x_1, x_2, \ldots, x_r]$

$$E' = \left[c_1 - \sum_{j=r+1}^{n} a_{1j}x_j,\ c_2 - \sum_{j=r+1}^{n} a_{2j}x_j \ldots, c_r - \sum_{j=r+1}^{n} a_{rj}x_j\right]$$

so that these r equations may be written

$$DY = E.$$

Then $Y = D^{-1}E$ is the solution.

Hence, if $n > r = r'$, $n - r$ of the variables may be given arbitrary values and the remaining r found uniquely in terms of these.

If $n = r = r'$, the equations

$$DX = C$$

have the unique solution

$$X = D^{-1}C,$$

which is also the unique solution of the given equations $AX = C$.

A set of *homogeneous* linear equations

$$\sum_{j=1}^{n} a_{ij}x_j = 0 \qquad (i=1, \ldots, m)$$

or

$$AX = 0$$

may be solved by the same methods, writing $c_i = 0$. If the rank r of $[a_{ij}]$ is equal to n, either method gives the unique solution

$$x_j = 0. \qquad (j=1, \ldots, n)$$

2.9. Polynomials

A polynomial (see § 12.1) is said to be *rational, real* or *complex* according as its coefficients are rational, real or complex. Any rational polynomial can be considered as a real or complex polynomial and any real polynomial as a complex polynomial.

If a polynomial A can be expressed as the product of several polynomials $A_1, A_2, \ldots, A_n$, each A_i is called a factor of A.

When we state that we can factorize a real or rational polynomial we mean that we can factorize it into real or rational polynomial factors respectively.

A polynomial is *prime* or *irreducible* if it has no factors other than constants and constant multiples of itself.

A rational polynomial which is prime need not be prime when regarded as a real or complex polynomial, e.g. x^3-2, and a real prime polynomial need not be prime when regarded as a complex polynomial, e.g. x^2+1.

A complex prime polynomial is real prime and a real prime one is rational prime.

A *monic* polynomial is one whose leading coefficient is unity.

Any polynomial can be expressed uniquely as the product of a constant and of prime monic polynomials.

All prime complex polynomials are linear, i.e. of degree one, and all prime real polynomials of degree one or two.

A real quadratic polynomial x^2+px+q is prime if, and only if, $p^2<4q$.

If a real polynomial, regarded as a complex polynomial, is factorized into linear complex factors $k\Pi(x-a_i)$, then the a_i are either real or can be arranged in pairs of conjugate complex numbers.

The *highest common factor* (H.C.F.) of several polynomials is the monic polynomial of highest degree which is a factor of them all. If the H.C.F. is 1, they are said to be *co-prime*.

The H.C.F. of several real polynomials is the same as their H.C.F. when they are considered as complex polynomials.

Euclid's algorithm (or algorism) for the highest common factor

Let A, B be two polynomials of degrees n, m, where $n \geqslant m \geqslant 1$.

Divide A by B, obtaining a remainder R_1, where

$$A \equiv BQ_1 + R_1$$

and R_1 is of degree $m_1 < m$. If $R_1 \neq 0$, divide B by R_1, obtaining a remainder R_2 of degree $m_2 < m_1$, then divide R_1 by R_2, and so on. Either some $R_i \equiv 0$, in which case R_{i-1} is the H.C.F., or some R_p is a constant, in which case the H.C.F. is 1.

If G is the H.C.F., co-prime polynomials L, M exist such that

$$LA + MB \equiv G.$$

L and M are of degrees less than $m-g$ and $n-g$ respectively, where g is the degree of G. The polynomials L and M can be obtained explicitly in terms of the quotients Q_i by the above process. A is prime to B if, and only if, polynomials L and M exist such that

$$LA+MB\equiv 1.$$

Given a monic polynomial Q of degree n, it can be written uniquely in the form

$$Q\equiv Q_1(Q_2)^2\ldots(Q_t)^t,$$

where the Q_i are co-prime monic polynomials, and no Q_i has a repeated factor. The Q_i can be found by the H.C.F. process thus: Let Q', Q'', ..., $Q^{(n)}$ be the successive derivates of Q, $Q^{(n)}$ being a constant. Let H_1 be the H.C.F. of Q and Q', H_2 that of H_1 and Q'', and so on.

Then $$Q_1=QH_2/H_1^2,\quad Q_2=H_1H_3/H_2^2,$$ and so on.

2.91. Partial fractions

Given two co-prime polynomials P and Q, there is a unique expression for the rational function

$$\frac{P}{Q}\equiv B+\sum_{r=1}^{t}\left\{\frac{A_{r1}}{Q_r}+\frac{A_{r2}}{Q_r^2}+\ldots+\frac{A_{rr}}{Q_r^r}\right\}$$

where B, A_{rs} are polynomials and the degree of each A_{rs} is less than that of Q_r. This form can be obtained by factorizing Q by the process given, even when the prime factors of Q are not known.

Given two co-prime polynomials P and Q, there is a unique expression for the rational function

$$\frac{P}{Q}=B+\sum_{r=1}^{k}\left\{\frac{c_{r1}}{T_r}+\frac{c_{r2}}{T_r^2}+\ldots+\frac{c_{rs_r}}{T_r^{s_r}}\right\},$$

where T_r are the prime factors of Q, s_r is the multiplicity of T_r in Q, B is a polynomial and c_{ri} are polynomials of degree less than the degree of T_r.

If it is desired to integrate P/Q, and the coefficients of $Q(x)$ are real, it is best to split up Q into powers of real prime factors. Corresponding to each factor $(x-a)^s$ assume a sum of partial fractions of the form

$$\frac{a_1}{x-a}+\frac{a_2}{(x-a)^2}+\ldots+\frac{a_s}{(x-a)^s},$$

and corresponding to each factor $(x^2+px+q)^t$, $(p^2<4q)$ assume a sum

$$\frac{b_1x+c_1}{x^2+px+q}+\frac{b_2x+c_2}{(x^2+px+q)^2}+\ldots+\frac{b_tx+c_t}{(x^2+px+q)^t}.$$

Then $$\frac{P(x)}{Q(x)}\equiv B(x)+\sum_{i=1}^{k}\sum_{j=1}^{s_i}\frac{a_{ij}}{(x-a_i)^j}+\sum_{i=1}^{l}\sum_{j=1}^{t_i}\frac{b_{ij}x+c_{ij}}{(x^2+p_ix+q_i)^j}, \qquad (2)$$

where $\sum_{i=1}^{k} s_i + 2\sum_{i=1}^{l} t_i = n$, the degree of $Q(x)$. The coefficients a, b, c can be found by multiplying the identity (2) by $Q(x)$ and equating coefficients of powers of x, or by giving x particular values. Begin by giving x the values α_i.

For other purposes, e.g. to find the nth derivate of P/Q, factorize $Q(X)$ into linear factors $(x-\alpha)$ whether α is real or not.

The values of the coefficients are given below for certain cases.

(i) If $Q(x)$ is the product of n distinct linear factors,

$$\frac{P(x)}{Q(x)} = B(x) + \sum \frac{P(\alpha)}{Q'(\alpha)} \cdot \frac{1}{(x-\alpha)}.$$

(ii) If α is an s-ple root of $Q(x)=0$,

$$\frac{P(x)}{Q(x)} = B(x) + \frac{\phi(x)}{(x-\alpha)^s f(x)} \equiv B(x) + \frac{R(x)}{(x-\alpha)^s}$$

say, where B, ϕ, f are polynomials and R is a rational function.

Then $$\frac{R(x)}{(x-\alpha)^s} \equiv \frac{a_1}{x-\alpha} + \dots + \frac{a_s}{(x-\alpha)^s} + \frac{b_1}{x-\beta} + \dots$$

Expanding $R(x)$ by Taylor's theorem in powers of $(x-\alpha)$, the value $a_i = \dfrac{R^{(s-i)}(\alpha)}{(s-i)!}$ is obtained.

CHAPTER 3

MATRICES AND DETERMINANTS

3.1. A *matrix* is an array of mn numbers, real or complex, arranged in m rows and n columns,

$$\begin{bmatrix} a_{11} & a_{12} & \cdot & \cdot & \cdot & a_{1n} \\ a_{21} & a_{22} & \cdot & \cdot & \cdot & a_{2n} \\ \cdot \\ \cdot \\ \cdot \\ a_{m1} & a_{m2} & & & & a_{mn} \end{bmatrix},$$

which obeys the laws of addition and multiplication given in § 3.3.

The order of the matrix is the number pair (m, n), usually written $m \times n$. The element in the ith row and jth column, a_{ij}, is called the (i, j)th element. The matrix is often denoted by $[a_{ij}]$ or A. If $m = n$, the matrix is square of order n.

An $m \times 1$ matrix is called a *column vector* or a *column matrix*

$$X = \begin{bmatrix} x_1 \\ x_2 \\ \cdot \\ \cdot \\ \cdot \\ x_m \end{bmatrix}.$$

A $1 \times n$ matrix is called a *row vector* or *one-row matrix*

$$U' = [u_1, u_2, \ldots, u_n].$$

The inner product of two row or column vectors $[x_1, x_2, \ldots, x_n]$, $[y_1, y_2, \ldots, y_n]$, each of n elements is $\sum_{r=1}^{n} x_r y_r$, written $(x \,.\, y)$. The *trace* or *spur* of a square matrix A is $\sum_{r=1}^{n} a_{rr}$.

3.2. Determinants

Definition. The *determinant* $|A|$ or $\|a_{ij}\|$ of a square matrix A of order n is defined by

$$|A| \equiv \|a_{ij}\| = \Sigma \pm a_{1\alpha} a_{2\beta} \ldots a_{n\nu} = \begin{vmatrix} a_{11} & a_{12} & \cdot & \cdot & \cdot & a_{1n} \\ a_{21} & a_{22} & \cdot & \cdot & \cdot & a_{2n} \\ \cdot \\ \cdot \\ \cdot \\ a_{n1} & a_{n2} & \cdot & \cdot & \cdot & a_{nn} \end{vmatrix}$$

the summation, of $n!$ terms, being extended over all arrangements $(\alpha, \beta, \ldots, \nu)$ of the second or column suffixes of the elements a_{ij}, and the sign $+$ or $-$ being prefixed to any element according as the arrangement is even or odd. (See § 1.6.)

E.g. $$\begin{vmatrix} a_{11} & a_{12} \\ a_{21} & a_{22} \end{vmatrix} = a_{11}a_{22} - a_{12}a_{21}.$$

Properties of determinants

(i) A determinant is unaltered by interchanging its rows with its columns. Hence every property stated for rows holds also for columns.

(ii) A determinant is altered only in sign by interchanging two rows.

(iii) A determinant with two rows identical has the value zero.

(iv) If the elements of one row are a constant multiple of those of another row, the determinant has the value zero.

(v) If a constant multiple of the elements of one row is added to the elements of another row, the value of the determinant is unaltered.

(vi) If the elements of one row of a determinant are multiplied by k, the determinant is multiplied by k.

(vii) A determinant $\|a_{ij}\|$, in which no special relation holds between the a_{ij}, cannot be factorized into rational factors; that is, it is a prime polynomial in its elements.

Minors. Methods of expansion

The determinant of the matrix formed from a square matrix A by suppressing the ith row and jth column of A is called the *minor* of a_{ij} in A. The *co-factor* $|A_{ij}|$ of a_{ij} in $|A|$ is $(-1)^{i+j}\times$minor of a_{ij} in A, and is equal to $\dfrac{\partial|A|}{\partial a_{ij}}$.* The terms involving a_{ij} in $|A|$ are $a_{ij}|A_{ij}|$.

Expansion by rows or columns. A determinant can be expanded or expressed in terms of the elements of any row and their co-factors:

$$a_{i1}|A_{i1}| + a_{i2}|A_{i2}| + \ldots + a_{in}|A_{in}| = |A|, \quad (i=1, 2, \ldots, n).$$

An expansion by alien co-factors is the inner product of the elements of one row and the co-factors of the elements of another row. Its value is zero.

$$\text{i.e. } a_{i1}|A_{k1}| + a_{i2}|A_{k2}| + \ldots + a_{in}|A_{kn}| = 0 \qquad (i \neq k)$$
$$= |A| \qquad (i=k).$$

Expanding by the jth column

$$a_{1j}|A_{1k}| + a_{2j}|A_{2k}| + \ldots + a_{nj}|A_{nk}| = 0, \qquad (j \neq k)$$
$$= |A|, \qquad (j=k).$$

* See § 12.5.

Complementary minors

The determinant of the matrix obtained by suppressing k rows and k columns of A is called a minor of A of order $n-k$. The determinant of the square matrix of order k, which is composed of the elements common to the rows and columns suppressed, is a minor of order k. These two minors are said to be complementary, e.g. in

$$|A| \equiv \begin{vmatrix} a_{11} & a_{12} & a_{13} & a_{14} \\ a_{21} & a_{22} & a_{23} & a_{24} \\ a_{31} & a_{32} & a_{33} & a_{34} \\ a_{41} & a_{42} & a_{43} & a_{44} \end{vmatrix}, \qquad (1)$$

$$\begin{vmatrix} a_{11} & a_{13} \\ a_{31} & a_{33} \end{vmatrix} \text{ and } \begin{vmatrix} a_{22} & a_{24} \\ a_{42} & a_{44} \end{vmatrix}$$

are complementary.

Laplace's expansion. Select k rows $i_1, i_2, \ldots, i_k$ of $|A|$. Form the $\binom{n}{k}$ minors of order k from these rows and multiply each by its co-factor i.e. by $(-1)^{i_1+i_2 \ldots +i_k+j_1+j_2+ \ldots +j_k} \times$ its complementary minor in A, when the minor of order k is formed from the columns $j_1, j_2, \ldots, j_k$. The sum of these products $=|A|$.

Example. The expansion of (1) by its first and third rows is

$$-\begin{vmatrix} a_{11} & a_{12} \\ a_{31} & a_{32} \end{vmatrix} \begin{vmatrix} a_{23} & a_{24} \\ a_{43} & a_{44} \end{vmatrix} + \begin{vmatrix} a_{11} & a_{13} \\ a_{31} & a_{33} \end{vmatrix} \begin{vmatrix} a_{22} & a_{24} \\ a_{42} & a_{44} \end{vmatrix}$$

$$-\begin{vmatrix} a_{11} & a_{14} \\ a_{31} & a_{34} \end{vmatrix} \begin{vmatrix} a_{22} & a_{23} \\ a_{42} & a_{43} \end{vmatrix} - \begin{vmatrix} a_{12} & a_{13} \\ a_{32} & a_{33} \end{vmatrix} \begin{vmatrix} a_{21} & a_{24} \\ a_{41} & a_{44} \end{vmatrix}$$

$$+\begin{vmatrix} a_{12} & a_{14} \\ a_{32} & a_{34} \end{vmatrix} \begin{vmatrix} a_{21} & a_{23} \\ a_{41} & a_{43} \end{vmatrix} - \begin{vmatrix} a_{13} & a_{14} \\ a_{33} & a_{34} \end{vmatrix} \begin{vmatrix} a_{21} & a_{22} \\ a_{41} & a_{42} \end{vmatrix}.$$

Similarly the Laplace expansion for any columns may be written down.

The Laplace expansion of a determinant by alien co-factors is zero; that is, the sum of the products of the minors of order k from k given rows by the co-factors of the corresponding minors of a different set of k rows is zero.

The Summation convention for repeated literal suffixes will be used. By this convention

$$(a_{ik}b_{kj}) \text{ denotes } \sum_{k=1}^{n} a_{ik}b_{kj}$$

and

$$(a_{ik}b_{ik}) \text{ denotes } \sum_{i=1}^{m} \sum_{k=1}^{n} a_{ik}b_{ik},$$

where the numbers m and n are known from the context. A repeated numerical suffix such as 1 in $a_{i1}x_1$ will not imply summation.

Multiplication of determinants of order n.

The product of two determinants, each of order n, can be expressed as a determinant of order n in four different ways:

$$|A|\ |B| = \|a_{ij}\|\ \|b_{ij}\| = \|(a_{ik}b_{kj})\| = \|(a_{ik}b_{jk})\|$$
$$= \|(a_{ki}b_{kj})\| = \|(a_{ki}b_{jk})\|.$$

Derivate of a determinant of order n. If the elements a_{ij} are functions of x, $\frac{d|A|}{dx}$ is equal to the sum of the n determinants obtained from $|A|$ by differentiating the elements of one row of $|A|$ and leaving the other rows unchanged.

3.3. Operations of matrix algebra

(i) Two matrices $[a_{ij}]$ and $[b_{ij}]$ are *equal* if, and only if, they are identical, i.e. if they are of the same order $m \times n$ and if $a_{ij} = b_{ij}$ for every i and j.

(ii) *Addition.* Two matrices may be added if, and only if, they are of the same order $m \times n$. They are then said to be *conformable for addition* and their *sum* is

$$A + B \equiv [a_{ij}] + [b_{ij}] = [(a_{ij} + b_{ij})].$$

(iii) Any matrix may be multiplied by a *scalar* λ, which may be real or complex. Then

$$\lambda A \equiv \lambda[a_{ij}] = [(\lambda a_{ij})] = A\lambda.$$

If $A, B, \ldots, K$ are matrices of the same order and $\alpha, \beta, \ldots, \kappa$ are scalars,

$$\alpha A + \beta B + \ldots + \kappa K \equiv \alpha[a_{ij}] + \beta[b_{ij}] + \ldots + \kappa[k_{ij}]$$
$$= [\alpha a_{ij} + \beta b_{ij} + \ldots + \kappa k_{ij}].$$

(iv) *Multiplication.* The matrices A and B (in that order) are *conformable for multiplication* if the number of columns of A is equal to the number of rows of B. If $A \equiv [a_{ij}]$ is of order $m \times n$ and $B \equiv [b_{ij}]$ of order $n \times p$, then

$$AB \equiv [a_{ij}][b_{ij}] = [(\sum_{k=1}^{n} a_{ik}b_{kj})] \equiv [(a_{ik}b_{kj})].$$

AB is of order $m \times p$ and its (i, j)th element is the inner product of the ith row of A and the jth column of B. To form AB, A is said to be *post-multiplied* by B or B *pre-multiplied* by A.

If A and B are conformable for multiplication, B and A need not be. AB and BA both exist only if A is of order $m \times n$ and B of order

$n \times m$. Then AB is square of order m and BA is square of order n. If $m=n$, AB is not in general equal to BA.

$$(AB)C=[(a_{i\beta}b_{\beta\gamma}c_{\gamma j})]=A(BC)=ABC,$$
$$ABC\ldots K=[(a_{i\beta}b_{\beta\gamma}c_{\gamma\delta}\ldots k_{\kappa j})],$$

where i and j are the only suffixes which do not imply summation.

The unit matrix I is a square matrix A in which $a_{ij}=0$ if $i\neq j$, $a_{ii}=1$, i.e. every element in the principal diagonal (top left to bottom right) is unity and all other elements are zero. The (i, j)th element of I is often denoted by δ_{ij}.

Then
$$I\,.\,I\equiv I^2=I,$$
$$IA=A=AI,$$

provided A and I are conformable for multiplication in the order taken. The symbol I_n is used for the unit matrix of order n if it is necessary to indicate the order.

A *null* or *zero matrix* O is a matrix of any order every element of which is zero.

Then
$$O\,.\,A=O,$$
$$A\,.\,O=O$$

for all matrices A, provided A and O are conformable for multiplication.

Laws of matrix algebra

Matrices which are conformable for addition and multiplication obey the associative and distributive laws and the commutative law of addition, I, III-IX in § 1.1, but do not in general obey the commutative law of multiplication II.

Transpose, adjugate and reciprocal of a matrix

The *transpose* of $A\equiv[a_{ij}]$ is the matrix $A'\equiv[a_{ji}]$, i.e. the matrix whose (i, j)th element is the (j, i)th element of A.

The *adjoint* or *adjugate* of a square matrix A is

$$\text{adj } A=[|A_{ji}|]=[|A_{ij}|]'.$$

It is the matrix whose (i, j)th element is the co-factor of the (j, i)th element in $|A|$. Its determinant $|\text{adj } A|$ is called the *adjugate determinant* of A, or the *adjugate* of $|A|$.

$$A\,(\text{adj } A)=(\text{adj } A)\,A=|A|\,I.$$

A square matrix is said to be *singular* if $|A|=O$ and *non-singular* if $|A|\neq O$. If A is singular

$$A\,(\text{adj } A)=(\text{adj } A)\,A=O.$$

The *reciprocal* matrix A^{-1} of A exists only if A is non-singular. It is defined by the equation $A^{-1}A=I$ and is unique. Moreover $AA^{-1}=I$ and the value of A^{-1} is

$$A^{-1}=\left[\frac{|A_{ji}|}{|A|}\right]=\frac{1}{|A|}\operatorname{adj} A.$$

A simple method of calculating A^{-1} is to reduce A to the reduced echelon form (see § 3.61) by a sequence of elementary row operations. If the reduced echelon form is I, A is non-singular. Perform the same sequence of elementary row operations on I. The result is A^{-1}.

The transpose of the transpose of A is A,

i.e. $$(A')'=A.$$

The reciprocal of the reciprocal of A is A,

i.e. $$(A^{-1})^{-1}=A.$$

The transpose of the reciprocal of A is the reciprocal of the transpose of A,

i.e. $$(A^{-1})'=(A')^{-1}.$$

Jacobi's theorem on minors of the adjugate

Any minor of order k in adj A is equal to the complementary signed minor in A' multiplied by $|A|^{k-1}$.

The theorem holds whether A is singular or not, provided that, if A is singular and $k=1$, $|A|^{k-1}$ is interpreted as 1.

If A is non-singular, the theorem may be stated as: Any minor of order k in A^{-1} is equal to the complementary signed minor in A' multiplied by $|A|^{-1}$.

Cauchy's theorem. If A is square of order n,

$$|\operatorname{adj} A|=|A|^{n-1}.$$

Transpose, adjugate and reciprocal of a product

The transpose of a product is the product of the transposes in the reverse order,

i.e. $$(A_1A_2\ldots A_k)'=A_k'A_{k-1}'\ldots A_2'A_1'.$$

The adjugate of a product is the product of the adjugates in the reverse order,

i.e. $$\operatorname{adj}(A_1A_2\ldots A_k)=(\operatorname{adj} A_k)\,.\,(\operatorname{adj} A_{k-1})\ldots(\operatorname{adj} A_2)\,.\,(\operatorname{adj} A_1).$$

The reciprocal of a product is the product of the reciprocals in the reverse order,

i.e. $$(A_1A_2\ldots A_k)^{-1}=A_k^{-1}A_{k-1}^{-1}\ldots A_2^{-1}A_1^{-1}.$$

Index law for square matrices. If r is a positive integer, A^r is defined to be $A.A. \ldots A$ (r factors) and A^{-r} to be $(A^{-1})^r$ and A° to be I. For all integers r and s,

$$A^r A^s = A^{r+s},$$
$$(A^r)^s = A^{rs}.$$

Rational functions of a matrix. If $a_0, a_1, \ldots, a_p$ are scalars and A is a square matrix, the matrix sum

$$f(A) \equiv a_0 I + a_1 A + \ldots + a_p A^p$$

is a single matrix and is called a polynomial in A. If $f(A)$ is non-singular, its reciprocal $[f(A)]^{-1}$ may be denoted by $\dfrac{1}{f(A)}$. If $g(A)$ is another polynomial in A, the product $\dfrac{1}{f(A)} \cdot g(A)$ is a single matrix said to be a rational function of A.

3.31. Matrix algebra differs from the algebra of real or complex numbers in that

$$AB \neq BA \text{ in general.}$$

If $AB = O$, it does not follow that either $A = O$ or $B = O$ or $BA = O$.
If $A^2 = I$, it does not follow that $A = \pm I$.
If $A^2 = B^2$, it does not follow that $A = \pm B$.
If $A^2 = O$, it does not follow that $A = O$.
But if $AB = O$ and A is non-singular, then $B = O$.
If $AB = O$ and B is non-singular, then $A = O$.
If $AX = B$ and A is non-singular, then $X = A^{-1}B$, and this solution is unique.
If $YA = B$ and A is non-singular, then $Y = BA^{-1}$, and this solution is unique.

3.32. Special matrices

A *scalar* matrix is a matrix γI, where γ is a scalar.

A *diagonal* or *quasi-scalar* matrix is a square matrix for which $a_{ij} = 0$ if $i \neq j$.

A *symmetric* matrix A satisfies the equation

$$A' = A,$$

i.e. $$a_{ij} = a_{ji}.$$

A *skew* matrix A satisfies the equation

$$A' = -A,$$

i.e. $$a_{ij} = -a_{ji},\ a_{ii} = 0.$$

The *complex conjugate* $\bar{A}$ of a matrix $A \equiv [a_{ij}]$ is the matrix $\bar{A} = [\bar{a}_{ij}]$.

A *Hermitian* matrix A satisfies the equation

$$\bar{A}' = A.$$

A *Skew-Hermitian* or *anti-Hermitian* matrix satisfies

$$\bar{A}' = -A.$$

An *orthogonal* matrix is a square matrix A which satisfies the equation

$$A'A = I.$$

Then $AA' = I$. Since $|A| = \pm 1$, A is non-singular and $A^{-1} = A'$.

A *unitary* matrix A satisfies the equation

$$\bar{A}'A = I.$$

3.33. A *submatrix* of order $r \times s$ of A is the array of elements common to the (not necessarily consecutive) rows $i_1, i_2, \ldots, i_r$ and columns $j_1, j_2, \ldots, j_s$. In particular, the rows of A are submatrices of order $1 \times n$, the columns are submatrices of order $m \times 1$ and the elements submatrices of order 1×1.

A minor of order r of a matrix A is the determinant of a square submatrix of order r of A.

A diagonal matrix A may be written diag $\{a_1, a_2, \ldots, a_n\}$, where $a_1, a_2, \ldots, a_n$ are the elements in the leading diagonal.* The notation has been extended to submatrices. If A_r is a square submatrix of order n_r, then diag $\{A_1, A_2, \ldots, A_k\}$ denotes the square matrix

$$\begin{bmatrix} A_1 & O & & O \\ O & A_2 & & O \\ & & & \\ & & & \\ O & O & & A_k \end{bmatrix}$$

of order $\sum_{r=1}^{k} n_r$.

If $A_1, A_2, \ldots, A_k$; $B_1, B_2, \ldots, B_k$ be two sets of square matrices each of order $n_1, n_2, \ldots, n_k$ respectively, and if

$$A = \text{diag}\,\{A_1, A_2, \ldots, A_k\}, \quad B = \text{diag}\,\{B_1, B_2, \ldots, B_k\},$$

then

$$AB = \text{diag}\,\{A_1B_1, A_2B_2, \ldots, A_kB_k\},$$

$$A^2 = \text{diag}\,\{A_1^2, A_2^2, \ldots, A_k^2\},$$

$$f(A) = \text{diag}\,\{f(A_1), f(A_2), \ldots, f(A_k)\},$$

where $f(A)$ is a polynomial in A or a rational function $g(A)/h(A)$, provided none of the matrices $h(A_i)$ is singular.

* The leading diagonal of $[a_{rs}]$ is the diagonal which includes the element a_{11}.

3.4. Rank and linear dependence

Definition. A matrix is of *rank* r if r is the largest integer for which the statement "not *all* minors of order r are zero" is true.

The rank of AB cannot exceed the rank of either factor.

If B and C are non-singular, then A, AB and CA have the same rank.

If A is square of order n and rank r, its *nullity* is $n-r$. If A is of order $m\times n$ and rank r, it has row nullity $m-r$ and column nullity $n-r$.

The nullity of $AB \leqslant$ nullity of $A+$nullity of B.

Definition. The rows of $A=[a_{ij}]$ are said to be *linearly dependent* if there is an identity

$$\lambda_1 a_{1j}+\lambda_2 a_{2j}+\ldots+\lambda_m a_{mj}\equiv 0 \quad (j=1, 2, \ldots, n), \quad . \quad . \quad (2)$$

i.e.

$$\lambda_i a_{ij}\equiv 0 \quad (j=1, 2, \ldots, n),$$

where the λ_i are scalars and are not all zero. If λ_s is not zero, the sth row of the matrix is said to be linearly dependent on the remaining rows or to be a sum of multiples of the remaining rows. The rows are *linearly independent* if (2) is satisfied only when $\lambda_1=\lambda_2=\ldots=\lambda_m=0$.

If A is of rank r, the maximum number of linearly independent rows (or columns) of A is r, and we can select r rows (columns) which are linearly independent and express any other row (column) as a sum of multiples of these r rows (columns).

3.5. Characteristic equation of a square matrix. Latent roots

A matrix $A-\lambda I$, where λ is a real or complex number, is associated with every square matrix A.

Definition. The equation

$$f(\lambda)\equiv|A-\lambda I|=0$$

is called the *characteristic equation* of A and its roots are the *latent* or *characteristic roots* or *eigen-values* of A.

$$|A-\lambda I|\equiv(-\lambda)^n+(-\lambda)^{n-1}(\text{trace } A)$$
$$+(-\lambda)^{n-2}\Sigma(\text{principal minors of A of order 2})+\ldots+|A|.$$

Theorem. Every square matrix satisfies its own characteristic equation; i.e. if

$$|A-\lambda I|\equiv(-1)^n(\lambda^n+p_1\lambda^{n-1}+\ldots+p_n)$$
$$\equiv(-1)^n(\lambda-\lambda_1)(\lambda-\lambda_2)\ldots(\lambda-\lambda_n),$$

then

$$A^n+p_1A^{n-1}+\ldots+p_nI\equiv(A-\lambda_1 I)(A-\lambda_2 I)\ldots(A-\lambda_n I)=0.$$

It does *not* follow that $A-\lambda_r I=0$ for any r.

If $g(\lambda)$ is a polynomial in λ and A is a square matrix, then

$$|g(A)| = g(\lambda_1)\, g(\lambda_2) \ldots g(\lambda_n),$$

where $\lambda_1, \lambda_2, \ldots, \lambda_n$ are the latent roots of A.

If $h(A) = g_1(A)/g_2(A)$, where $g_1(A)$ and $g_2(A)$ are polynomials in A and $g_2(A)$ is non-singular, then

$$|\lambda I - h(A)| = \prod_{r=1}^{n} \{\lambda - h(\lambda_r)\}.$$

Hence the latent roots of $h(A)$ are $h(\lambda_r)$, $(r = 1, \ldots, n)$.

3.6. Elementary operations on a matrix

The *elementary row* (*column*) operations on a matrix are:

(I) The interchange of two rows (columns).

(II) The multiplication of the elements of a row (column) by a number k other than zero.

(III) The addition to the elements of one row (column) of a multiple d of the corresponding elements of another row (column).

Let K_{ij} be a square matrix having 1 in the (i, j)th place and zero elsewhere.

An *elementary* square row-matrix E of order m is a matrix obtained from I_m by one elementary row operation of type (I), (II) or (III). It is of one of the types.

(I) E_{ij}, obtained from I_m by interchanging its ith and jth rows.

(II) $M_{k,\,i} \equiv I + (k-1)K_{ii}$, obtained by multiplying the ith row of I_m by k.

(III) $P_{i;\,d,\,j} \equiv I + dK_{ij}$, obtained by adding d times the jth row of I_m to the ith.

Elementary matrices are non-singular since

$$|E_{ij}| = -1, \quad |M_{k,\,i}| = |I + (k-1)K_{ii}| = k, \quad |I + dK_{ij}| = |P_{i;\,d,\,j}| = 1.$$

The inverse of an elementary matrix is an elementary matrix of the same type.

$$E_{ij}^{-1} = E_{ij}, \quad M_{k,i}^{-1} = M_{1/k,\,i},$$
$$P_{i;\,d,j}^{-1} = P_{i;\,-d,\,j}, \quad i \neq j.$$

The result of an elementary row operation on any $m \times n$ matrix A is the matrix EA obtained by pre-multiplying A by the corresponding elementary matrix E of order $m \times m$ obtained from I_m by the same row operation.

A matrix B is *row-equivalent* to A if it can be obtained from A by a finite sequence of elementary row operations. The relation is *reflexive*, i.e. A is then row-equivalent to B. Row equivalence is *transitive*, i.e. if A is row-equivalent to B and B to C, then A is row-equivalent to C.

The matrices A and B are row-equivalent if $B=QA$, where Q is non-singular. The converse holds.

A square matrix Q is non-singular if, and only if, it can be written as a product of a finite number of elementary square matrices.

3.61. Row-reduced matrices

The *leading entry* in a non-zero row is the first non-zero entry in that row.

A matrix A is *row-reduced* if

(*a*) every leading entry (of a non-zero row) is 1,

(*b*) every column containing such a leading entry 1 has all its other entries zero.

A (row) *reduced echelon* matrix is one for which (*a*), (*b*), (*c*) and (*d*) hold, where

(*c*) each zero row of A lies below all non-zero rows,

(*d*) there are r non-zero rows and the leading entry in the ith row is in column t_i, where

$$t_1 < t_2 < \dots < t_r.$$

An *echelon* matrix is one which satisfies (*a*), (*c*) and (*d*).

There is a reduced echelon matrix row-equivalent to any matrix.

It may be found in many ways. A systematic method is as follows:

(In these instructions a_{ij} indicates the element standing in the $(i, j)^{\text{th}}$ place at the moment considered.)

(1) Interchange rows so that all zero rows are below the non-zero rows.

(2) Suppose column s is the first non-zero column. If $a_{1s}=0$, interchange row 1 and row k, where $a_{ks} \neq 0$, $a_{is}=0$ for all $i<k$.

(3) Multiply the first row by $1/a_{1s}$.

(4) Subtract from each element a_{ij} in the ith row, $a_{is} \times$ the corresponding element a_{1j} of the first row for all $i \geqslant 2$.

(5) Suppose the next non-zero column is column t. If $a_{2t}=0$, interchange row 2 and row k, where $a_{kt} \neq 0$, $a_{it}=0$ for $2 \leqslant i < k$.

(6) Multiply row 2 by $1/a_{2t}$.

(7) Subtract from each element a_{ij} in the ith row, $a_{it} \times$ the corresponding element a_{2j} of the second row, for all $i \neq 2$; and so on.

This gives a reduced echelon form.

For the echelon form, perform processes (1) to (6) and then perform (7) for all $i \geqslant 3$; and so on.

The rank of a matrix A is equal to the number of non-zero rows in any echelon matrix row-equivalent to A.

3.62. Column operations

The result of the elementary column operation on I, corresponding to the row operation I, II or III of § 3.6, is the matrix E'_{ij}, $M'_{k,\, i}$, $P'_{i;\, d,\, j}$, respectively. The result of an elementary column operation on an $m \times n$ matrix A is AE, where E is the elementary matrix of order $n \times n$ obtained from I_n by the same operation.

A can be transformed into B by a succession of elementary column operations if, and only if, A' can be transformed into B' by an equivalent succession of elementary row operations. If $B' = QA'$, then $B = AQ' = AP$, where $P = Q'$.

3.63. General equivalence

Two $m \times n$ matrices A and B are *equivalent* if, and only if, B can be obtained from A by a finite sequence of elementary row and column operations. Then

$$B = QAP,$$

where P and Q are non-singular square matrices of orders n and m respectively. Every such matrix QAP is equivalent to A. Equivalence is transitive.

An $m \times n$ matrix A of rank r is equivalent to the $m \times n$ diagonal matrix

$$\begin{bmatrix} I_r & O_{r,\, n-r} \\ O_{m-r,\, r} & O_{m-r,\, n-r} \end{bmatrix},$$

where O_{ij} denotes a null $i \times j$ matrix. Matrices are equivalent if, and only if, they have the same order and rank.

3.7. Equivalent λ-matrices

In this section all matrices are square and their elements are polynomials in a variable λ with scalar coefficients.

A λ-matrix, $A = [a_{ij}]$, is a matrix whose elements are polynomials in λ. The determinant $|A|$ is in general a polynomial in λ. It may be a constant.

A λ-matrix A is said to be singular if $|A| \equiv O$ and to be non-singular if $|A|$ is not identically zero. A non-singular λ-matrix need not have a λ-matrix inverse to it.

A λ-matrix is of rank r if r is the largest integer for which the statement "not all minors of order r are identically zero" holds.

The elementary λ-operations of a matrix are the operations (I) and (II) in § 3.6 and

(IIIλ) The addition to the elements of the ith row (column) of the corresponding elements of the jth row (column) multiplied by a polynomial in λ or by a constant.

Such operations can be effected by matrix multiplication. If H_{ij} has the polynomial in λ in the (i, j)th place and zero elsewhere, and $X=I+H_{ij}$, $Y=I+H_{ji}=X'$, the operation IIIλ on rows (columns) is effected by pre- (post-) multiplying A by X (Y). Moreover, $|X|=1=|Y|$; $[I+H_{ij}]^{-1}=I-H_{ij}$, which is a matrix of an operation IIIλ.

Two matrices are λ-equivalent if it is possible to pass from one to the other by a finite sequence of λ-operations.

The following theorem gives the simplest form QAP to which a λ-matrix can be reduced by a finite number of λ-operations of the types I, II and IIIλ, and corresponding column operations. P and Q are the product of the finite number of the elementary matrices of the operations.

Theorem. Let A by a λ-matrix of order n and rank $r \geqslant 1$. If $r<n$, A is λ-equivalent to a matrix of the form

$$N \equiv \begin{bmatrix} E & O \\ O & O \end{bmatrix},$$

where the Os denote null sub-matrices and

$$E=\text{diag}\,\{E_1, E_2, \ldots, E_r\},$$

each E_s being either unity or a polynomial in λ with unity as the coefficient of the highest power of λ. Further, E_1 is a factor of E_2, E_2 a factor of E_3, . . ., E_{r-1} a factor of E_r and $E_1, E_2, \ldots, E_r$ are called the *invariant factors* of A. If $r=n$, A is λ-equivalent to E. N is called the equivalent normal form of the λ-matrix A.

The highest common factor

of the elements of A is	E_1,
of the 2-rowed minors of A is	E_1E_2,
of the 3-rowed minors of A is	$E_1E_2E_3$,
. . . .	. . .
of the r-rowed minors of A is	$E_1E_2 \ldots E_r$.

If A is non-singular, $|A|=E_1E_2 \ldots E_n$.

Theorem. If A is λ-equivalent to B, then A and B have the same rank r, the same normal λ-equivalent form N, and, for $t=1, 2, \ldots, r$, the same H.C.F. of t-rowed minors.

Conversely, if A and B have the same rank r and order n, and, for $t=1, 2, \ldots, r$, the same H.C.F. of t-rowed minors, then A and B are λ-equivalent and have the same normal λ-equivalent form N.

3.71. Elementary divisors

If the entries in the matrix are regarded as complex polynomials, then on factorizing, the invariant factors are

$$E_1=(\lambda-\alpha)^{a_1}(\lambda-\beta)^{b_1}\ldots(\lambda-\kappa)^{k_1},$$
$$E_2=(\lambda-\alpha)^{a_2}(\lambda-\beta)^{b_2}\ldots(\lambda-\kappa)^{k_2},$$
$$\cdots\cdots\cdots\cdots\cdots$$
$$\cdots\cdots\cdots\cdots\cdots$$
$$E_r=(\lambda-\alpha)^{a_r}(\lambda-\beta)^{b_r}\ldots(\lambda-\kappa)^{k_r},$$

where
$$a_1<a_2<\ldots<a_r,$$
$$b_1<b_2<\ldots<b_r,$$
$$\vdots$$
$$k_1<k_2<\quad<k_r.$$

Those of the factors $(\lambda-\alpha)^{a_1}$, . . ., $(\lambda-\kappa)^{k_r}$ which are not unity are called the *elementary divisors* of A.

Necessary and sufficient conditions for λ-equivalence

Each one of the following is a necessary and sufficient condition for two square matrices A and B of order n, whose elements are complex polynomials, to be λ-equivalent.

(i) That there are λ-matrices P and Q for which $|P|$ and $|Q|$ are non-zero constants and

$$QAP=B.$$

(ii) That A and B have the same invariant factors.

(iii) That A and B have the same set of elementary divisors.

Definition. The *minimal polynomial* of a matrix A is the polynomial $h(\lambda)\equiv\lambda^m+h_1\lambda^{m-1}+\ldots+h_m$, of lowest degree m, for which $h(A)=0$. This polynomial is unique. It is also called the *reduced characteristic function* of the matrix A or the *minimum function* of A.

If A is square of order n and the invariant factors of $(\lambda I-A)$ are $E_1(\lambda)$, $E_2(\lambda)$, . . ., $E_n(\lambda)$, then the minimal polynomial of the matrix A is $E_n(\lambda)$.

If $g(\lambda)$ is a polynomial, then $g(A)=0$ if, and only if, $g(\lambda)$ contains $E_n(\lambda)$ as a factor.

3.72. *Matrices that are linear in λ*, i.e. in which each element is a constant or is linear in λ.

Let a_1, a_2, b_1, b_2 be matrices whose elements are scalars and let

b_1, b_2 be non-singular. If the matrices $A_1 \equiv a_1 - \lambda b_1$, $A_2 \equiv a_2 - \lambda b_2$ are λ-equivalent, then there are non-singular matrices p, q, with scalar elements for which

$$A_2 = qA_1p.$$

Further

$$a_2 = qa_1p, \quad b_2 = qb_1p.$$

If a_1 and a_2 are matrices with scalar elements such that $A_1 \equiv a_1 - \lambda I$ and $A_2 \equiv a_2 - \lambda I$ are λ-equivalent, then there is a non-singular matrix P with scalar elements for which

$$A_2 = P^{-1}A_1P, \quad a_2 = P^{-1}a_1P.$$

Conversely, if $a_2 = P^{-1}a_1P$, then $A_2 = P^{-1}A_1P$, and A_1 and A_2 are λ-equivalent.

If a_1 and a_2 are matrices with scalar elements, then a necessary and sufficient condition that a matrix P, with scalar elements, exists, for which $a_2 = P^{-1}a_1P$, is that the two matrices $a_1 - \lambda I$, $a_2 - \lambda I$ have the same invariant factors, or what is the same thing, the same set of elementary divisors.

If A is a square matrix whose elements are constants, then $|\lambda I - A|$ is equal to the product of the invariant factors of $(\lambda I - A)$.

3.8. Transforms of a square matrix. Similarity

Definition. If P is a non-singular matrix whose elements are scalars and

$$B = P^{-1}AP, \qquad \ldots \qquad (3)$$

B is said to be *similar* or *c-equivalent* to A or to be a *transform* of A written $B \sim A$.

The relation is reflexive and transitive.

If $f(A)$ and $g(A)$ are polynomials in A and $g(A)$ is non-singular, and (3) holds, then

$$\frac{f(B)}{g(B)} = P^{-1}\frac{f(A)}{g(A)}P,$$

i.e. any rational function of A is transformed by pre- and post-multiplying it by the same matrices P^{-1} and P.

If A and B are similar,

$$|B - \lambda I| = |A - \lambda I|,$$

i.e. A and B have the same characteristic equation.

If $A \sim B$, then $(A - \lambda I) \sim (B - \lambda I)$.

3.81. *Geometrical interpretation.* Let X be a column matrix whose elements are the homogeneous co-ordinates of a point x in a space of dimension $[n-1]$ or of a vector x in $[n]$, where $X' = [x_1, \ldots, x_n]$, and let $L' = [l_1, \ldots, l_n]$ be the tangential co-ordinates (q.v.) of a prime l in the space. The matrix equation

$$Y = AX$$

expresses a relation between the variable points x and y.

If the co-ordinate system be changed from X to X^* by the transformation

$$X = PX^*, \quad |P| \neq 0,$$

so that $X^* = P^{-1}X$ and $Y^* = P^{-1}Y$ are the new co-ordinates of the points x and y, then

$$Y^* = P^{-1}APX^*.$$

The bilinear form $L'AX$ (q.v.) becomes $L^{*\prime}P^{-1}APX$. Thus the effect of replacing A by $P^{-1}AP$ is equivalent to considering the same relation in a new co-ordinate system.

3.82. Elementary classical submatrices

The matrix

$$C_s(\lambda) \equiv \begin{bmatrix} \lambda & 1 & & & \\ & \lambda & 1 & & \\ & & & & \\ & & & \lambda & 1 \\ & & & & \lambda \end{bmatrix},$$

where $C_s(\lambda)$ is of order s, each diagonal element is λ, each element immediately above the diagonal is unity, and all other elements are zero, is called an *elementary classical submatrix*.

The expression

$$\text{diag}\,\{C_1{}^p(\lambda),\, C_2{}^q(\lambda),\, \ldots\}$$

denotes a matrix D in which the submatrices are arranged diagonally so that their diagonals lie along the principal diagonal of D and in which $C_1(\lambda)$ enters p times, $C_2(\lambda)$ enters q times, and so on, all the other elements being zero. D is a diagonal matrix only if it is diag $\{C_1{}^p(\lambda)\}$.

Classical canonical form of a square matrix A

A matrix A of order n, with complex elements, k of whose characteristic roots are distinct, is similar to a matrix

$$C \equiv \text{diag}\,\{D_1, D_2, \ldots, D_k\}$$

in which $D_1, \ldots, D_k$ are submatrices which correspond to the k distinct roots $\lambda_1, \ldots, \lambda_k$, and each D_i is of the form

$$D_i \equiv \text{diag}\,\{C_1{}^p(\lambda_i),\, C_2{}^q(\lambda_i),\, \ldots\},$$

where $p + 2q + \ldots$ is the multiplicity of the root λ_i.

The classical canonical form C is usually the simplest matrix of the set of matrices similar to A. For many purposes one may work with C instead of A as this merely implies a change of co-ordinates. With proper safeguards, C can be used when considering functions of A and convergence properties.

A square matrix of order n and rank r is equivalent (by transformations of the type QAP) to a pure diagonal matrix having r non-zero elements in the leading diagonal and zeros elsewhere. This statement is also true for λ-equivalence of λ-matrices. It is true for similarity (by transformations of type $P^{-1}AP$) of matrices A when all the roots of $|A-\lambda I|=0$ are distinct and it is sometimes, but not always, true when two or more of the latent roots are equal. A necessary and sufficient condition that a matrix A have a transform which is diagonal is that all the elementary divisors of $(\lambda I-A)$ be linear. The transform is then diag $\{\lambda_1, \lambda_2, \ldots, \lambda_n\}$.

CHAPTER 4

ALGEBRAIC FORMS

4.1. Quadratic forms

Let a_{ij} be constants and x_i, y_i variables, and let A be the square matrix $[a_{ij}]$ of order n. The sets of elements of the matrices X, Y, where

$$X' \equiv [x_1, x_2, \ldots, x_n], \quad Y' \equiv [y_1, y_2, \ldots, y_n],$$

may be interpreted as co-ordinates of a vector in a vector space V_n or as homogeneous co-ordinates of a point* in $[n-1]$.

$$\sum_{i=1}^{n} \sum_{j=1}^{n} a_{ij}x_iy_j, \text{ written } (a_{ij}x_iy_j) \text{ or } X'AY,$$

is a *bilinear form* in x_i and y_i; whereas

$$\sum_{i=1}^{n} \sum_{j=1}^{n} a_{ij}x_ix_j, \text{ written } (a_{ij}x_ix_j), \text{ where } a_{ij}=a_{ji}, \text{ or } X'AX,$$

where $A'=A$, is a *quadratic* form in x_i. If the variables are real numbers, the form is said to be a "form in real variables". A *real form* is one in which both constants and variables are real.

A form $(b_{ij}x_ix_j)$ can be written as a quadratic form $(a_{ij}x_ix_j)$, where $a_{ij}=a_{ji}$, by writing $a_{ii}=b_{ii}$, $a_{ij}=a_{ji}=\frac{1}{2}(b_{ij}+b_{ji})$.

The *discriminant* of the quadratic form $X'AX$ is $|A|$.

4.2. Linear transformations

The set of equations

$$x_i = \sum_{j=1}^{n} m_{ij}z_j \equiv (m_{ij}z_j) \quad i=1, 2, \ldots, n,$$

or

$$X=MZ$$

is a *linear transformation* connecting the variables x_i and z_i. The transformation is real if the m_{ij} are real. The correspondence between X and Z is or is not (1, 1) according as the transformation is non-singular or singular, i.e. according as its *modulus* $|M|$ is not or is zero.

* In n-dimensional projective Geometry (cf. Chapter 10), a point may be defined as an ordered set of $n+1$ numbers $(x_0, x_1, \ldots, x_n)$, where $(\lambda x_0, \lambda x_1, \ldots, \lambda x_n)$ is the same point as $(x_0, x_1, \ldots, x_n)$. A linear space $[r]$ of dimension r is the aggregate of points

$$(\lambda_0 x_0^{(1)} + \ldots + \lambda_s x_0^{(s)}, \ldots, \lambda_0 x_n^{(1)} + \ldots \lambda_s x_n^{(s)}),$$

where the matrix $[x_i^{(j)}]$ is of rank $r+1$.

The product of the two transformations

$$X^{(1)} = M_1 X^{(2)}, \quad X^{(2)} = M_2 X^{(3)}$$

is the transformation

$$X^{(1)} = M_1 M_2 X^{(3)}.$$

If a transformation $X = MZ$ is applied to a quadratic form $X'AX$, the result is the quadratic form $Z'CZ$, where $C = M'AM$. The discriminant of the new form is $|C| = |M|^2 |A|$.

If transformations $X = MZ$, $Y = NW$ are applied to a bilinear form $Y'AX$, the result is a bilinear form $W'N'AMZ$.

The transformation $X = MZ$ is orthogonal if $M'M = I$.

4.3. Definite real forms

Definition. The real quadratic form $X'AX$ is said to be *positive definite* if it is positive for every set of real values of $X' = [x_1, x_2, \ldots, x_n]$ other than the set $X^1 = 0$. It is *negative definite* if it is negative for every set of real values of X^1 other than $X^1 = 0$. It is positive *semi-definite* if $X'AX \geqslant 0$ for all real values of X and *indefinite* if it is neither positive nor negative semi-definite.

Theorem I. If $X'AX$ is positive definite and is transformed into $Z'CZ$ by a real non-singular transformation, then $Z'CZ$ is positive definite.

Theorem II. Every real positive definite form $X'AX$ can be transformed by a real transformation of unit modulus into $c_{11}z_1^2 + c_{22}z_2^2 + \ldots + c_{nn}z_n^2$ wherein each c_{rr} is positive. It can also be transformed by a real transformation to $\sum_{i=1}^{n} w_i^2$.

Theorem III. A set of necessary and sufficient conditions that the real quadratic form $X'AX$ be positive semi-definite is

$$a_{11} \geqslant 0, \quad \begin{vmatrix} a_{11} & a_{12} \\ a_{21} & a_{22} \end{vmatrix} \geqslant 0, \quad \ldots, \quad \begin{vmatrix} a_{11} & a_{12} & \cdot & \cdot & \cdot & a_{1n} \\ a_{21} & a_{22} & \cdot & \cdot & \cdot & a_{2n} \\ \cdot & \cdot & \cdot & \cdot & \cdot & \cdot \\ \cdot & \cdot & \cdot & \cdot & \cdot & \cdot \\ a_{n1} & a_{n2} & \cdot & \cdot & \cdot & a_{nn} \end{vmatrix} \geqslant 0.$$

Theorem IV. A set of necessary and sufficient conditions that the real quadratic form $X'AX$ be negative semi-definite is

$$a_{11} \leqslant 0, \quad \begin{vmatrix} a_{11} & a_{12} \\ a_{21} & a_{22} \end{vmatrix} \geqslant 0, \quad \begin{vmatrix} a_{11} & a_{12} & a_{13} \\ a_{21} & a_{22} & a_{23} \\ a_{31} & a_{32} & a_{33} \end{vmatrix} \leqslant 0, \quad \ldots$$

and so on, n conditions in all.

In Theorems III and IV, if the inequality signs hold throughout, the forms are positive and negative definite respectively.

Other sets of necessary and sufficient conditions can be obtained by altering the order in which the variables are considered.

The real quadratic form $X'AX$ is positive definite if and only if there exists a real non-singular matrix P such that $A=PP'$.

4.4. The λ-equation of two quadratic forms

$$X'AX \text{ and } X'CX$$

is the equation

$$|A-\lambda C|=0.$$

The roots of the λ-equation of any two quadratic forms in n variables are unaltered by a non-singular linear transformation.

If C is the matrix of a positive definite form and A is any symmetric matrix with real elements, then all the roots of the equation $|A-\lambda C|=0$ are real. If the form $X'AX$ is also positive definite, all the roots are positive. In particular, if A is any symmetric matrix with real elements, the roots of the equation $|A-\lambda I|=0$ are real. If $X'AX$ is positive definite, every root is positive.

4.5. Canonical forms

The *rank* of a quadratic form is the rank of the matrix of its coefficients.

A quadratic form in n variables, of rank r, can be transformed by a non-singular transformation into the form $\alpha_1 z_1^2+\alpha_2 z_2^2+\ldots+\alpha_r z_r^2$, where $\alpha_1, \ldots \alpha_r$ are numbers, no one of which is zero.

If $X'AX$ be a real quadratic form and $X'BX$ a positive definite quadratic form in n variables, then there is a real non-singular transformation $X=HZ$ which expresses the two forms as

$$\lambda_1 z_1^2+\lambda_2 z_2^2+\ldots+\lambda_n z_n^2, \quad z_1^2+z_2^2+\ldots+z_n^2,$$

where $\lambda_1, \lambda_2, \ldots, \lambda_n$ are the roots of $|A-\lambda B|=0$ and are all real.

A real quadratic form $X'AX$ in n variables can be reduced by a real orthogonal transformation to the form

$$\lambda_1 z_1^2+\lambda_2 z_2^2+\ldots+\lambda_n z_n^2,$$

where $\lambda_1, \ldots, \lambda_n$ are the roots of $|A-\lambda I|=0$.

All these roots are real and the number of non-zero roots is equal to the rank of A.

Signature of a quadratic form

If a given real quadratic form of rank r is reduced by two real non-singular transformations to the forms

$$\beta_1 y_1^2+\beta_2 y_2^2+\ldots+\beta_r y_r^2, \quad \gamma_1 z_1^2+\gamma_2 z_2^2+\ldots+\gamma_r z_r^2,$$

then the number P of positive β_i is equal to the number of positive γ_i, and the number N of negative β_i is equal to the number of negative γ_i. The number $P-N$ is called the *signature* of the form.

If $Y'BY$, $Z'CZ$ be two real quadratic forms having the same rank r and the same signature s, then there is a real non-singular transformation $Y=PZ$ which transforms $Y'BY$ into $Z'CZ$.

4.6. Invariants and covariants of an algebraic form

An *algebraic form* of degree k in the n variables $x_1, x_2, \ldots, x_n$ is a homogeneous polynomial of degree k

$$\sum a_{\alpha, \beta, \ldots, \lambda} \frac{k!}{\alpha!\beta! \ldots \lambda!} x_1^{\alpha} x_2^{\beta} \ldots x_n^{\lambda}, \qquad (1)$$

wherein the $a_{\alpha \ldots \lambda}$ are constants and the sum is taken over all sets of integer or zero values of $\alpha, \beta, \ldots, \lambda$, which satisfy the conditions

$$0 \leqslant \alpha \leqslant k,\ 0 \leqslant \beta \leqslant k,\ \ldots,\ 0 \leqslant \lambda \leqslant k,\ \alpha+\beta+\ldots+\lambda=k.$$

We denote the form by $F(a, x)$ or by $F(a, x)_n{}^k$.

Let the variables be subject to a non-singular linear transformation $X=MZ$ which changes $F(a, x)$ into $G(A, z)$.

A function $\phi(a)$ of the coefficients a of an algebraic form $F(a, x)$ is said to be an *invariant* of the form if, for every non-singular M, the same function $\phi(A)$ of the coefficients of $G(A, z)$ is equal to $\phi(a)$ multiplied by a power of $|M|$, the power in question being independent of M.

E.g. for the quadratic form $X'AX$ in three variables, the discriminant $||a_{ij}||$ is an invariant.

An algebraic function $\phi(a)$ of the coefficients a of a number of algebraic forms $F_r(a, x)$ is said to be an *invariant* (or a *joint-invariant*) of the forms if, whatever the non-singular matrix M of the transformation $X=MZ$, the same function $\phi(A)$ of the coefficients A of the resulting forms $G_r(A, z)$ is equal to $\phi(a)$ multiplied by a certain power of $|M|$.

A *covariant* is a function $\phi(a; x)$ of the coefficients and variables of a form $F(a, x)$ or of a number of forms $F_r(a, x)$, which is such that the same function $\phi(A; z)$, of the transformed form or forms $G(A, z)$ or $G_r(A, z)$, is equal to $\phi(a; x)$ multiplied by a power of $|M|$.

E.g. if $f(a, x)$ is a form in three variables x, y, z, then the *Hessian*

$$\begin{vmatrix} f_{xx} & f_{xy} & f_{xz} \\ f_{yx} & f_{yy} & f_{yz} \\ f_{zx} & f_{zy} & f_{zz} \end{vmatrix}$$

is a covariant of $f(a, x)$.

Weight of a form

The *weight* of the coefficient $a_{\alpha, \beta, \ldots, \lambda}$ in the form (1) is the suffix λ corresponding to the power of x_n in the term. The weight of a product of coefficients is defined to be the sum of the weights of its constituent factors.

E.g. in the binary form $a_0x^k + ka_1x^{k-1}y + \ldots + a_k y^k$ the weight of each term is equal to its suffix.

Invariants of an algebraic form are algebraic forms in its coefficients. If $\phi(a)$ is a polynomial invariant of (1) of degree q in the a_i, then $\phi(a)$ must be isobaric and of weight kq/n, which is an integer.

An *irreducible* invariant of $f(a, x)$ is one which cannot be expressed rationally and integrally in terms of invariants of equal or lower degree.

An *irreducible* covariant is one which cannot be expressed rationally and integrally in terms of invariants and covariants of equal or lower degree in the coefficients a.

The number of irreducible covariants and invariants of a given form is finite.

4.7. Irreducible invariants and covariants of binary quadratic, cubic and quartic

Binary quadratic

$$f(x, y) \equiv a_0x^2 + 2a_1xy + a_2y^2$$

Invariant

$$\Delta \equiv a_0a_2 - a_1^2$$

Covariant

$$f(x, y).$$

Binary cubic

$$f(x, y) \equiv a_0x^3 + 3a_1x^2y + 3a_2xy^2 + a_3y^3$$

Invariant

$$\Delta \equiv (a_0a_3 - a_1a_2)^2 - 4(a_0a_2 - a_1^2)(a_1a_3 - a_2^2).$$

Covariants

(i) $$f(x, y),$$

(ii) $$H \equiv \tfrac{1}{36} \begin{vmatrix} f_{xx} & f_{xy} \\ f_{yx} & f_{yy} \end{vmatrix} *,$$

(iii) $$G \equiv \tfrac{1}{3} \begin{vmatrix} f_x & f_y \\ H_x & H_y \end{vmatrix}.$$

* See § 12.5.

Δ is the discriminant of the binary cubic. If $\Delta=0$, it has a repeated factor. H is its Hessian. If $\Delta\neq 0$, then

$$\Delta f^2 = G^2 + 4H^3.$$

Binary quartic

$$f(x, y) \equiv a_0x^4 + 4a_1x^3y + 6a_2x^2y^2 + 4a_3xy^3 + a_4y^4.$$

Invariants

(i) $I \equiv a_0a_4 - 4a_1a_3 + 3a_2^2.$

(ii) $J \equiv a_0a_2a_4 + 2a_1a_2a_3 - a_0a_3^2 - a_1^2a_4 - a_2^3.$

Covariants

(i) $$f(x, y).$$

(ii) $$H \equiv \tfrac{1}{144}\begin{vmatrix} f_{xx} & f_{xy} \\ f_{yx} & f_{yy} \end{vmatrix},$$

(iii) $$G \equiv \tfrac{1}{8}\begin{vmatrix} f_x & f_y \\ H_x & H_y \end{vmatrix}.$$

If $J=0$, the lines $f=0$ form an harmonic pencil. If $I=0$, the lines $f=0$ form an equianharmonic pencil (see § 10.4). The discriminant of $f(x, y)$ is $\Delta \equiv 256\,(I^3 - 27J^2)$, which vanishes if $f(x, y)$ has a repeated factor. If $H \equiv f(x, y) \times$ constant, f has two repeated factors. If $G \equiv 0$, f has two repeated factors. If $I=J=0$, f has a cubed factor. If $H\equiv 0$, f has a fourfold factor.

If $\Delta\neq 0$, the invariants and covariants are connected by the relation

$$G^2 + 4H^3 - IHf^2 + Jf^3 \equiv 0.$$

See also § 2.24.

4.8. Contragredients and mixed concomitants

If $(x_1, \ldots, x_n)$ are homogeneous co-ordinates (q.v.) in $[n-1]$ and are subjected to the transformation $X=MZ$, then the corresponding tangential or prime co-ordinates (q.v.) are transformed by $U=(M^{-1})'W$. The vectors x and u are said to be *transformed contragrediently*.

A *mixed concomitant* is a function $\phi(a;\ x;\ u)$ of the coefficients and variables of a form or forms $F(a, x)$, $G(a, u)$, which is such that the same function $\phi(A;\ z;\ w)$ of the transformed form or forms $F(A, X)$, $G(A, w)$ is equal to $\phi(a;\ x;\ u)$ multiplied by a power of $|M|$. If ϕ is a function of the coefficients and of the variables u only, it is called a *contravariant* of G.

CHAPTER 5

SETS AND FINITE GROUPS

5.1. Sets

Generally the words *set, class, aggregate* are used for collection of objects of any type, called the members of the set.

$x \in S$ denotes "x is a member of the set S".

Two sets, S and T, are said to be equal if they contain the same objects, not only the same number of objects. We write $S=T$.

A *subset* of S is a set of some or all of the members of S. The subset T is a *proper subset* if it is not identical with S. If T is a subset of S, we write $T \subseteq S$ or $S \supseteq T$. If T is a proper subset of S, $T \subset S$ or $S \supset T$.

The *union* of S and T, written $S \cup T$, is the set of objects belonging to either S or T or to both S and T.

The *intersection* of S and T, written $S \cap T$, is the set of objects in both S and T.

When discussing subsets of a given set S, the set of elements of S which are not in a subset T is called the *complement* of T, written $\mathscr{C}(T)$ or T'.

If S and T are both subsets we write $S-T$ or $S \cap \mathscr{C}(T)$ for the set of all the elements in S which are not in T (but see below).

Notations

$\{x|x$ has the property $A\}$ denotes the set of all objects x which have the property A.

$$\bigcup_{r=1}^{n} S_r = S_1 \cup S_2 \cup \ldots \cup S_n.$$

$$\bigcap_{r=1}^{n} S_r = S_1 \cap S_2 \cap \ldots \cap S_n.$$

$$\bigcup_{\mathrm{A}} S_\alpha = \{x | x \in S_\alpha \text{ for at least one } \alpha \in \mathrm{A}\}$$

$$\text{and } \bigcap_{\mathrm{A}} S_\alpha = \{x | x \in S_\alpha \text{ for all } \alpha \in \mathrm{A}\}$$

if $\{S_\alpha | \alpha \in \mathrm{A}\}$ is a set of subsets.

Unions and intersections of subsets obey the following laws:—

$$(S \cup T) \cup V = S \cup (T \cup V),$$

$$(S \cap T) \cap V = S \cap (T \cap V),$$

$$S\cap(T\cup V)=(S\cap T)\cup(S\cap V),$$

$$S\cup(T\cap V)=(S\cup T)\cap(S\cup V),$$

$$\mathscr{C}(S\cap T)=\mathscr{C}(S)\cup\mathscr{C}(T),$$

$$\mathscr{C}(S\cup T)=\mathscr{C}(S)\cap\mathscr{C}(T).$$

5.2. A *mapping* $\mathscr{F}$ of a set S *into* a set T is a rule which assigns to each $x \in S$ an element $y=\mathscr{F}x \in T$. We write $\mathscr{F}: S \to T$ (read "$\mathscr{F}$ maps S into T").

If $U \subseteq S$, $\mathscr{F}U$ denotes $\{y|y=\mathscr{F}x$ for some $x \in U\}$. The set $\mathscr{F}S$ may be a proper subset of T or may be the set T. If $\mathscr{F}S=T$, $\mathscr{F}$ is said to map S *onto* T.

A (1, 1) *mapping* is one such that $\mathscr{F}x_1=\mathscr{F}x_2$ implies $x_1=x_2$, i.e. not more than one element of S is mapped on any given element of T. There may be elements of T on which no element of S is mapped.

If $\mathscr{F}$ is a (1, 1) mapping of S ONTO T, $\mathscr{F}$ is said to be a (1, 1) *correspondence* between S and T, i.e. one point of S is mapped on one and only one point of T and vice versa.

If $\mathscr{F}$ maps R into S and $\mathscr{G}$ maps S into T, $\mathscr{G}\mathscr{F}$ is the mapping of R into T that takes $x \in R$ into $\mathscr{G}(\mathscr{F}x)$. This mapping is called the *product* of $\mathscr{F}$ and $\mathscr{G}$. This form of multiplication is associative but not in general commutative, even if $R=S=T$.

5.3. A *ring* is a set R on which two operations $a+b$ and $a\times b$ or ab are defined, such that if a and b belong to the set, so do $a+b$ and ab, and such that these operations obey the laws (I), (III)–(VII), (IX), of § 1.1.

E.g. square matrices of any definite order n.

An *integral domain* is a ring which also satisfies the laws (I)–(IX) of § 1.1 and (XI), viz.:

If $\qquad c \neq 0$ and $ca=cb$, then $a=b$. . . . (XI)

E.g. (i) Set of integers including zero.

(ii) Polynomials whose coefficients lie in an integral domain.

A *field* is a ring which satisfies (I)–(X) of § 1.1.

E.g. The real numbers,

The complex numbers.

5.4. Finite groups

Notation. In the theory of groups the word multiplication and the symbol AB are used in a generalized sense to express the result of combining two elements A and B according to some given law of composition. The result C of this process is written AB. Sometimes the word addition is used for the operation, the result being then written $A+B$.

Definition. A *group* is a set of a finite or infinite number of elements $A, B,$ C, . . ., for which a single law of composition ("multiplication") is given by which any ordered pair* of elements A, B yields a unique product AB for which the following axioms hold:

(i) *Closure.* The product of any two elements distinct or not, belongs to the set.

(ii) *Associative law.* If A, B, C are any three elements of the set, distinct or not,

$$(AB)C=A(BC),$$

so each side may be written ABC.

(iii) *Unit element.* The set contains a unit element I, for which $IA=AI=A$ for every member of the set. If the group is written additively, the unit element is denoted by 0.

(iv) *Reciprocal or inverse element.* Every element A has an inverse A^{-1}, for which $AA^{-1}=A^{-1}A=I$. In an additive group the inverse element is written $-A$.

E.g. the following form groups:

(i) The positive rational numbers, if the law of composition is ordinary multiplication.

(ii) The set of all integers, if the law of composition is addition. Here 0 is the unit element and the inverse of A is $-A$.

(iii) The set z, $1/z$, $1-z$, $1/(1-z)$, $(z-1)/z$, $z/(1-z)$ (z a fixed non-zero number, $z\neq 1$), if the law of composition is "substitute A for the variable z in B".

(iv) The non-singular square matrices of given order n.

(v) The elements of a ring, under addition.

(vi) The non-zero elements of a field, under multiplication.

Theorem. A *finite* set of elements, for which a law of composition of two elements A, B is given, form a group if axioms (i) and (ii) above hold and

(v) Each of the equations

$$AX=BX, \qquad YA=YB$$

implies that

$$A=B,$$

where A, B, X, Y are members of the set, i.e. right and left cancelling is allowable.

* A, B and B, A are distinct pairs if $A\neq B$.

Two elements A, B *commute* if $AB=BA$.

An *Abelian* group is one for which

$$AB=BA$$

for every pair of elements A, B. It is customary to write the result of the group operation of A on B as $A+B$ in Abelian groups.

The *order* of a finite group is the number of elements which it contains.

A finite set S of elements of a group G is a *set of generators* if every element of G can be expressed as a finite product of elements of S. The group generated by $A, B, \ldots, D$ is denoted by $\{A, B, \ldots, D\}$.

5.5. Subsets

A *subset* or *complex* S of a group G is a subset of elements of G. The *product* ST of two subsets S and T is the subset consisting of all elements expressible as the product of an element of S by an element of T. (In an additive group, $S+T$ denotes the set of all sums of an element of S with an element of T.) Multiplication is associative but not, in general, commutative. Thus

$$S(TV)=(ST)V.$$

If A is an element of G and S, T are subsets of G, $AS=\{x|x=AB$ for some $B\in S\}$.

The subset S^{-1} is the set of inverses of all elements in S.

The equation $ST=TS$ means that every element of ST is an element of TS and vice versa; not that every element of S commutes with every element of T.

The cancelling rule does not in general apply to subsets, i.e. if $ST=SV$ it does *not* follow that $T=V$, but if A is an element of the group G of which S and T are subsets, and $AS=AT$ or $SA=TA$, then $S=T$.

If $S\subseteq T$, then $AS\subseteq AT$ and $SA\subseteq TA$.

5.6. Subgroups

A *subgroup* of G is a subset of G, which is itself a group under the same group operation.

Every group has two improper subgroups, viz. G itself and the group consisting of the element I alone. All other subgroups are proper subgroups.

E.g. the group $\{1, +i, -1, -i\}$ has the proper subgroup $\{1, -1\}$, where the law of composition is ordinary multiplication.

The intersection M of several subgroups $\mathsf{H}, \mathsf{J}, \mathsf{K}, \ldots$, of G is a subgroup (proper or improper) of each of the groups $\mathsf{H}, \mathsf{J}, \mathsf{K}, \ldots$

A subgroup of a subgroup is a subgroup of the original group.

A non-empty subset S of a group G is a subgroup if, and only if, $SS^{-1} \subseteq S$.

A non-empty subset S of a finite group G is a subgroup

(i) if, and only if, it is closed with respect to multiplication,

or (ii) if, and only if,

$$S^2 \subseteq S,$$

or (iii) if, and only if,

$$S^2 = S.$$

5.7. Right and left cosets

If H is a subgroup of G and A_1 is any member of H, then $\mathsf{H}A_1 = \mathsf{H} = A_1\mathsf{H}$. If A_2 is any member of G, then $\mathsf{H}A_2$ is called a right coset of H. If A_3 is a member of G not contained in $\mathsf{H}A_2$, then the coset $\mathsf{H}A_3$ has no element in common with $\mathsf{H}A_2$. The cosets $\mathsf{H}A$ and $\mathsf{H}B$ are identical if, and only if, $BA^{-1} \subseteq \mathsf{H}$, i.e. $B \subseteq \mathsf{H}A$, otherwise they have no element in common. The group G can be expressed as the union of the right cosets of H, where no two of the cosets have an element in common. Thus a set of n elements $A_1, A_2, \ldots, A_n$ of G can be found such that

$$\mathsf{G} = \mathsf{H}A_1 \cup \mathsf{H}A_2 \cup \ldots \cup \mathsf{H}A_n, \quad . \quad . \quad . \quad (1)$$

or, in particular,

$$\mathsf{G} = \mathsf{H} \cup \mathsf{H}A_2 \cup \ldots \cup \mathsf{H}A_n,$$

if the group is finite.

Similarly, if $D \in \mathsf{G}$, $D\mathsf{H}$ is a left coset of H. Moreover, $D\mathsf{H}$ and $C\mathsf{H}$ are identical if, and only if, $D^{-1}C \in \mathsf{H}$, i.e. $C \in D\mathsf{H}$. Otherwise they have no element in common. A set of n elements $D_1, \ldots, D_n$ of G can be found such that

$$\mathsf{G} = D_1\mathsf{H} \cup D_2\mathsf{H} \cup \ldots \cup D_n\mathsf{H}, \quad . \quad . \quad . \quad (2)$$

giving the decomposition of G into left cosets relative to H, no two of which have an element in common.

Lagrange's theorem. If H is a subgroup of order h of the group G whose order is g, then h is a factor of g, i.e. $g = nh$. The integer n is called the *index* of H in G.

5.8. If A is an element of a finite group, then $A^h = I$ for some integer h. The *period* or *order* of an element A is the least positive integer h for which $A^h = I$.

A *cyclic* group is a group which is generated by a single element. The general form of a cyclic group C of order g is

$$\mathsf{C} : I, A, A^2, \ldots, A^{g-1}.$$

If a group of order g contains an element of period g, then the group is cyclic. The period of every element of a group of order g is a factor of g. A group of prime order has no proper subgroups and is necessarily cyclic. All subgroups of a cyclic group are cyclic. If $\{A\}$ is a cyclic group of order g and if h is a factor of g, then there is one and only one subgroup of order h and this is generated by $A^{g/h}$.

5.9. Homomorphisms and isomorphisms

A mapping $\mathscr{F}$ of one group G_1 into another G_2 is called a *homomorphism* if

$$\mathscr{F}(AB) = \mathscr{F}A\mathscr{F}B,$$
$$\mathscr{F}A^{-1} = (\mathscr{F}A)^{-1},$$

for all A and B in G_1.

E.g, the mapping of the group of non-singular square matrices of given order n into the group of their determinants.

The *kernel* of a homomorphism is the set of elements mapped on the unit element of G_2.

A (1, 1) homomorphism of G_1 INTO G_2 is called an *isomorphic mapping* or *isomorphism*. Two groups G_1 and G_2 are said to be *isomorphic* if there is an isomorphism of G_1 ONTO G_2.

E.g. the following groups are isomorphic:

$$1, \quad i, \quad -1, \quad i \qquad \text{(ordinary multiplication)}$$

$$\begin{bmatrix}1 & 0\\0 & 1\end{bmatrix}, \begin{bmatrix}0 & 1\\-1 & 0\end{bmatrix}, \begin{bmatrix}-1 & 0\\0 & -1\end{bmatrix}, \begin{bmatrix}0 & -1\\1 & 0\end{bmatrix} \qquad \text{(matrix multiplication)}.$$

An *automorphism* is an isomorphism of G onto itself.

If H is a subgroup of G and if A is any element of G, then the subset

$$\mathsf{H}' = A^{-1}\mathsf{H}A$$

is a subgroup isomorphic with H. (H and H' may be identical.)

Two elements A and B of a group G are said to be *conjugate* with respect to G if

$$D^{-1}AD = B$$

for some element D in G. D is called the transforming element. It may not be unique. The subset (A), which consists of all elements conjugate with A, is called the *class* of A. The element $A \in (A)$.

The elements of G which commute with a given element A form a subgroup N called the *normalizer* of A. If

$$\mathsf{G} = \mathsf{N}D_1 \cup \mathsf{N}D_2 \cup \ldots \cup \mathsf{N}D_h,$$

where $g = nh$, then the class (A) contains h distinct elements which may be written

$$D_1^{-1}AD_1, \; D_2^{-1}AD_2, \ldots, D_h^{-1}AD_h.$$

An element of G is an *invariant* or *self-conjugate element* if it commutes with every element of G, i.e. if $AX = XA$ for every element X of G.

An *invariant subgroup* is a subgroup H such that $A^{-1}\mathsf{H}A = \mathsf{H}$ for all A in the group.

A left coset with respect to an invariant subgroup is also a right coset.

The cosets of a group with respect to an invariant subgroup H are themselves the elements of a group G/H, with unit element H. This is called the *quotient group* of G with respect to H. The group G is mapped homomorphically onto G/H by the mapping that takes A to $A\mathsf{H}$. The kernel of this homomorphism is H.

The kernel of a homomorphism is an invariant subgroup.

If any group G is mapped homomorphically onto a group G_1, then G_1 is isomorphic with G/K, where K is the kernel of the homomorphism.

CHAPTER 6

PLANE TRIGONOMETRY

IT is assumed that the reader is familiar with the relation between circular and sexagesimal measure of an angle, i.e. π radians$=180°$.

6.1. Trigonometrical ratios

Let P be the point (x, y) in a plane rectangular co-ordinate system (§ 9.21) with axes Ox, Oy, and let P be (r, θ) in polar co-ordinates with pole O and initial line Ox. Here r is positive.

The *sine, cosine, tangent, cotangent, secant* and *cosecant* of the angle $\theta = POx$ are defined as:

$$\sin\theta = y/r, \quad \cos\theta = x/r, \quad \tan\theta = y/x,$$
$$\operatorname{cosec}\theta = r/y, \quad \sec\theta = r/x, \quad \cot\theta = x/y.$$

The signs of the ratios for angles in the four quadrants are:

Quadrant	Angle	sin	cos	tan	cot
I	0°-90°	+	+	+	+
II	90°-180°	+	−	−	−
III	180°-270°	−	−	+	+
IV	270°-360°	−	+	−	−

Ratios for supplementary and complementary angles:

Angle	$-\alpha$	$\frac{1}{2}\pi\pm\alpha$	$\pi\pm\alpha$	$\frac{3}{2}\pi\pm\alpha$	$2n\pi\pm\alpha$
sin	$-\sin\alpha$	$\cos\alpha$	$\mp\sin\alpha$	$-\cos\alpha$	$\pm\sin\alpha$
cos	$\cos\alpha$	$\mp\sin\alpha$	$-\cos\alpha$	$\pm\sin\alpha$	$\cos\alpha$
tan	$-\tan\alpha$	$\mp\cot\alpha$	$\pm\tan\alpha$	$\mp\cot\alpha$	$\pm\tan\alpha$
cot	$-\cot\alpha$	$\mp\tan\alpha$	$\pm\cot\alpha$	$\mp\tan\alpha$	$\pm\cot\alpha$

Identities

$$\tan\alpha = \sin\alpha/\cos\alpha = 1/\cot\alpha.$$
$$\sec\alpha = 1/\cos\alpha.$$
$$\operatorname{cosec}\alpha = 1/\sin\alpha.$$

$$\sin^2\alpha+\cos^2\alpha=1.$$
$$1+\tan^2\alpha=\sec^2\alpha.$$
$$1+\cot^2\alpha=\operatorname{cosec}^2\alpha.$$

Inverse circular functions

Notation. $y=f^{-1}(x)$ if $x=f(y)$, e.g. $y=\sin^{-1}x$ if $x=\sin y$. I.e. $\sin^{-1}x$ is an angle whose sine is x.

Principal value of $\sin^{-1}x$ satisfies $-\frac{1}{2}\pi\leqslant y\leqslant\frac{1}{2}\pi$.

,, ,, ,, $\cos^{-1}x$,, $0\leqslant y\leqslant\pi$.

,, ,, ,, $\tan^{-1}x$,, $-\frac{1}{2}\pi\leqslant y\leqslant\frac{1}{2}\pi$.

General values of inverse circular functions

If $\sin\theta=\sin\alpha$ or $\operatorname{cosec}\theta=\operatorname{cosec}\alpha$, then $\theta=n\pi+(-1)^n\alpha$,

If $\cos\theta=\cos\alpha$ or $\sec\theta=\sec\alpha$, then $\theta=2n\pi\pm\alpha$,

If $\tan\theta=\tan\alpha$ or $\cot\theta=\cot\alpha$, then $\theta=n\pi+\alpha$,

where n is an integer, positive, negative or zero.

6.11. Functions of compound angles

Addition formulae

$$\sin(\alpha\pm\beta)=\sin\alpha\cos\beta\pm\cos\alpha\sin\beta,$$
$$\cos(\alpha\pm\beta)=\cos\alpha\cos\beta\mp\sin\alpha\sin\beta,$$
$$\tan(\alpha\pm\beta)=(\tan\alpha\pm\tan\beta)/(1\mp\tan\alpha\tan\beta),$$
$$\cot(\alpha\pm\beta)=(\cot\alpha\cot\beta\mp1)/(\cot\beta\pm\cot\alpha).$$

In particular

$$\sin 2\alpha=2\sin\alpha\cos\alpha,$$
$$\cos 2\alpha=\cos^2\alpha-\sin^2\alpha=1-2\sin^2\alpha=2\cos^2\alpha-1,$$
$$\sin\alpha=\frac{2\tan\frac{1}{2}\alpha}{1+\tan^2\frac{1}{2}\alpha},\quad \cos\alpha=\frac{1-\tan^2\frac{1}{2}\alpha}{1+\tan^2\frac{1}{2}\alpha}.$$
$$\tan 2\alpha=2\tan\alpha/(1-\tan^2\alpha),\quad \cot 2\alpha=(\cot^2\alpha-1)/(2\cot\alpha),$$
$$\tan\alpha=\{(1-\cos 2\alpha)/(1+\cos 2\alpha)\}^{\frac{1}{2}}=\sin 2\alpha/(1+\cos 2\alpha)$$
$$=(1-\cos 2\alpha)/\sin 2\alpha,$$
$$\sin 3\alpha=3\sin\alpha-4\sin^3\alpha,$$
$$\cos 3\alpha=4\cos^3\alpha-3\cos\alpha,$$

$$\tan 3\alpha = (3 \tan \alpha - \tan^3 \alpha)/(1 - 3 \tan^2 \alpha),$$
$$\cot 3\alpha = (\cot^3 \alpha - 3 \cot \alpha)/(3 \cot^2 \alpha - 1).$$

For a positive integer n

$$\sin n\alpha = \binom{n}{1} \cos^{n-1} \alpha \sin \alpha - \binom{n}{3} \cos^{n-3} \alpha \sin^3 \alpha + \binom{n}{5} \cos^{n-5} \alpha \sin^5 \alpha \pm \ldots .$$

$$\cos n\alpha = \cos^n \alpha - \binom{n}{2} \cos^{n-2} \alpha \sin^2 \alpha + \binom{n}{4} \cos^{n-4} \alpha \sin^4 \alpha \mp \ldots .$$

$$\tan n\alpha = \left\{\binom{n}{1} \tan \alpha - \binom{n}{3} \tan^3 \alpha + \binom{n}{5} \tan^5 \alpha \mp \ldots\right\} \Big/ \left\{1 - \binom{n}{2} \tan^2 \alpha + \binom{n}{4} \tan^4 \alpha \mp \ldots\right\}.$$

Transformations of sums and products

$$\sin \alpha + \sin \beta = 2 \sin \tfrac{1}{2}(\alpha+\beta) \cos \tfrac{1}{2}(\alpha-\beta),$$
$$\sin \alpha - \sin \beta = 2 \cos \tfrac{1}{2}(\alpha+\beta) \sin \tfrac{1}{2}(\alpha-\beta),$$
$$\cos \alpha + \cos \beta = 2 \cos \tfrac{1}{2}(\alpha+\beta) \cos \tfrac{1}{2}(\alpha-\beta),$$
$$\cos \alpha - \cos \beta = 2 \sin \tfrac{1}{2}(\alpha+\beta) \sin \tfrac{1}{2}(\beta-\alpha).$$

$$\sin \alpha \sin \beta = \tfrac{1}{2}\{\cos (\alpha-\beta) - \cos (\alpha+\beta)\},$$
$$\sin \alpha \cos \beta = \tfrac{1}{2}\{\sin (\alpha+\beta) + \sin (\alpha-\beta\},$$
$$\cos \alpha \cos \beta = \tfrac{1}{2}\{\cos (\alpha+\beta) + \cos (\alpha-\beta)\}.$$

$$\cot \alpha + \tan \alpha = 2 \operatorname{cosec} 2\alpha,$$
$$\cot \alpha - \tan \alpha = 2 \cot 2\alpha,$$

$$(1 + \tan \alpha)/(1 - \tan \alpha) = \tan (45^\circ + \alpha) = (\cot \alpha + 1)/(\cot \alpha - 1) = \cot (45^\circ - \alpha).$$

6.2. The triangle

Two triangles are similar, if they have

(*a*) three pairs of sides proportional, or

(*b*) two angles of the first equal to two of the second, or

(*c*) two pairs of sides proportional and the angles between these sides equal, or

(*d*) two pairs of sides proportional and the angles opposite to the larger side of each pair equal.

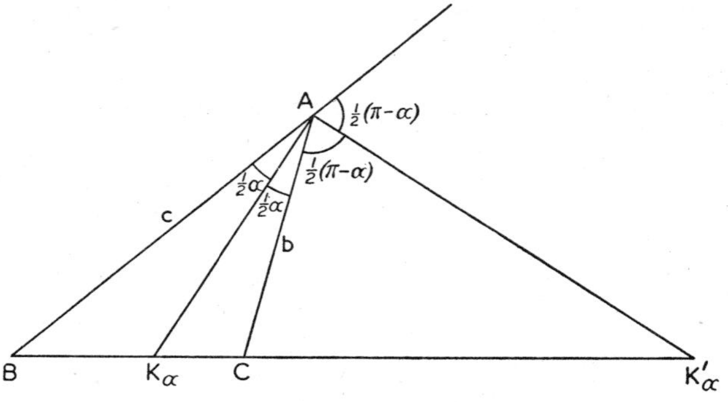

Fig. 6.1

The internal and external bisectors of an angle of a triangle divide the opposite side internally and externally in the ratio of the sides.

$$\text{i.e. } BK_\alpha : K_\alpha C = AB : AC = c : b.$$
$$BK'_\alpha : K'_\alpha C = c : -b.$$

in Fig. 6.1.

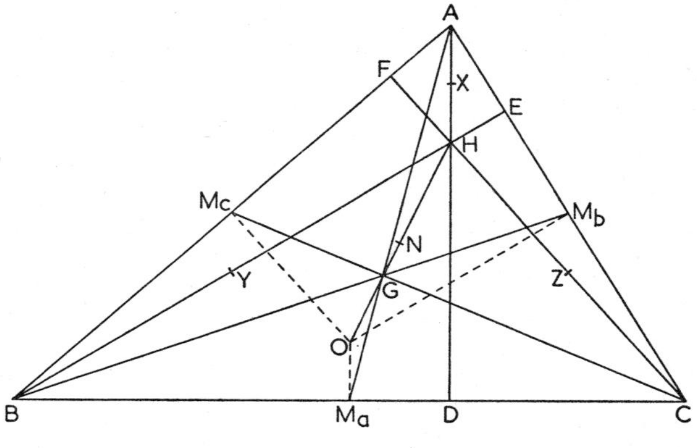

Fig. 6.2

In a triangle ABC:—

(i) The perpendicular bisectors of the sides are concurrent at the circumcentre O, which is equidistant from the vertices.

(ii) The interior bisectors of the angles are concurrent at the incentre I, which is equidistant from the sides.

(iii) The interior bisector of one angle α and the exterior bisectors of the other two are concurrent at an e-centre I_a, which is equidistant from the sides.

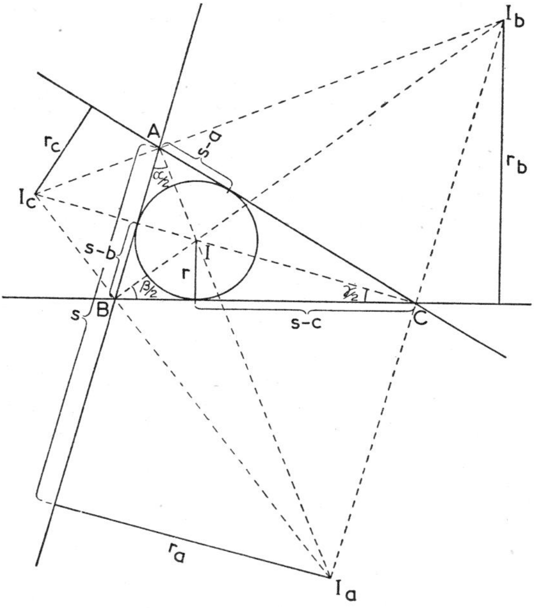

Fig. 6.3

(iv) The medians (lines joining the vertices to the mid-points M_a, M_b, M_c of the sides) are concurrent in the centroid G, where

$$AG : GM_a = BG : GM_b = CG : GM_c = 2 : 1.$$

(v) The perpendiculars AD, BE, CF from the vertices on the opposite sides are concurrent in the orthocentre H. The triangle DEF is called the pedal triangle of the triangle ABC.

(vi) The orthocentre H, the centroid G and the circumcentre O are collinear and $OG = \frac{1}{3}OH$.

(vii) The three points D, E, F, the three mid-points M_a, M_b, M_c of the sides and the three mid-points X, Y, Z of HA, HB, HC lie on a circle called the nine-points circle. Its centre N is the mid-point of OH. The nine-points circle touches the incircle and the escribed circles. See Figs. 6.2 and 6.3.

Ceva's theorem. If three concurrent lines through the vertices A, B, C of a triangle meet the opposite sides in A_1, B_1, C_1 respectively, then

$$\overline{BA_1} \cdot \overline{CB_1} \cdot \overline{AC_1} = \overline{A_1C} \cdot \overline{B_1A} \cdot \overline{C_1B}.$$

Menelaus' theorem. If a transversal cuts the sides BC, CA, AB of a triangle at A_1, B_1, C_1, then

$$\overline{BA_1}\,.\,\overline{CB_1}\,.\,\overline{AC_1} = -\overline{A_1C}\,.\,\overline{B_1A}\,.\,\overline{C_1B}.$$

Apollonius' theorem.

$$AB^2 + AC^2 = 2AM_a^2 + 2BM_a^2.$$

Circle of Apollonius. The locus of the vertex of a triangle lying on one side of a given base c, such that the sides a and b are in a given ratio $\lambda : 1$, is a semicircle described on the line joining the points which divide the base c internally and externally in the ratio $\lambda : 1$.

Notation. Triangle ABC; sides a, b, c; opposite angles α, β, γ; perpendiculars from the vertices on the opposite sides h_a, h_b, h_c; radii of circumscribed, inscribed and escribed circles R, r, r_a, r_b, r_c respectively; circumcentre O, incentre I, e-centres I_a, I_b, I_c, orthocentre H and centroid G; area Δ; perimeter $2s$; medians m_a, m_b, m_c; lengths of bisectors of interior and exterior angles ω_α, ω_β, ω_γ; ω_α', ω_β', ω_γ' respectively.

All formula hold after cyclical interchange of a, b, c; α, β, γ.

$$\alpha + \beta + \gamma = \pi.$$

$$\sin(\beta+\gamma) = \sin\alpha, \qquad \cos(\beta+\gamma) = -\cos\alpha,$$

$$\sin\tfrac{1}{2}(\beta+\gamma) = \cos\tfrac{1}{2}\alpha, \qquad \cos\tfrac{1}{2}(\beta+\gamma) = \sin\tfrac{1}{2}\alpha.$$

Sine formula

$$a/\sin\alpha = b/\sin\beta = c/\sin\gamma.$$

Cosine formula

$$a^2 = b^2 + c^2 - 2bc\cos\alpha.$$

A form of this, useful for logarithmic computation, is

$$a = (b-c)\cos\tfrac{1}{2}\alpha\sec\theta, \text{ where } \tan\theta = \frac{b+c}{b-c}\tan\tfrac{1}{2}\alpha, \text{ or}$$

$$a = (b+c)\sin\phi, \text{ where } \cos\phi = \frac{2\sqrt{(bc)}}{b+c}\cos\tfrac{1}{2}\alpha,$$

and ϕ is an acute angle.

$$a = b\cos\gamma + c\cos\beta.$$

Half-angle formulae

$$\frac{a+b}{a-b} = \frac{\tan\frac{1}{2}(\alpha+\beta)}{\tan\frac{1}{2}(\alpha-\beta)}.$$

$$(b+c)\sin\tfrac{1}{2}\alpha = a\cos\tfrac{1}{2}(\beta-\gamma).$$

$$(b-c)\cos\tfrac{1}{2}\alpha = a\sin\tfrac{1}{2}(\beta-\gamma).$$

$$\sin \tfrac{1}{2}\alpha = \{(s-b)(s-c)/(bc)\}^{\frac{1}{2}},$$
$$\cos \tfrac{1}{2}\alpha = \{s(s-a)/(bc)\}^{\frac{1}{2}},$$
$$\tan \tfrac{1}{2}\alpha = [(s-b)(s-c)/\{s(s-a)\}]^{\frac{1}{2}},$$
$$\sin \alpha = 2\{s(s-a)(s-b)(s-c)\}^{\frac{1}{2}}/(bc).$$

The roots take their positive values.

6.21. Area of triangle

$$\Delta = \tfrac{1}{2}ab \sin \gamma = 2R^2 \sin \alpha \sin \beta \sin \gamma$$
$$= \{s(s-a)(s-b)(s-c)\}^{\frac{1}{2}}.$$
$$R = \tfrac{1}{2}a/\sin \alpha = \tfrac{1}{2}b/\sin \beta = \tfrac{1}{2}c/\sin \gamma = abc/(4\Delta).$$
$$r = (s-a) \tan \tfrac{1}{2}\alpha = \Delta/s = 4R \sin \tfrac{1}{2}\alpha \sin \tfrac{1}{2}\beta \sin \tfrac{1}{2}\gamma.$$
$$r_a = s \tan \tfrac{1}{2}\alpha = \Delta/(s-a) = 4R \sin \tfrac{1}{2}\alpha \cos \tfrac{1}{2}\beta \cos \tfrac{1}{2}\gamma.$$
$$1/r = 1/r_a + 1/r_b + 1/r_c.$$
$$\Delta^2 = r \,.\, r_a \,.\, r_b \,.\, r_c, \qquad r_a + r_b + r_c - r = 4R.$$

Radius of nine-points circle $= R/2$.

$$h_a = b \sin \gamma = c \sin \beta = a \sin \beta \sin \gamma/\sin \alpha = bc/(2R).$$
$$2m_a{}^2 = b^2 + c^2 - \tfrac{1}{2}a^2.$$
$$m_a{}^2 + m_b{}^2 + m_c{}^2 = \tfrac{3}{4}(a^2 + b^2 + c^2).$$
$$\omega_\alpha = 2\{s(s-a)bc\}^{\frac{1}{2}}/(b+c).$$
$$\omega'_\alpha = 2\{(s-b)(s-c)bc\}^{\frac{1}{2}}/(b-c).$$

Distances between special points

If ω_α and ω'_α meet BC at K_α and K'_α, then $BK_\alpha = (ac)/(b+c)$, $K_\alpha C = (ab)/(b+c)$, $BK'_\alpha = (ac)/(c-b)$, $K'_\alpha C = (ab)/(b-c)$.

The pedal triangle is DEF, where $EF = a \cos \alpha$.

$$AH = 2R \cos \alpha.$$
$$DH = 2R \cos \beta \cos \gamma.$$
$$IA = r \operatorname{cosec} \tfrac{1}{2}\alpha = 4R \sin \tfrac{1}{2}\beta \sin \tfrac{1}{2}\gamma.$$
$$I_aA = r_a \operatorname{cosec} \tfrac{1}{2}\alpha = 4R \cos \tfrac{1}{2}\beta \cos \tfrac{1}{2}\gamma.$$
$$OI^2 = R^2 - 2Rr. \qquad OI_a{}^2 = R^2 + 2Rr_a.$$
$$OH^2 = R^2 - 8R^2 \cos \alpha \cos \beta \cos \gamma.$$
$$IH^2 = 2r^2 - 4R^2 \cos \alpha \cos \beta \cos \gamma.$$
$$I_aH^2 = 2r_a{}^2 - 4R^2 \cos \alpha \cos \beta \cos \gamma.$$
$$IN = \tfrac{1}{2}R - r. \qquad I_aN = \tfrac{1}{2}R + r_a.$$

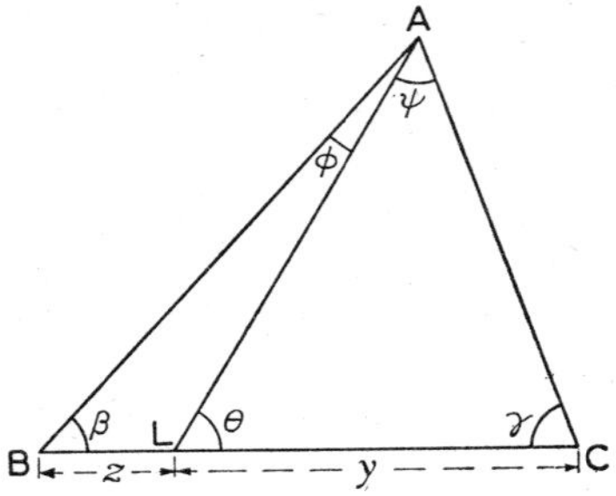

Fig. 6.4

If AL is any line through the vertex A making angles θ, ϕ, and ψ with BC, AB and AC respectively and meeting BC at L, where $BL=z$, $LC=y$ (see Fig. 6.4), then

$$(y+z)\cot\theta = y\cot\beta - z\cot\gamma$$
$$= z\cot\phi - y\cot\psi.$$

6.22. Solution of triangles

(1) Given a, β, γ.

$$\alpha = 180° - (\beta+\gamma),\ b = a\sin\beta/\sin\alpha,\ c = a\sin\gamma/\sin\alpha.$$

(2) Given b, c, α.

$\frac{1}{2}(\beta+\gamma) = 90° - \frac{1}{2}\alpha.$

$\tan\frac{1}{2}(\beta-\gamma) = \{(b-c)\tan\frac{1}{2}(\beta+\gamma)\}/(b+c)$

giving β and γ.

$a = b\sin\alpha/\sin\beta.$

OR

$\tan\beta = b\sin\alpha/(c-b\cos\alpha)$

$a = b\sin\alpha/\sin\beta$

$= (c-b\cos\alpha)/\cos\beta.$

(3) Given a, b, c.

$$\tan\tfrac{1}{2}\alpha = [(s-b)(s-c)/\{s(s-a)\}]^{\frac{1}{2}},$$
$$\tan\tfrac{1}{2}\beta = [(s-a)(s-c)/\{s(s-b)\}]^{\frac{1}{2}}.$$

(4) Given a, b, β.

(i) $b > a$.

$$\sin\alpha = (a\sin\beta)/b,\quad \alpha < 90°.$$
$$\gamma = 180 - (\alpha+\beta).$$
$$c = b\sin\gamma/\sin\beta = a\sin\gamma/\sin\alpha.$$

(ii) $a\sin\beta < b < a$.

$$\sin\alpha = (a\sin\beta)/b.$$

There are two solutions α and $180° - \alpha$, giving two possible values for the third angle, $\gamma_1 = 180 - \alpha - \beta$, $\gamma_2 = \alpha - \beta$ and two values for c:

$$c_1 = a\sin(\alpha+\beta)/\sin\alpha,\quad c_2 = a\sin(\alpha-\beta)/\sin\alpha.$$

(iii) $a\sin\beta = b$. One solution $\alpha = 90°$.

(iv) $a\sin\beta > b$. No solution.

6.3. Quadrilateral

Sides $AB=a$, $BC=b$, $CD=c$, $DA=d$. Diagonals $AC=x$, $BD=y$ intersecting at O. $A\hat{O}B=\theta$. Angles α, β, γ, δ. $2s=a+b+c+d$, $S=$area $ABCD$. See Fig. 6.5.

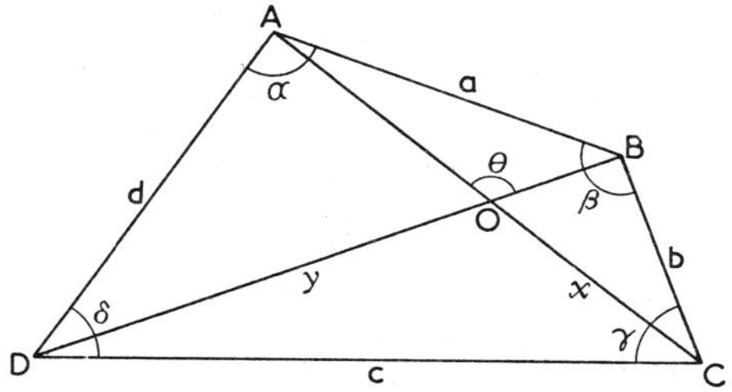

Fig. 6.5

$$S^2=(s-a)(s-b)(s-c)(s-d)-abcd\cos^2\tfrac{1}{2}(\beta+\delta).$$

$$S=\tfrac{1}{2}xy\sin\theta=\tfrac{1}{4}(b^2+d^2-a^2-c^2)\tan\theta.$$

$$x^2y^2=a^2c^2+b^2d^2-2abcd\cos(\beta+\delta).$$

Cyclic quadrilateral. Necessary and sufficient condition that a quadrilateral be cyclic is

$$\alpha+\gamma=\pi.$$

Then $\beta+\delta=\pi$.

$$S^2=(s-a)(s-b)(s-c)(s-d).$$

$$x^2=(ac+bd)(ad+bc)/(ab+cd),\ y^2=(ac+bd)(ab+cd)/(ad+bc).$$

Ptolemy's theorem: $xy=ac+bd$.

Circumradius R given by

$$16R^2S^2=(ab+cd)(ac+bd)(ad+bc)$$

$$\sin\alpha=2S/(bc+ad),$$

$$\cos\alpha=(a^2+d^2-b^2-c^2)/\{2(ad+bc)\}.$$

$$\tan^2\tfrac{1}{2}\alpha=(s-a)(s-d)/\{(s-b)(s-c)\}.$$

Circumscribable quadrilateral, i.e. one in which a circle can be inscribed. A necessary and sufficient condition that a quadrilateral be circumscribable is

$$a+c=b+d.$$

Then $$S^2=abcd\sin^2\tfrac{1}{2}(\beta+\delta).$$

In-radius $r=S/s$.

A *Trapezium* is a quadrilateral with a pair a, c of parallel sides. Height h = distance between parallel sides.

$$S=\tfrac{1}{2}(a+c)h.$$

$$h^2=4\{(s-a)(s-c)(s-c-d)(s-b-c)\}/(a-c)^2.$$

Diagonal $x=AC$ is given by

$$x^2=ac+(ad^2-cb^2)/(a-c).$$

6.4. Polygons with the same number n of sides are similar if their corresponding angles are equal and their corresponding sides are proportional. The diagonals through two corresponding vertices of two similar polygons divide the polygons into triangles similar in pairs. Conversely, if two polygons are divided by the diagonals through two vertices into triangles which, taken in the same order, are similar in pairs, the polygons are similar.

The perimeter of similar polygons are to one another as the lengths of corresponding sides and their areas as the squares of the lengths of corresponding sides.

Regular polygon of n sides

Notation. a side. R, r radii of circumscribed and inscribed circles. S area.

Angle subtended at the centre by a side $=2\pi/n$.

Interior angle of polygon $=(n-2)\pi/n$.

$$R=\tfrac{1}{2}a \operatorname{cosec}(\pi/n),\ r=\tfrac{1}{2}a\cot(\pi/n),\ S=\tfrac{1}{4}na^2\cot(\pi/n).$$

6.5. The Circle, radius r

1. The angle subtended by a chord BC at a point P of the arc BAC is called the angle in the segment BAC. It is equal to half the angle subtended by the chord BC at the centre O of the circle. All angles in the same segment are equal.

2. The angle TBC between the chord BC and the tangent at B is equal to the angle in the alternate segment, i.e. $\alpha=\alpha'$, $\beta=\beta'$ in Fig. 6.6.

3. An angle in a semicircle is a right angle.

4. If a circle is cut by two secants PMQ, $P'MQ'$ intersecting at a point M, then

$$PM\,.\,MQ=P'M\,.\,MQ'.$$

The point M may be inside or outside the circle.

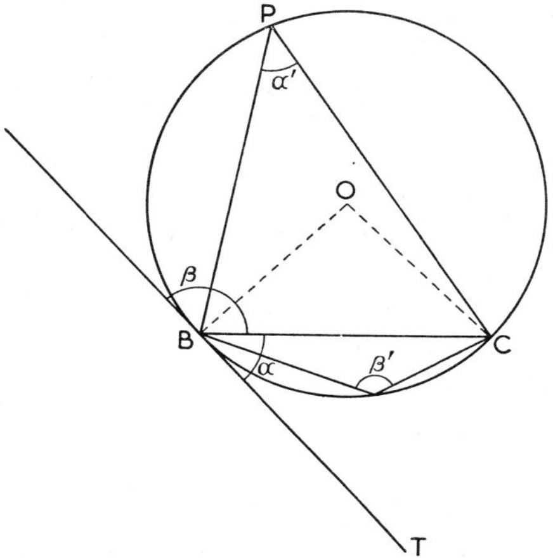

Fig. 6.6

5. If a tangent at T to a circle meets a secant MPQ at M, then

$$MT^2 = MP \, . \, MQ.$$

Perimeter $= 2\pi r$, where π is a constant.

Approximations to π are $\frac{22}{7}$, 3·14159.

Area $= \pi r^2$.

The angle α radians $= \alpha \dfrac{180°}{\pi}$ subtended at the centre of a circle of radius r by an arc of length l is given by $\alpha = l/r$.

Area of the sector on an arc of length l is $\frac{1}{2}r^2\alpha = \frac{1}{2}lr$.

Area of the segment whose chord subtends an angle α radians at the centre is $\frac{1}{2}r^2\ (\alpha - \sin \alpha)$.

CHAPTER 7

SPHERICAL TRIGONOMETRY

7.1. All formulae are given for a unit sphere. If radius is R, replace

$$a, b, c \text{ by } a/R, b/R, c/R.$$

A *great circle* on a sphere is a section by a plane through the centre O of the sphere. Through two points A and B on a sphere, which are not ends of a diameter, passes a unique great circle. The shortest distance along the surface of the sphere between A and B is the smaller of the great circle arcs AB.

A *small circle* is a section by a plane which does not pass through the centre.

A *zone* is the portion of the surface which lies between two circles whose planes are parallel.

A *lune* is any one of the four segments into which the surface of the sphere is divided by any two great circles.

A *spherical triangle* ABC is the figure formed by the arcs (each subtending $<180°$ at O) of three great circles. The *sides* a, b, c of the triangle are the arcs BC, CA, AB and the *angles* α, β, γ are the dihedral angles between the planes of the great circles. α is equal to the angle between the tangents at A to the arcs AB, AC.

The *poles* of a great circle are the points in which the diameter perpendicular to the plane of the circle meets the sphere. The *polar triangle* of a spherical triangle ABC is the triangle $A'B'C'$, where A' is that pole of the arc BC which lies on the same side of BC as A does, etc. The polar triangle of $A'B'C'$ is ABC. If $a', b', c', \alpha', \beta', \gamma'$ are the sides and angles of the polar triangle $A'B'C'$, then on a unit sphere

$$a'+\alpha=\pi, \ldots, \alpha'+a=\pi \ldots \qquad (1)$$

Applying any formula for a spherical triangle to the polar triangle, we obtain another formula by making the substitutions (1).

A triangle is *equilateral, isosceles* or *scalene* if it has three, two or no equal sides. A triangle is *quadrantal, biquadrantal* or *triquadrantal* if it has one, two or three sides quadrants, i.e. sides of length $\frac{1}{2}\pi$. A *right* spherical triangle has one angle a right angle. A spherical triangle may have two or three right angles or two or three obtuse angles.

If the corresponding sides and angles of two spherical triangles are equal, they are said to be *congruent* or to be *symmetrically equal* according as it is or is not possible to move one over the surface of the sphere into coincidence with the other. E.g. if AA', BB', CC' are diameters of the sphere and ABC is a spherical triangle, then $A'B'C'$ is symmetrically equal to ABC.

7.2. Two spherical triangles on equal spheres are either congruent or symmetrically equal if they have equal

(1) two sides and their included angle,

(2) a side and two adjacent angles,

(3) the three sides,

(4) the three angles,

(5) two sides (angles) and the angle (side) opposite one of them equal, and the angle (side) opposite the second side (angle) is in both triangles $\lesseqgtr \frac{1}{2}\pi$.

In every spherical triangle,

(1) the angles opposite equal sides are equal and conversely,

(2) the greatest side is opposite the greatest angle and conversely,

(3) $b+c>a, \qquad c+a>b, \qquad a+b>c.$

(4) $\beta+\gamma<\pi+\alpha,\ \gamma+\alpha<\pi+\beta,\ \alpha+\beta<\pi+\gamma.$

(5) $\alpha+\beta$ and $a+b$ are both $<\pi$ or both $=\pi$ or both $>\pi$.

(6) $0<a+b+c<2\pi.$

(7) $\pi<\alpha+\beta+\gamma<3\pi.$

7.3. Formula for a spherical triangle ABC on a unit sphere

All formulae may be cyclically interchanged.

Notation

Spherical excess $\quad E\equiv\alpha+\beta+\gamma-\pi.$

Spherical defect $\quad d\equiv 2\pi-(a+b+c).$

$$2S\equiv\alpha+\beta+\gamma, \quad 2s\equiv a+b+c.$$

Norm of angles of ΔABC

$$=N\equiv\tfrac{1}{2}\begin{vmatrix} 1 & -\cos\gamma & -\cos\beta \\ -\cos\gamma & 1 & -\cos\alpha \\ -\cos\beta & -\cos\alpha & 1 \end{vmatrix}^{\frac{1}{2}}$$

$$=\{-\cos S\cos(S-\alpha)\cos(S-\beta)\cos(S-\gamma)\}^{\frac{1}{2}}.$$

Norm of sides of ΔABC

$$=n\equiv\tfrac{1}{2}\begin{vmatrix} 1 & \cos c & \cos b \\ \cos c & 1 & \cos a \\ \cos b & \cos a & 1 \end{vmatrix}^{\frac{1}{2}}$$

$$=\{\sin s \sin(s-a) \sin(s-b) \sin(s-c)\}^{\frac{1}{2}}.$$

Sine formula

$$\frac{\sin a}{\sin \alpha}=\frac{\sin b}{\sin \beta}=\frac{\sin c}{\sin \gamma}$$

$$=\frac{\sin a \sin b \sin c}{2n}=\frac{2N}{\sin \alpha \sin \beta \sin \gamma}. \quad (2)$$

Cosine formula for sides: $\cos a=\cos b \cos c+\sin b \sin c \cos \alpha.$

Cosine formula for angles: $\cos \alpha=-\cos \beta \cos \gamma+\sin \beta \sin \gamma \cos a.$

$$\cos a \cos \beta=\sin a \cot c-\sin \beta \cot \gamma,$$

$$\cos a \cos \gamma=\sin a \cot b-\sin \gamma \cot \beta.$$

Half-angle formulae

$$\sin \tfrac{1}{2}\alpha=\{\sin(s-b) \sin(s-c)/(\sin b \sin c)\}^{\frac{1}{2}},$$

$$\cos \tfrac{1}{2}\alpha=\{\sin s \sin(s-a)/(\sin b \sin c)\}^{\frac{1}{2}},$$

$$\tan \tfrac{1}{2}\alpha=[\sin(s-b) \sin(s-c)/\{\sin s \sin(s-a)\}]^{\frac{1}{2}},$$

$$\cot \tfrac{1}{2}\alpha=\{\sin s \sin(s-a)\}/n,$$

$$\sin \tfrac{1}{2}a=\{-\cos S \cos(S-\alpha)/(\sin \beta \sin \gamma)\}^{\frac{1}{2}},$$

$$\cos \tfrac{1}{2}a=\{\cos(S-\beta) \cos(S-\gamma)/(\sin \beta \sin \gamma)\}^{\frac{1}{2}},$$

$$\tan \tfrac{1}{2}a=[-\cos S \cos(S-\alpha)/\{\cos(S-\beta) \cos(S-\gamma)\}]^{\frac{1}{2}},$$

$$=\{\cos S \cos(S-\alpha)\}/N.$$

Delambre's analogies

$$\sin \tfrac{1}{2}\alpha \cos \tfrac{1}{2}(b+c)=\cos \tfrac{1}{2}a \cos \tfrac{1}{2}(\beta+\gamma),$$

$$\cos \tfrac{1}{2}\alpha \sin \tfrac{1}{2}(b-c)=\sin \tfrac{1}{2}a \sin \tfrac{1}{2}(\beta-\gamma),$$

$$\sin \tfrac{1}{2}\alpha \sin \tfrac{1}{2}(b+c)=\sin \tfrac{1}{2}a \cos \tfrac{1}{2}(\beta-\gamma),$$

$$\cos \tfrac{1}{2}\alpha \cos \tfrac{1}{2}(b-c)=\cos \tfrac{1}{2}a \sin \tfrac{1}{2}(\beta+\gamma).$$

Napier's analogies

$$\tan \tfrac{1}{2}(b+c) \cos \tfrac{1}{2}(\beta+\gamma)=\tan \tfrac{1}{2}a \cos \tfrac{1}{2}(\beta-\gamma),$$

$$\tan \tfrac{1}{2}(\beta+\gamma) \cos \tfrac{1}{2}(b+c)=\cot \tfrac{1}{2}\alpha \cos \tfrac{1}{2}(b-c),$$

$$\tan \tfrac{1}{2}(b-c) \sin \tfrac{1}{2}(\beta+\gamma)=\tan \tfrac{1}{2}a \sin \tfrac{1}{2}(\beta-\gamma),$$

$$\tan \tfrac{1}{2}(\beta-\gamma) \sin \tfrac{1}{2}(b+c)=\cot \tfrac{1}{2}\alpha \sin \tfrac{1}{2}(b-c).$$

Area of a lune of angle α is 2α.

Area of a spherical triangle $ABC = \alpha+\beta+\gamma-\pi = E$ on unit sphere,
$= R^2E$ on sphere of radius R.

$$\sin \tfrac{1}{2}E = n/\{2 \cos \tfrac{1}{2}a \cos \tfrac{1}{2}b \cos \tfrac{1}{2}c\},$$

$$\tan \tfrac{1}{4}E = \{\tan \tfrac{1}{2}s \tan \tfrac{1}{2}(s-a) \tan \tfrac{1}{2}(s-b) \tan \tfrac{1}{2}(s-c)\}^{\frac{1}{2}},$$

$$\tan \tfrac{1}{4}d = [-\tan (\tfrac{1}{4}\pi+\tfrac{1}{2}S) \tan \{\tfrac{1}{4}\pi-\tfrac{1}{2}(S-\alpha)\} \tan \{\tfrac{1}{4}\pi-\tfrac{1}{2}(S-\beta)\} \times \times \tan \{\tfrac{1}{4}\pi-\tfrac{1}{2}(S-\gamma)\}]^{\frac{1}{2}}.$$

7.4. Circumscribed, inscribed and escribed circles of a spherical triangle

The *circumscribed, inscribed* and *escribed* circles of a triangle are the small circles which respectively pass through the vertices, touch the sides internally, or touch one side internally and two sides externally. Denote their angular radii (i.e. the angle subtended at the centre of the sphere) by R, r, r_a, r_b, r_c respectively.

The great circle arcs perpendicular to the sides of a triangle and through their mid-points are concurrent in the pole M of the circum-circle.

The great circle arcs bisecting the interior and exterior angles of a triangle are concurrent in I, I_a, I_b, I_c, the poles of the inscribed and escribed circles.

$$\tan R = -\frac{\cos S}{N},$$

$$\tan r = \frac{n}{\sin s} = \tan \tfrac{1}{2}\alpha \sin (s-a) = \frac{N}{2 \cos \tfrac{1}{2}\alpha \cos \tfrac{1}{2}\beta \cos \tfrac{1}{2}\gamma},$$

$$\tan r_a = \frac{n}{\sin (s-a)} = \tan \tfrac{1}{2}\alpha \sin s = \frac{N}{2 \cos \tfrac{1}{2}\alpha \sin \tfrac{1}{2}\beta \sin \tfrac{1}{2}\gamma}.$$

7.5. Right-angled triangles. $(\gamma = \tfrac{1}{2}\pi)$

The hypoteneuse is acute if a and b are both acute or both obtuse. c is obtuse if one of a and b is acute and the other obtuse. The following formulae are obtained immediately from the sine and cosine formulae:

(1) $\cos c = \cos a \cos b$.

(2) $\sin a = \sin \alpha \sin c$,
$\sin b = \sin \beta \sin c$.

(3) $\cos c = \cot \alpha \cot \beta$.　　$(\tfrac{1}{2}\pi < \alpha+\beta < \tfrac{3}{2}\pi.)$

(4) $\cos \alpha = \cos a \sin \beta$,
$\cos \beta = \cos b \sin \alpha$.　　$(-\tfrac{1}{2}\pi < \alpha-\beta < \tfrac{1}{2}\pi.)$

(5) $\cos \alpha = \cot c \tan b$,　　$\cos \beta = \cot c \tan a$.

(6) $\sin b = \tan a \cot \alpha$,　　$\sin a = \tan b \cot \beta$.

A side and its opposite angle are either both acute or both obtuse.

Napier's rules give a mnemonic for the formulae (1)-(6). Write

$$\bar{a}=\tfrac{1}{2}\pi-\alpha,\ \bar{\beta}=\tfrac{1}{2}\pi-\beta,\ \bar{c}=\tfrac{1}{2}\pi-c,$$

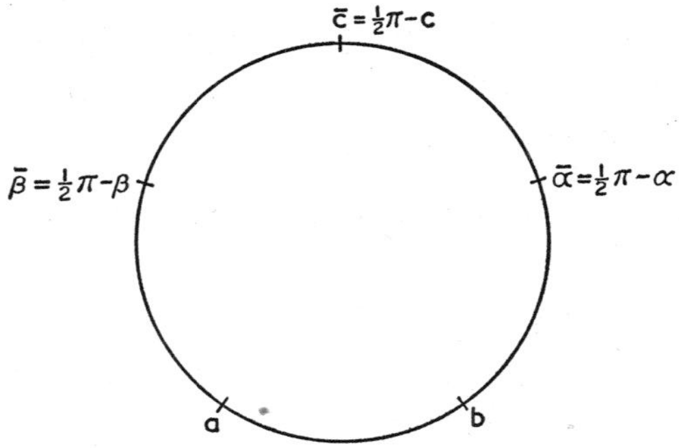

Fig. 7.1

and arrange a, b, $\bar{a}$, $\bar{c}$, $\bar{\beta}$ as in Fig. 7.1. If a is the middle part, then b and $\bar{\beta}$ are adjacent parts and $\bar{a}$ and $\bar{c}$ are opposite parts. Similarly for any other middle part.

Rules. I. The sine of the middle part is equal to the product of the tangents of the adjacent parts.

II. The sine of the middle part is equal to the product of the cosines of the opposite parts.

7.6. Solution of triangles

7.61. *Given a, b, c.*

$$a+b+c=2s, \qquad n=\{\sin s\sin(s-a)\sin(s-b)\sin(s-c)\}^{\frac{1}{2}}.$$

$$\cot\tfrac{1}{2}\alpha=\{\sin(s-a)\sin s\}/n,\ \cot\tfrac{1}{2}\beta=\{\sin(s-b)\sin s\}/n,\ \cot\tfrac{1}{2}\gamma=\{\sin(s-c)\sin s\}/n.$$

A solution exists only if the sum of any two of the sides is greater than the third and if $a+b+c<2\pi$.

7.62. *Given α, β, γ.*

$$\alpha+\beta+\gamma=2S, \qquad N=\{-\cos S\cos(S-\alpha)\cos(S-\beta)\cos(S-\gamma)\}^{\frac{1}{2}}.$$

$$\tan\tfrac{1}{2}a=\{\cos(S-\alpha)\cos S\}/N,\ \tan\tfrac{1}{2}b=\{\cos(S-\beta)\cos S\}/N,$$

$$\tan\tfrac{1}{2}c=\{\cos(S-\gamma)\ \cos S\}/N.$$

A solution exists only if $\pi<\alpha+\beta+\gamma<3\pi$ and if the sum of any two sides exceeds the third by less than π.

7.63. *Given a, b, γ.*

$$\tan\tfrac{1}{2}(\alpha+\beta)=\cot\tfrac{1}{2}\gamma\cos\tfrac{1}{2}(a-b)/\cos\tfrac{1}{2}(a+b),$$

$$\tan\tfrac{1}{2}(\alpha-\beta)=\cot\tfrac{1}{2}\gamma\ \sin\tfrac{1}{2}(a-b)/\sin\tfrac{1}{2}(a+b),$$

giving α and β.

$$\sin\tfrac{1}{2}c=\cos\tfrac{1}{2}\gamma\sin\tfrac{1}{2}(a-b)/\sin\tfrac{1}{2}(\alpha-\beta).$$

7.64. *Given* α, β, c.

$$\tan \tfrac{1}{2}(a+b) = \tan \tfrac{1}{2}c \cos \tfrac{1}{2}(\alpha-\beta)/\cos \tfrac{1}{2}(\alpha+\beta),$$
$$\tan \tfrac{1}{2}(a-b) = \tan \tfrac{1}{2}c \sin \tfrac{1}{2}(\alpha-\beta)/\sin \tfrac{1}{2}(\alpha+\beta),$$

giving a and b.

$$\sin \tfrac{1}{2}\gamma = \cos \tfrac{1}{2}c \cos \tfrac{1}{2}(\alpha+\beta)/\cos \tfrac{1}{2}(a+b).$$

7.65. *Given* a, b, α.

$$\sin \beta = \{\sin b \sin \alpha\}/\sin a.$$

Then
$$\tan \tfrac{1}{2}\gamma = \sin \tfrac{1}{2}(a-b) \operatorname{cosec} \tfrac{1}{2}(a+b) \cot \tfrac{1}{2}(\alpha-\beta),$$
$$\tan \tfrac{1}{2}c = \sin \tfrac{1}{2}(\alpha+\beta) \operatorname{cosec} \tfrac{1}{2}(\alpha-\beta) \tan \tfrac{1}{2}(a-b).$$

For a solution to be possible, $\sin b \sin \alpha \leqslant \sin a$.

If $\sin b \sin \alpha < \sin a$, the sine formula gives two solutions β_1 and $\beta_2 = \pi - \beta_1$ for β. For a real triangle $\alpha-\beta$ and $a-b$ have the same sign and $a+b \gtreqqless \pi$ and $\alpha+\beta \gtreqqless \pi$ hold together. One or both of β_1 and β_2 will satisfy these conditions. If both do, there are two triangles satisfying the data and the case is said to be ambiguous.

7.66. *Given* α, β, a.

$$\sin b = \{\sin a \sin \beta\}/\sin \alpha.$$

c and γ follow as in case 7.65.

If $\sin a \sin \beta > \sin \alpha$, there is no solution.

If $\sin a \sin \beta = \sin \alpha$, $b = \tfrac{1}{2}\pi$, and there is one triangle.

If $\sin a \sin \beta < \sin \alpha$, we have two values b_1 and $b_2 = \pi - b_1$ for b. If both satisfy the conditions that $b-a$ and $\beta-\alpha$ are of the same sign and that $a+b \gtreqqless \pi$ and $\alpha+\beta \gtreqqless \pi$ hold together, there are two triangles satisfying the data and the case is said to be ambiguous.

Cases 7.62, 7.64, 7.66 can be solved by applying the methods of 7.61, 7.63 and 7.65 respectively to the polar triangle of the given triangle.

CHAPTER 8

MENSURATION

8.1. Two non-coplanar lines are said to be skew.

The *angle* between two skew lines is the angle between one and a parallel to the second through a point on the first.

The shortest distance between two skew lines is the length of the unique line which intersects both at right angles.

The *angle* between a line and a plane is the complement of the angle between the line and a normal to the plane.

8.2. Solid angles

A *solid angle** is the figure formed by three concurrent non-coplanar lines OP, OQ, OR, where the angles QOR, ROP and POQ are all less than 180°. It is measured by the spherical triangle ABC on a unit sphere centre O, where A, B, and C are the points in which OP, OQ, OR meet the sphere. Its *plane angles* are the angles BOC, COA, AOB, its *sides* are the arcs BC, etc., and the *dihedral angles* or *angles* of the solid angle are the angles between the pairs of planes BOC, COA, AOB, i.e. the angles α, β, γ of the spherical triangle ABC.

If the words "dihedral angle" are substituted for angle, the properties given in 7.2 for spherical triangles hold for solid angles. In a solid angle:

(*a*) The planes bisecting the sides at right angles are line-concurrent in a line which is the axis of a right circular cone through the three line-vertices of the three dihedral angles.

(*b*) The planes bisecting the dihedral angles internally are line-concurrent and the planes bisecting one dihedral angle internally and the other two externally are line-concurrent. These four lines are the axes of four right circular cones which touch the planes of the angle.

(*c*) A *median plane* is a plane through the line-vertex of one dihedral angle and the mid-point of the opposite side. The three median planes are line-concurrent.

(*d*) An *orthogonal plane* is a plane through the line-vertex of one dihedral angle and perpendicular to the opposite side. The three orthogonal planes are line-concurrent.

* The term 'solid angle subtended at a point O' by a figure A is also used for the area of the unit sphere, centre O, which lies within the cone vertex O and base A.

8.3. Polyhedra

A *polyhedron* is a solid bounded by finite plane polygons. It is convex if the interior dihedral angles between adjacent bounding planes are all less than 180°.

Euler's theorem. If E, F and K are the numbers of vertices, faces and edges of a convex polyhedron,

$$E+F=K+2.$$

The number of angles of the plane faces is $2K$.

Cavalieri's theorem. If two bodies have equal height and equal bases and if all sections which are parallel to and the same distance from the respective bases are equal to each other, the bodies are of equal volume.

A *pyramid* is a polyhedron bounded by one polygon of n sides and by n triangles.

A section of a pyramid by a plane parallel to the base is a polygon similar to the base. The ratio of the area of the section to that of the base is the square of the ratio of their distances from the apex.

8.4. Mensuration formulae

Notation. M = area of curved surface; A = total area; G = area of base; V = volume; G_1 = area of plane surface parallel to the base; h = height; r = radius of base; r_1 = radius of plane surface parallel to the base; a, b, c lengths of sides; d = length of diagonal; l = slant height;

R = radius of a sphere.

Rectangular block or *parallelepiped*:

$$A=2(bc+ca+ab),$$
$$V=abc,\quad d=(a^2+b^2+c^2)^{\frac{1}{2}}.$$

Prism: $$V=Gh.$$

Regular right six-sided prism (side of base $=a$):

$$V=\tfrac{3}{2}a^2h\sqrt{3},\quad A=3a(2h+a\sqrt{3}).$$

Pyramid: $$V=\tfrac{1}{3}Gh.$$

Right pyramid, base a regular hexagon side a:

$$V=\tfrac{1}{2}a^2h\sqrt{3},\quad A=3a\{\tfrac{1}{2}a\sqrt{3}+\sqrt{(h^2+\tfrac{3}{4}a^2)}\}.$$

Cylinder on circular base:

Volume: $V=\pi r^2h$, whether generators are perpendicular to base or not.

Right Cylinder: $M=2\pi rh$, $A=2\pi r(h+r)$.

Hollow cylinder: $V=(r^2-r_2{}^2)\pi h$. (r_2 = inner radius of cross-section.)

Circular cone:

General: $V=\frac{1}{3}\pi r^2 h.$

Right: $M=\pi rl,\ A=\pi r(l+r),\ l=(r^2+h^2)^{\frac{1}{2}}.$

Frustum of a pyramid (top parallel to the base):

$$V=\tfrac{1}{3}h\{G+\sqrt{(GG_1)}+G_1\}.$$

Frustum of a circular cone (top parallel to the base):

General: $V=\frac{1}{3}\pi h(r^2+rr_1+r_1^2).$

Right: $M=(r_1+r_2)\pi l.$

Oblique frustum (cut from a triangular right prism):

$$V=G(a+b+c)/3.$$

Sphere: $A=4\pi R^2,\ V=4\pi R^3/3.$

Zone of a sphere (cut off between two planes at a distance h from each other):

$$M=2\pi Rh,\ A=\pi(r^2+2Rh+r_1^2).$$
$$V=\pi h(3r^2+3r_1^2+h^2)/6.$$

Spherical cap of height h:

$$M=2\pi Rh=\pi(r^2+h^2),\ A=\pi(2r^2+h^2).$$
$$V=\pi h(3r^2+h^2)/6=\tfrac{1}{3}\pi h^2(3R-h).$$

Sector of a sphere:

r=radius of base of spherical cap and h=height of the spherical cap on which the cone stands.

$$A=\pi R(r+2h),\ V=2\pi R^2h/3.$$

Spherical wedge of angle α: $V=2R^3\alpha/3.$

Ellipsoid: $V=4\pi abc/3.$ (a, b, c semi-axes.)

Elliptic paraboloid: $V=\frac{1}{2}\pi abh.$ (a, b, semi-axes of base, h height.)

Frustum of an elliptic paraboloid:

$V=\frac{1}{2}\pi(ab+a_1b_1)h.$ (a, b and a_1, b_1 semi-axes of the ends, h height.)

Anchor ring or tore:

Radius of circle rotated$=r$, distance of its centre from the axis of rotation$=R$.

$$V=2\pi^2Rr^2,\quad A=4\pi^2Rr.$$

Oblique segment of a right circular cylinder:

h_1, h_2 the longest and shortest generators.

$$V = \tfrac{1}{2}\pi r^2(h_1 + h_2), \quad M = \pi r(h_1 + h_2).$$

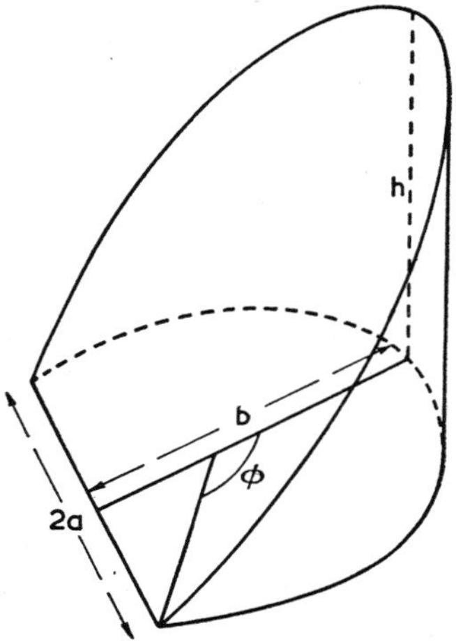

Fig. 8.1

Incomplete segment of a right circular cylinder:

h = longest generator, b the length of the perpendicular from the foot of h to the base chord of length $2a$; 2ϕ the angle which the curved arc of the base subtends at the centre of the circle of which the base is a segment. See Fig. 8.1.

$$V = \tfrac{1}{3}h\{a(3r^2 - a^2) + 3r^2(b - r)\phi\}/b.$$

$$M = 2rh\{(b - r)\phi + a\}/b.$$

8.5. Regular polyhedra

A regular polyhedron is a polyhedron whose faces are congruent regular polygons and in whose vertices an equal number of polygons meet.

There are five regular convex polyhedra:

(*a*) the tetrahedron, bounded by 4 equilateral triangles.

(*b*) the cube, ,, ,, 6 squares.

(*c*) the octahedron, ,, ,, 8 equilateral triangles.

(*d*) the dodecahedron, ,, ,, 12 regular pentagons.

(*e*) the isocahedron, ,, ,, 20 equilateral triangles.

Notation. R, r = radii of circumscribing and inscribed spheres respectively, a = edge.

Tetrahedron: $R=\frac{1}{4}a\sqrt{6}$, $r=\frac{a}{12}\sqrt{6}$, $A=a^2\sqrt{3}$, $V=\frac{a^3}{12}\sqrt{2}$.

Cube: $R=\frac{1}{2}a\sqrt{3}$, $r=\frac{1}{2}a$, $A=6a^2$, $V=a^3$.

Octahedron: $R=\frac{1}{2}a\sqrt{2}$, $r=\frac{a}{6}\sqrt{6}$, $A=2a^2\sqrt{3}$, $V=\frac{1}{3}a^3\sqrt{2}$.

Dodecahedron: $R=\sqrt{3}a\cos 36°$.

$r=a\cot 36°\cos 36°$.

$A=15a^2\cot 36°$.

$V=4Fr$ (F = area of a face),

$=5a^3\cot^2 36°\cos 36°$.

Isocahedron: $R=a\cos 18°$.

$$r=\frac{2a}{\sqrt{3}}\cos^2 36°.$$

$A=5a^2\sqrt{3}$.

$$V=\frac{20Fr}{3}=\frac{10}{3}a^3\cos^2 36°.$$

CHAPTER 9

PLANE ANALYTICAL GEOMETRY

9.1. Geometrical formulae are capable of different interpretations depending on the axioms assumed or on the definitions given. Often the same names are used and the same equations hold for geometrical constructs in geometries based on different initial assumptions. It is necessary to distinguish clearly which formulae follow from any given set of initial assumptions and how these formulae are to be interpreted.

Euclidean Geometry was suggested by physical bodies and is based on a certain set of axioms. To *represent* the points of a plane or of space, Descartes introduced his co-ordinates which are real numbers. Abstract Geometry may be based on a set of axioms of incidence which state relations between entities, called "points" and "lines", which are themselves undefined. Alternatively, in abstract plane Cartesian Geometry a point may be *defined* as an ordered pair (x, y) of numbers which obey certain laws of Algebra, where x and y are defined to be either real or complex, or some other restriction may be imposed on them. A curve of order n is defined as the set of points which satisfy one equation in x and y of degree n; in particular a line is the set of points satisfying a linear equation $ax+by+c=0$. It can be shewn that this is the set

$$(\lambda x_1+\mu x_2, \lambda y_1+\mu y_2),$$

where (x_1, y_1), (x_2, y_2) are two fixed distinct members of the set and λ and μ vary over the set of numbers. Two lines may or may not meet.

Again, in homogeneous plane Geometry a point may be defined as a trio of numbers (x, y, z) with the convention that $(\lambda x, \lambda y, \lambda z)$ is the same point as (x, y, z), provided $\lambda \neq 0$. There is no point $(0, 0, 0)$. The co-ordinates x, y, z may be defined as real numbers or complex numbers or as some other kind of number. A line is defined as the set of points $(\lambda x_1+\mu x_2, \lambda y_1+\mu y_2, \lambda z_1+\mu z_2)$, where (x_1, y_1, z_1), (x_2, y_2, z_2) are two fixed distinct points. The co-ordinates of the points of a line so defined satisfy a homogeneous linear relation in x, y, z, viz. $ax+by+cz=0$. A curve of order n is defined as the set of points which satisfy a homogeneous equation in x, y, z of degree n, so that a line is a curve of order unity.

If $z\neq 0$, there is a (1, 1) correspondence between the point (x, y, z) and the point whose Cartesian co-ordinates are $(x/z, y/z)$. The latter point does not exist if $z=0$, but in this case the point $(a, b, 0)$ satisfies the equation $bx-ay+cz=0$ for all c, and the convention is that the system of parallel lines $bx-ay+\lambda=0$ intersect in a point which corresponds to $(a, b, 0)$. The aggregate of such points is a line $z=0$ called the "*line at infinity*". In the complex homogeneous Cartesian plane the two points $(1, \pm i, 0)$ are called the *absolute* or *circular points,* and the $(1, 1)$ correspondence between points and between curves of order n in the complex Cartesian (x, y) plane and the homogeneous Cartesian (x, y, z) plane is preserved if a circle in the latter plane is defined as a conic (q.v.) which passes through the absolute points. The significance of the absolute points is deeper than this, for all properties of distance and direction which enter into a geometrical figure in the (x, y) plane can be interpreted in terms of the relation with the absolute points of the corresponding configuration in the (x, y, z) plane. The ideas of distance and direction play no part in these relations.

Other particular systems of homogeneous co-ordinates may be set up, e.g. trilinears or areals (q.v.), which have a physical significance. In abstract Geometry no physical significance is attached to the co-ordinates and no particular significance is attached to any particular line or any particular points. Direction and distance in their physical sense are meaningless terms.

The equations in x, y given below hold for Cartesian co-ordinates whether (x, y) is interpreted as representing a point or as being a point, and, unless the contrary is stated, whether x and y are complex or restricted to be real. Similar remarks apply for the homogeneous co-ordinates x, y, z.

A set of *axioms of incidence* for a plane are: Through an arbitrary point pass an infinite number of lines, of which one passes through any other arbitrary point. The point is determined by any two distinct lines through it. A line contains an infinite number of points and is determined by any two of them. Two lines have a point in common or coincide. Any two points determine a line unless they coincide.

Pappus' theorem states that if $A, B, C;\ A', B', C'$ be two trios of points lying on two intersecting lines, then the points $(AB', A'B)$, $(BC', B'C)$, $(CA', C'A)$ are collinear, where $(AB', A'B)$ denotes the intersection of the lines AB', $A'B$.

Pappus' theorem cannot be deduced from the axioms of incidence for a plane, nor indeed from the axioms of incidence for space of any dimensions. The theorems obtained by the operation of the commutative and associative laws of addition, the associative law of multiplication and the distributive law on the co-ordinate symbols can be deduced geometrically using the axioms of incidence. Theorems obtained by the operation of these laws and of the commutative law of multiplication on the symbols follow geometrically from the axioms of incidence in a plane together with Pappus' theorem assumed as an axiom. The assumption of Pappus' theorem as an axiom is equivalent to the assumption that the symbols obey the commutative law of multiplication.

Two triangles are *in perspective* if the lines joining corresponding vertices are concurrent.

Desargues' theorem states that if ABC, $A'B'C'$ be two triangles in perspective, then the points $(BC, B'C')$, $(CA, C'A')$, $(AB, A'B')$ are collinear. The converse holds. The theorem holds for triangles in a plane or in space. It can be deduced from the propositions of incidence in a plane together with Pappus' theorem, or from the propositions of incidence in space. It can be deduced by using the symbols if the commutative law of multiplication holds.

9.2. Euclidean plane geometry. Cartesian co-ordinates

Co-ordinates on a line. Two points O, the origin, and A, the unit point, are chosen on the line. The co-ordinate of any point P on the line is $x=\overline{OP}/\overline{OA}$, where $\overline{OP}$ is a directed length. $\overline{OA}$ is the positive direction on the line.

If A, B, C are any three collinear points

$$\overline{AB}=-\overline{BA}, \quad \overline{AB}+\overline{BC}+\overline{CA}=0.$$

The point C divides the line AB in the ratio $\lambda:1$ if $\overline{AC}/\overline{CB}=\lambda$. The value of the ratio is independent of the positive direction along the line.

The values which λ takes, if C lies in the portion of the line indicated, are given in the following table:

C moves	λ takes
from $-\infty$ to A	the negative values from -1 to 0
from A to B	the positive values from 0 to $+\infty$
from B to $+\infty$	the negative values from $-\infty$ to -1.

We assume that only one point on the line is non-finite. It is called the point at infinity on the line. Then to each value of λ corresponds one point C on the line, and conversely. One value of λ corresponds to the point at infinity on the line and one point on the line corresponds to the non-finite value of λ.

9.21. Rectangular Cartesian co-ordinates in a plane

(Unless otherwise stated all formulae for Cartesian co-ordinates are for rectangular axes.)

Two perpendicular lines Ox, Oy are taken such that the angle between the positive direction Ox and the positive direction Oy is 90°, and unit points A and B are chosen on Ox and Oy. These fix the scales used. Perpendiculars PM and PN are drawn from a point P onto Ox and Oy respectively. The co-ordinates (x, y) of P are the signed ratios OM/OA, ON/OB. O is called the *origin*, Ox, Oy the *axes*, x the *absissa* and y the *ordinate* of P. To each finite point P in the plane corresponds one ordered pair of real co-ordinates (x, y), and conversely. We call this point $P(x, y)$.

Oblique axes. Two lines Ox, Oy, intersecting at an angle ω measured in the anti-clockwise direction from Ox to Oy, are chosen as axes, and unit points A and B fixed on them. Lines PN and PM parallel to Ox, Oy are drawn meeting Oy, Ox in N and M respectively. The co-ordinates of P referred to Ox, Oy are $x=OM/OA$, $y=ON/OB$.

Polar co-ordinates. A fixed point O is chosen as pole and a line Ox as initial line. The polar co-ordinates of P are (r, θ), where $r=|OP|$, $\theta=P\hat{O}x$. If (x, y) are the Cartesian co-ordinates of P referred to rectangular axes Ox, Oy, then (see Fig. 1.1)

$$x=r\cos\theta,\ y=r\sin\theta,\ r=|(x^2+y^2)^{\frac{1}{2}}|.$$

Tangential polar co-ordinates (p, r). A point O is taken as pole, $r=$distance OP and p is the length of the perpendicular from O to the tangent (q.v.) to the curve at P. The (p, r) equation is called the *pedal equation* of a curve. These must not be confused with tangential or prime co-ordinates.

Parametric co-ordinates. $x=\phi(u, v)$, $y=\psi(u, v)$ are functions of two parameters u and v, called the parameters of the point x, y. A curve is given by one equation $f(u, v)=0$ or by $x=f_1(t)$, $y=f_2(t)$ where x and y are functions of one parameter, called the parameter of the point t.

9.22. Change of axes

Take new axes $O'x'$, $O'y'$, parallel to Ox, Oy through the point $O'(a, b)$, and let the co-ordinates of P referred to the old and new axes be (x, y), (x', y') respectively. Then

$$x=a+x',\quad y=b+y'.$$

If OX, OY be rectangular axes through O such that the angles $XOx=\theta$ and the co-ordinates of P referred to OX, OY are (X, Y), then

$$\left.\begin{aligned}X&=x\cos\theta+y\sin\theta\\ Y&=-x\sin\theta+y\cos\theta\end{aligned}\right\},\quad \left.\begin{aligned}x&=X\cos\theta-Y\sin\theta\\ y&=X\sin\theta+Y\cos\theta\end{aligned}\right\}.$$

Transformation from one set of oblique axes to another. Let Ox, Oy be oblique axes intersecting at an angle ω and $O'x'$, $O'y'$ make angles α and β respectively with Ox, where O' is (a, b) referred to Ox, Oy.

Then if P is the point (x, y) and (x', y') referred to Ox, Oy and $O'x'$, $O'y'$ respectively,

$$x = a + \{x' \sin(\omega - \alpha) + y' \sin(\omega - \beta)\}/\sin \omega,$$
$$y = b + \{x' \sin \alpha + y' \sin \beta\}/\sin \omega.$$
$$x' = \{(x-a) \sin \beta - (y-b) \sin(\omega - \beta)\}/\sin(\beta - \alpha),$$
$$y' = \{-(x-a) \sin \alpha + (y-b) \sin(\omega - \alpha)\}/\sin(\beta - \alpha).$$

9.3. Co-ordinates of a point $P(x, y)$ which divides the line P_1P_2 in the ratio $\lambda : 1$, i.e. such that $P_1P : PP_2 = \lambda : 1$, where P_1 and P_2 are the points (x_1, y_1), (x_2, y_2), are

$$x = (x_1 + \lambda x_2)/(1+\lambda), \quad y = (y_1 + \lambda y_2)/(1+\lambda).$$

For the position of P relative to P_1 and P_2 for different values of λ, see § 9.2.

The above formulae hold for rectangular and oblique axes.

Distance between two points $P_1(x_1, y_1)$, $P_2(x_2, y_2)$ in rectangular axes is

$$d = |\sqrt{\{|x_2 - x_1|^2 + |y_2 - y_1|^2\}}|.$$

In oblique axes intersecting at an angle ω

$$d = |\sqrt{\{(x_2 - x_1)^2 + (y_2 - y_1)^2 + 2(x_2 - x_1)(y_2 - y_1) \cos \omega\}}|.$$

If the points are $P_1(r_1, \theta_1)$, $P_2(r_2, \theta_2)$ in polar co-ordinates

$$d = |\sqrt{\{r_1^2 + r_2^2 - 2r_1r_2 \cos(\theta_2 - \theta_1)\}}|.$$

Area of a triangle, vertices $P_1(x_1, y_1)$, $P_2(x_2, y_2)$, $P_3(x_3, y_3)$ (rectangular axes), is Δ, where

$$\Delta = \text{numerical value of } \tfrac{1}{2} \begin{vmatrix} x_1 & y_1 & 1 \\ x_2 & y_2 & 1 \\ x_3 & y_3 & 1 \end{vmatrix}.$$

Area of a triangle, vertices $P_i(r_i, \theta_i)$, $(i = 1, 2, 3)$, is

$$\tfrac{1}{2}|r_2r_3 \sin(\theta_3 - \theta_2) + r_3r_1 \sin(\theta_1 - \theta_3) + r_1r_2 \sin(\theta_2 - \theta_1)|.$$

Area of a polygon, vertices $P_i(x_i, y_i)$, $(i = 1, 2, \ldots, n)$, is

$$\tfrac{1}{2}|x_1(y_2 - y_n) + x_2(y_3 - y_1) + x_3(y_4 - y_2) + \ldots + x_n(y_1 - y_{n-1})|.$$

9.4. Equation of a line

General form: $\quad ax + by + c = 0.$

Gradient form. The line making an angle α with the positive direction Ox and an intercept* c on Oy is

$$y = x \tan \alpha + c.$$

* The term intercept means the signed length OP, where P is the point of intersection with the axis.

Intercept form. The line making intercepts a and b on the x and y axes is

$$x/a+y/b=1.$$

Perpendicular form. If the perpendicular from the origin in the line is of length p and makes an angle α with the positive direction of the x-axis, the equation is

$$x \cos \alpha+y \sin \alpha=p.$$

In polar co-ordinates: $r \cos (\theta-\alpha)=p.$

Any line through (x_1, y_1): $y-y_1=m(x-x_1)$.

Line joining (x_1, y_1), (x_2, y_2):

$$\begin{vmatrix} x & y & 1 \\ x_1 & y_1 & 1 \\ x_2 & y_2 & 1 \end{vmatrix}=0, \quad \text{or} \quad y-y_1=\frac{y_2-y_1}{x_2-x_1}(x-x_1).$$

Any line through the point of intersection of $L_1=0$, $L_2=0$, where $L_i \equiv a_i x+b_i y+c_i$, is

$$\lambda L_1+\mu L_2=0.$$

The equation of any line which makes an angle α with the line $ax+by+c=0$ is

$$y=\frac{b \tan \alpha-a}{a \tan \alpha+b}x+d.$$

The equation of any line parallel to $ax+by+c=0$ is $ax+by+c_1=0$.

The condition that the points (x_i, y_i), $i=1, 2, 3$, be collinear:

$$\begin{vmatrix} x_1 & y_1 & 1 \\ x_2 & y_2 & 1 \\ x_3 & y_3 & 1 \end{vmatrix}=0.$$

Length of the perpendicular from $P(x_1, y_1)$ on the line

$x \cos \alpha+y \sin \alpha-p=0$ is $p_1=|x_1 \cos \alpha+y_1 \sin \alpha-p|$,
$ax+by+c=0$ is $p_1=|(ax_1+by_1+c)/\sqrt{(a^2+b^2)}|$.

The angle α between the lines

$$y=m_i x+d_i \qquad (i=1, 2),$$

or between

$$a_i x+b_i y+c_i=0 \quad (i=1, 2),$$

is given by

$$\tan \alpha=(m_2-m_1)/(1+m_1 m_2) \text{ or } \tan \alpha=(a_1 b_2-a_2 b_1)/(a_1 a_2+b_1 b_2).$$

The angle α is the positive angle through which the first line must be rotated to be parallel to the second.

The lines are parallel, if

$$m_1 = m_2 \text{ or } a_1 : a_2 = b_1 : b_2;$$

identical, if

$$m_1 = m_2,\ d_1 = d_2 \text{ or } a_1 : a_2 = b_1 : b_2 = c_1 : c_2;$$

perpendicular, if

$$m_1 m_2 = -1 \text{ or } a_1 a_2 + b_1 b_2 = 0.$$

Three lines $L_i \equiv a_i x + b_i y + c_i = 0 \quad (i = 1, 2, 3)$ are concurrent if

$$\begin{vmatrix} a_1 & b_1 & c_1 \\ a_2 & b_2 & c_2 \\ a_3 & b_3 & c_3 \end{vmatrix} = 0.$$

Then constants λ_i exist such that

$$\lambda_1 L_1 + \lambda_2 L_2 + \lambda_3 L_3 \equiv 0.$$

The point of intersection may be at infinity, in which case the lines are parallel.

9.5. Equation of an algebraic curve

An equation $f(x, y) = 0$, where $f(x, y)$ is a polynomial* of degree n in x and y, is, or represents, an *algebraic curve of order n*. It is met by a general straight line in the complex plane in n points. The degree of the polynomial $f(x, y)$ is unchanged by any of the changes of axes given in § 9.22, or by any linear transformation of the co-ordinates.

The points of intersection of the curves $f_1(x, y) = 0$, $f_2(x, y) = 0$ are the pairs of values of (x, y) which satisfy both equations. If f_1 and f_2 are of orders n_1 and n_2 and are co-prime, the number of points of intersection is $\leqslant n_1 n_2$ if the co-ordinates are real, and is $n_1 n_2$ if they are complex, coincident points of intersection being suitably counted. If λ is a constant, $f_1(x, y) + \lambda f_2(x, y) = 0$ is a curve through the points of intersection of the two curves.

The *tangent* AT a point $P(x_1, y_1)$ ON the curve is the limiting position of the chord PQ as $Q \to P$ along the curve. Its equation is

$$(y - y_1)\frac{\partial f_1}{\partial y_1} + (x - x_1)\frac{\partial f_1}{\partial x_1} = 0. \qquad \text{(See § 12.5.)}$$

* The *degree* of a polynomial in several variables is its degree in all the variables taken together.

9.6. The conic

Apollonius defined a conic as a plane section of a right circular cone. In Cartesian Geometry the *conic* is the curve whose equation is

$$S(x, y) \equiv ax^2+by^2+2hxy+2gx+2fy+c=0, \quad \quad (1)$$

or

$$X'\Gamma X=0,$$

where

$$X=\begin{bmatrix} x \\ y \\ 1 \end{bmatrix}, \quad \Gamma=\begin{bmatrix} a & h & g \\ h & b & f \\ g & f & c \end{bmatrix}.$$

Notation: $P=\tfrac{1}{2}\dfrac{\partial S}{\partial x}=ax+hy+g,\ Q=\tfrac{1}{2}\dfrac{\partial S}{\partial y}=hx+by+f,$

$$R=gx+fy+c.$$

$$P_1=ax_1+hy_1+g, \text{ etc.}$$

Then

$$xP_1+yQ_1+R_1 \equiv x_1P+y_1Q+R,$$
$$xP+yQ+R \equiv S(x, y).$$
$$\Delta \equiv |\Gamma|.$$

A, B, C, F, G, H are the co-factors (q.v.) of $a, b, \ldots, h$ in Δ.

The conic degenerates into a pair of straight lines if, and only if, $\Delta=0$. The lines then intersect at the point of intersection of the concurrent lines $P=0$, $Q=0$, $R=0$.

The following properties hold for non-degenerate or proper conics.

The conic is of class two, i.e. two tangents, real or not, pass through any point P not on the curve. The line joining their points of contact is called the *chord of contact* of the tangents from P.

Pole and polar. The locus of the point of intersection P of tangents at the extremities of a variable chord through a fixed point A lies in a straight line l called the *polar* of A with respect to the conic. The point A is the *pole* of l. The pole of a line l is unique. The polar of A coincides with the chord of contact of tangents from A. The pole of a line l is the point of intersection of the tangents at the points of intersection of l with the conic. The polar of A contains the locus of the harmonic conjugate (q.v.) of A with respect to the points B, D of intersection of a chord through A with the conic. The polar of a point P on the conic is the tangent at P.

If a point Q lies on the polar of P, then P lies on the polar of Q. P and Q are said to be *conjugate* with respect to the conic.

If a line m passes through the pole of a line l, then l passes through the pole of m. Then l and m are *conjugate* with respect to the conic.

If a point P moves on a line l, its polar passes through a fixed point

L, the pole of l. The range of points P on l and the pencil of lines through L are homographic (q.v.).

If a line p passes through a fixed point L, the locus of its pole is a line l, the polar of L.

The polar of the point of intersection of two lines is the join of their poles. The pole of the line joining two points A and B is the point of intersection of the polars of A and B.

The equation of the polar of $A(x_1, y_1)$ with respect to $S(x, y)=0$ given by (1), is

$$L_1(x, y) \equiv x(ax_1+hy_1+g)+y(hx_1+by_1+f)+gx_1+fy_1+c=0, \quad . \quad (2)$$

i.e. $$xP_1+yQ_1+R_1=0,$$

or $$x_1P+y_1Q+R=0,$$

i.e. $$X'\Gamma X_1=0, \text{ or } X_1'\Gamma X=0,$$

where $$X'_1=[x_1, y_1, 1].$$

This is the equation of the chord of contact of the tangents from A, and, if A lies ON the conic S, of the tangent AT A.

The combined equation of the tangents from $P_1(x_1, y_1)$ to the curve is

$$S(x, y)S_1(x_1, y_1)-\{L_1(x, y)\}^2=0.$$

The condition that the line

$$ux+vy+w=0 \quad . \quad . \quad . \quad . \quad (2')$$

shall touch the curve is

$$\begin{vmatrix} a & h & g & u \\ h & b & f & v \\ g & f & c & w \\ u & v & w & 0 \end{vmatrix} = 0,$$

i.e. $$Au^2+Bv^2+2Huv+2Guw+2Fvw+Cw^2=0, \quad . \quad . \quad (3)$$

or $$U'(\text{adj } \Gamma)U=0, \text{ where } U'=[u,v,w].$$

The *centre* of a conic is the pole of the line at infinity. If $\Delta \neq 0$, $C \neq 0$, the conic has a finite centre M given by $P=Q=0$ and every chord through M is bisected at M.

The locus of the mid-points of a system of parallel chords of a conic is a straight line through the centre called a *diameter*. Two diameters are *conjugate* when each is the locus of the mid-points of chords parallel to the other.

The equation of the diameter which bisects the chords which cut the x-axis at an angle β is

$$P \cos \beta + Q \sin \beta = 0,$$

i.e. $$(ax+hy+g) \cos \beta + (hx+by+f) \sin \beta = 0.$$

A conic has one pair of perpendicular diameters which are called its *principal axes*. The angle α which a principal axis makes with the axis of x is given by

$$\tan 2\alpha = 2h/(a-b).$$

If a principal axis is taken as x-axis and a tangent to the curve as y-axis, the equation of any proper conic is

$$y^2 = 2lx - (1-e^2)x^2. \quad . \quad . \quad . \quad . \quad (4)$$

The conic is the locus of a point P such that $SP = ePM$, where S is a fixed point, the *focus*, and PM is the perpendicular distance from P to a fixed line, the *directrix*, and e is a constant, the *eccentricity*, which is given by

$$(2-e^2)^2/(1-e^2) = (a+b)^2/(ab-h^2).$$

In the form (4) the x-axis passes through the focus and is perpendicular to the directrix. The y-axis divides the segment of the x-axis between the directrix and S in the ratio $1 : e$. The ordinate through S is of length l and l is called the *semi-latus rectum*. The distance of the focus from the directrix is l/e. The conic is an *ellipse, parabola* or *hyperbola* according as $e \lesseqgtr 1$. For a circle $e=0$.

Two conics

$$a_i x^2 + b_i y^2 + 2h_i xy + 2g_i x + 2f_i y + c_i = 0 \quad (i=1, 2)$$

are similar if

$$(a_1 b_1 - h_1^2)/(a_1+b_1)^2 = (a_2 b_2 - h_2^2)/(a_2+b_2)^2.$$

They are similar and similarly situated if

$$a_1/a_2 = b_1/b_2 = h_1/h_2.$$

9.7. In polar co-ordinates r, θ the equation of a proper conic is

$$l = r(1 + e\cos\theta),$$

where the pole is the focus, a principal axis the initial line and θ is measured from the perpendicular from S to the directrix.

If the pole is the focus and the axis is inclined at an angle γ to the initial line, the equation is

$$l = r\{1 + e\cos(\theta-\gamma)\}.$$

The equation of the directrix is then

$$l = re\cos(\theta-\gamma).$$

The equation of the chord joining the points whose vectorial angles are α and β is

$$\frac{l}{r} - e\cos(\theta-\gamma) = \sec\tfrac{1}{2}(\alpha-\beta)\cos\{\theta-\tfrac{1}{2}(\alpha+\beta)\}.$$

9.8. Special conics

9.81. The circle

The theorems given in § 9.6 for conics hold for circles. See also § 6.5.

Centre of similitude. Lines joining the ends of parallel radii of two coplanar circles pass through one or other of two points called the inner and outer *centres of similitude* of the circles. The centres of similitude lie on the line of centres and divide it harmonically (see § 10.41). Each common tangent passes through a centre of similitude.

Monge's theorem. The three outer centres of similitude of three circles taken in pairs are collinear. Any two of the inner centres of similitude is collinear with one of the outer centres of similitude. The four lines of collinearity are called *axes of similitude.*

Radical axis

The *power* of a point S with respect to a circle is the (constant) product of the segments $SP \,.\, SQ$ of a secant SPQ through S. If O is the centre of the circle and T a point of contact of a tangent from S,

$$SP \,.\, SQ = OS^2 - r^2 = ST^2.$$

The locus of a point which has equal powers with respect to two circles is a line perpendicular to the line of centres. It is called their *radical axis*. The tangents to the two circles from any point on their radical axis are equal. If the circles intersect, their radical axis is their common chord. If they touch, it is the tangent at their point of contact. The radical axis of two concentric circles is the line at infinity.

The radical axes of three circles taken in pairs are concurrent in the *radical centre* of the circles. If the centres of the circles are collinear, the radical axes are parallel and the radical centre is on the line at infinity.

Equation of a circle: $S(x, y) \equiv x^2 + y^2 + 2gx + 2fy + c = 0$.

Centre: $(-g, -f)$; radius $= |\sqrt{(g^2 + f^2 - c)}|$.

Circle centre (α, β), radius a: $(x-\alpha)^2 + (y-\beta)^2 = a^2$.

Parametrically: $x = \alpha + a \cos t$, $y = \beta + a \sin t$.

Conditions that (1) is a circle: $a = b$, $h = 0$.

Equation of circle through $P_i(x_i, y_i)$, $i = 1, 2, 3$, is

$$\begin{vmatrix} x^2+y^2 & x & y & 1 \\ x_1^2+y_1^2 & x_1 & y_1 & 1 \\ x_2^2+y_2^2 & x_2 & y_2 & 1 \\ x_3^2+y_3^2 & x_3 & y_3 & 1 \end{vmatrix} = 0.$$

Substituting x_4, y_4 for x, y, we obtain the necessary and sufficient condition that $P_i(x_i, y_i)$, $i=1, 2, 3, 4$, are concyclic.

Equation of circle centre (α, β), radius a, in oblique axes intersecting at angle ω is

$$(x-\alpha)^2+(y-\beta)^2+2(x-\alpha)(y-\beta)\cos\omega=a^2.$$

Equation in polar co-ordinates, centre (c, α), radius a is

$$r^2-2rc\cos(\theta-\alpha)+c^2=a^2.$$

Condition that the line (2′) shall touch the circle centre (α, β), radius a, is

$$a^2(u^2+v^2)-(\alpha u+\beta v+w)^2=0.$$

Polar of (x_1, y_1) with respect to $S(x, y)=0$ is

$$xx_1+yy_1+g(x+x_1)+f(y+y_1)+c=0.$$

This is also the equation of the tangent AT (x_1, y_1) ON $S(x, y)=0$.

Equation of any circle through the points of intersection of two circles $S_i=0$, $i=1, 2$, where

$$S_i\equiv x^2+y^2+2g_ix+2f_iy+c_i=0,$$

is

$$S_1+\lambda S_2=0 \quad . \quad . \quad . \quad . \quad . \quad (5)$$

The radical axis of the two circles is

$$S_1-S_2=0,$$

i.e.

$$2(g_1-g_2)x+2(f_1-f_2)y+c_1-c_2=0. \quad . \quad . \quad (6)$$

The family of circles (5) is a co-axial system and (6) is the radical axis of any pair of the system.

If PQR is any secant through $P(x_1, y_1)$ to S and t is the length of the tangent from P, then the power of $P=PQ\,.\,PR=t^2$, where

$$t^2=x_1^2+y_1^2+2gx_1+2fy_1+c.$$

Two circles S_1, S_2 are orthogonal, if

$$2g_1g_2+2f_1f_2-c_1-c_2=0.$$

Inversion with respect to a circle

The *inverse* of P, with respect to a circle, centre O and radius a, is the point P' in OP on the same side of O as P, such that $OP\,.\,OP'=a^2$.

As P describes a curve C, the inverse P' of P describes the inverse of C with respect to the circle. If $P(x, y)$, $P'(x', y')$ or $P(r, \theta)$, $P'(r', \theta')$

are inverses with respect to the circle, centre the origin or pole and radius a, then

$$rr'=a^2,\ \theta'=\theta,$$

$$x'=a^2x/(x^2+y^2),\ y'=a^2y/(x^2+y^2).$$

The inverse of $f(x, y)=0$ is $f\left(\frac{a^2x}{x^2+y^2}, \frac{a^2y}{x^2+y^2}\right)=0,$

and that of $\phi(r, \theta)=0$ is $\phi\left(\frac{a^2}{r}, \theta\right)=0.$

The inverse of a line not through the pole is a circle through the pole; that of a circle not through the pole is a circle not through the pole.

9.82. The ellipse and hyperbola referred to their principal axes

Ellipse: $x^2/a^2+y^2/b^2=1$ . . (7) *Hyperbola:* $x^2/a^2-y^2/b^2=1$. (8)

a=major axis, b=minor axis (imaginary for the hyperbola).

Condition that equation (1) represents an

ellipse: $h^2-ab<0$. hyperbola: $h^2-ab>0$.

Parametric representations:

$x=a\cos\theta,\ y=b\sin\theta$; $x=a\sec\theta,\ y=b\tan\theta$.

θ is called the *eccentric* angle.

$x=a\left(\frac{1-t^2}{1+t^2}\right),\ y=\frac{2bt}{1+t^2}$; $x=a\left(\frac{1+t^2}{1-t^2}\right),\ y=\frac{2bt}{1-t^2}$;

$x=\frac{1}{2}a(s+s^{-1}),\ y=\frac{1}{2}b(s-s^{-1})$. (9)

One branch is given by

$x=a\cosh\phi,\ y=a\sinh\phi$,

the other by

$x=-a\cosh\phi,\ y=a\sinh\phi$.

Polar equation, centre the pole, and major axis the initial line:

$r^2(1-e^2\cos^2\theta)=b^2$; $r^2(1-e^2\cos^2\theta)+b^2=0$.

Condition that the line (2′) shall touch the curve:

$a^2u^2+b^2v^2=w^2$; $a^2u^2-b^2v^2=w^2$.

Pedal equation with respect to a focus as pole:

$\frac{b^2}{p^2}=\frac{2a}{r}-1$; $\frac{b^2}{p^2}=1\pm\frac{2a}{r}$ (near and far branches respectively).

Pedal equation with respect to the centre as pole:

$$p^2r^2+a^2b^2=(a^2+b^2)p^2; \qquad p^2r^2-a^2b^2=(a^2-b^2)p^2.$$

In the remainder of this paragraph, the upper sign refers to the ellipse (7) and the lower to the hyperbola (8).

Polar of a point (x_1, y_1): $\dfrac{xx_1}{a^2}\pm\dfrac{yy_1}{b^2}=1.$

Pole of $lx+my+n=0$: $(-a^2l/n, \mp b^2m/n)$.

Tangents of gradient m:

$$y-mx=+\sqrt{(m^2a^2\pm b^2)}, \; y-mx=-\sqrt{(m^2a^2\pm b^2)}.$$

Asymptotes of the hyperbola, i.e. tangents at its points of intersection with the line at infinity:

$$x/a+y/b=0, \; x/a-y/b=0.$$

The angle between the asymptotes is 2ϕ given by $\tan\phi=b/a$.

A *rectangular* hyperbola is one whose asymptotes are perpendicular. Its equation referred to its axes is $x^2-y^2=a^2$;

referred to its asymptotes is $xy=c^2$,

a parametric representation of which is $(ct, c/t)$.

A diameter $y=mx$ cuts the hyperbola (8) in real finite points, touches it at infinity or meets it in unreal points according as $m^2 \lesseqgtr b^2/a^2$.

Normal at (x_1, y_1): $(y-y_1)x_1/a^2=\pm(x-x_1)y_1/b^2$.

Diameter conjugate to $Ax+By=0$ is $Bx/a^2\mp Ay/b^2=0$.

The equation of the curve referred to two conjugate diameters, one of length $2a_1$, as oblique axes is

$$x^2/a_1^2\pm y^2/b_1^2=1, \text{ where } a_1^2\pm b_1^2=a^2\pm b^2.$$

If ϕ_1, ϕ_2 are the angles these conjugate diameters make with the x-axis,

$$\tan\phi_1\tan\phi_2=\mp b^2/a^2, \qquad a_1b_1\sin(\phi_2-\phi_1)=ab.$$

Hence the area of the triangle formed by two conjugate radii of an ellipse and the chord joining their end points is constant.

If $P(a\cos\theta, b\sin\theta)$, $Q(a\cos\phi, b\sin\phi)$ are the extremities of two conjugate diameters of the ellipse, then $\theta=\frac{1}{2}\pi+\phi$.

Equation of a hyperbola referred to its asymptotes as oblique axes:

$$xy=\tfrac{1}{4}(a^2+b^2).$$

Equation of the chord PQ joining the points θ and ϕ on the ellipse is:

$$\frac{x}{a}\cos\tfrac{1}{2}(\theta+\phi)+\frac{y}{b}\sin\tfrac{1}{2}(\theta+\phi)=\cos\tfrac{1}{2}(\theta-\phi).$$

The chord joining $(a \sec \theta, b \tan \theta), (a \sec \phi, b \tan \phi)$ on the hyperbola is:

$$\frac{x}{a} \cos \tfrac{1}{2}(\theta - \phi) - \frac{y}{b} \sin \tfrac{1}{2}(\theta + \phi) = \cos \tfrac{1}{2}(\theta + \phi).$$

Eccentricity e given by

$$a^2 e^2 = a^2 \mp b^2.$$

Latus rectum is of length $\pm 2a(1 - e^2)$.

There are two foci $(ae, 0)$, $(-ae, 0)$ and two directrices $x = a/e$, $x = -a/e$.

Distances of a point $P(x_1, y_1)$ on the curve from the foci $S(ae, 0)$ and $H(-ae, 0)$ are

$$r_1 = a + x_1 e, \qquad r_2 = \pm(a - x_1 e), \qquad r_1 \pm r_2 = 2a.$$

Area of the ellipse cut off between the minor axis and the ordinate $x = x_1$ $(0 \leqslant x_1 \leqslant a)$ is

$$\frac{b}{a} x_1 \underset{+}{\sqrt{}}(a^2 - x_1^2) + ab \sin^{-1} \frac{x_1}{a}, \qquad 0 \leqslant \sin^{-1} \frac{x_1}{a} \leqslant \tfrac{1}{2}\pi.$$

Area of ellipse $= \pi ab$.

Area of hyperbola cut off by the line $x = x_1$ $(x_1 \geqslant a)$ which meets the curve at (x_1, y_1) where $y_1 > 0$ is

$$x_1 y_1 - ab \ln \left(\frac{x_1}{a} + \frac{y_1}{b} \right).$$

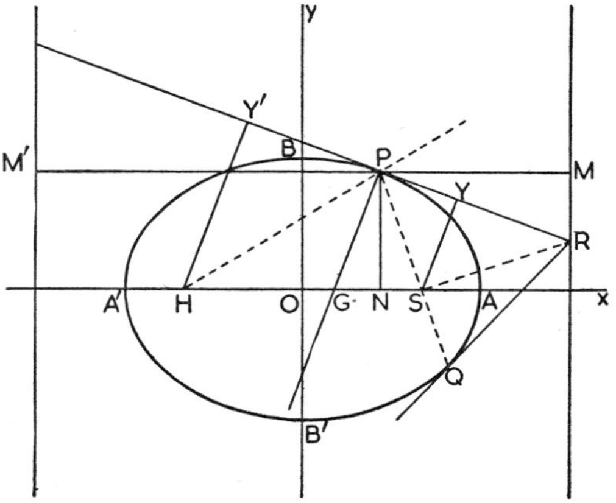

Fig. 9.1

The locus of the feet Y and Y' of the perpendiculars SY, HY' from the foci on a tangent is the auxiliary circle

$$x^2 + y^2 = a^2.$$

$$SY \,.\, HY' = \text{constant} = b^2.$$

Locus of the point of intersection of perpendicular tangents is the director circle

$$x^2+y^2=a^2\pm b^2.$$

For any point P on the ellipse, $PS+PH=2a$; on the hyperbola, $PS-PH=\pm 2a$. This gives a construction for the curve.

The tangent and normal at a point P bisect the angles between the focal distances PH and PS.

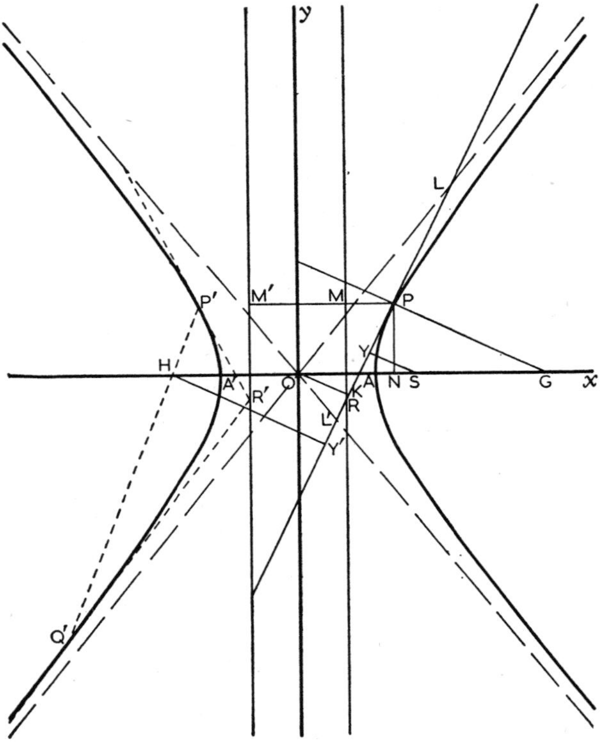

Fig. 9.2

On any secant of a hyperbola the two intercepts between the curve and the two asymptotes are equal. This gives a construction for the curve if the asymptotes and one point on the curve are given.

The intercept that the asymptotes make on a tangent is bisected at the point of contact.

The area of a triangle formed by a tangent and the asymptotes of a hyperbola is constant.

The diagonals of a circumscribed parallelogram are conjugate diameters. In an inscribed parallelogram the sides are parallel to two conjugate diameters.

The tangents from any point are equally inclined to the focal distances of the point.

The tangents at the ends of a focal chord intersect at a point R on the directrix and the line SR is perpendicular to the chord.

9.83. The parabola

The condition that (1) is a parabola is that the terms of the second degree form a perfect square i.e. $h^2=ab$. A repeated line also satisfies this condition.

Equation when axis of parabola and tangent at the vertex are axes of reference: $y^2=4ax$, parametric representation: $(at^2, 2at)$.

Condition that the line (2′) shall touch curve: $uw=av^2$.

Focus: $(a, 0)$, directrix: $x+a=0$.

Polar equation with focus as pole, axis as initial line: $r(1\pm\cos\theta)=2a$; (lower or upper sign according as positive direction on initial line is from S on directrix or vice versa).

Pedal equation with focus as pole: $p^2=ar$.

Polar of (x_1, y_1): $yy_1=2a(x+x_1)$.

Tangent at t, i.e. $(at^2, 2at)$: $ty=x+at^2$.

Tangent with gradient m: $y=mx+a/m$.

Pole of $lx+my+n=0$ is $(n/l, -2am/l)$.

Chord joining t_1, t_2: $x-\frac{1}{2}(t_1+t_2)y+at_1t_2=0$.

Normal at t: $y+tx=2at+at^3$.

Equation of the diameter bisecting the chords of slope m: $y=2a/m$.

Locus of the point of intersection of perpendicular tangents is the directrix.

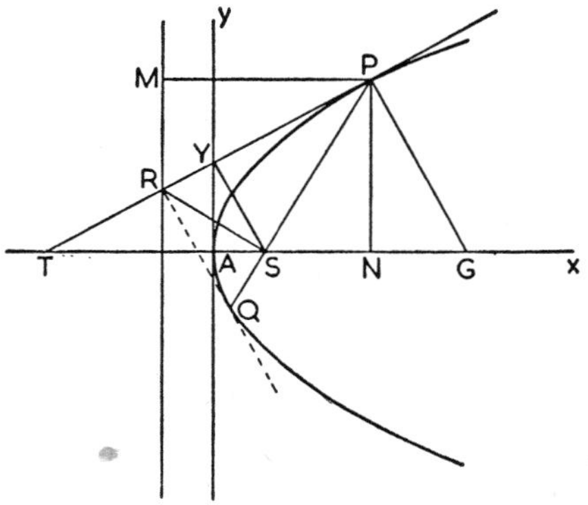

Fig. 9.3

The tangents at the ends of a focal chord PQ intersect at right angles at a point R on the directrix. SR is perpendicular to the chord.

The foot of the perpendicular from the focus on a tangent lies on the tangent at the vertex. (This gives a construction for the tangents.)

The distance TS from the focus to the point of intersection of the tangent at P with the axis is equal to the focal distances PS. (This gives a construction for the tangent at any point P.)

The tangent and normal at P bisect the angles between the focal distance SP and the diameter PM through P. (This gives a construction for the tangent and normal).

The vertex bisects the intercept on the axis between the point of intersection of the tangent with the axis and the foot of the perpendicular from its point of contact on the axis, i.e. $TA = AN$.

The sub-normal NG (q.v.) is constant and equal to $2a$.

The area of the segment cut off by the chord joining (x_1, y_1) to (x_2, y_2) is $(y_1 - y_2)^3/(24a) \equiv a^2(t_1 - t_2)^3/3$.

9.9. Confocal conics

The equation

$$\frac{x^2}{a^2+\lambda} + \frac{y^2}{b^2+\lambda} = 1 \quad (a^2 > b^2) \quad . \quad . \quad . \quad (10)$$

represents, for variable λ, a family of confocal ellipses and hyperbolae with foci $\{\pm\sqrt{(a^2-b^2)}, 0\}$.

If $\lambda < -a^2$, the conic is unreal,

if $-a^2 < \lambda < -b^2$, the conic is a hyperbola,

if $\lambda > -b^2$, it is an ellipse.

Through any point in the plane pass two confocals, one an ellipse and one a hyperbola. They intersect at right angles at all their common points.

The four points of intersection of an ellipse, parameter λ, and a hyperbola, parameter μ, are

$$x = \pm\{(a^2+\lambda)(a^2+\mu)/(a^2-b^2)\}^{\frac{1}{2}}, \; y = \pm\{(b^2+\lambda)(b^2+\mu)/(b^2-a^2)\}^{\frac{1}{2}},$$

where either sign may be taken in each case.

To each point (x, y) in the first quadrant corresponds one pair of values of λ and μ, and conversely. The *confocal* or *elliptic co-ordinates* of (x, y) are λ, μ.

The condition that the line (2′) shall touch (10) is

$$a^2u^2 + b^2v^2 - w^2 + \lambda(u^2+v^2) = 0.$$

The confocals are a tangential pencil (see § 10.8) of conics, touching the four tangents from the circular points to the base ellipse. The real foci are the real points of intersection of these tangents, one from each circular point.

Confocal parabolas

The equation

$$y^2=4\lambda(x+\lambda)$$

represents a system of parabolas, focus the origin and axis along Ox. Through every point in the plane pass two parabolas of the system and these intersect at right angles. The condition that the line (2′) shall touch the parabola is

$$\lambda(u^2+v^2)+uw=0.$$

The system is a tangential pencil of conics touching the tangents from the circular points to any one parabola of the system.

CHAPTER 10

PLANE PROJECTIVE GEOMETRY. HOMOGENEOUS CO-ORDINATES

10.1. Homogeneous co-ordinates on a line

Two fixed points A, B are chosen on the line. The homogeneous co-ordinates (x, y) of P are given by $y:x=AP:PB$. The point is determined if the ratio $y:x$ is known. If $\lambda\neq 0$, $(\lambda x, \lambda y)$ is the same point as (x, y). There is no point $(0, 0)$.

10.11. Homogeneous co-ordinates in a plane

A fixed triangle ABC is chosen, called the *triangle of reference*. The *trilinear co-ordinates* (α, β, γ) of a point P are the signed lengths of the perpendiculars from P on the sides BC, CA, AB respectively, of the triangle of reference. The perpendicular α is positive or negative according as P is or is not on the same side of BC as A is, and similarly for β and γ. The co-ordinates satisfy the identity

$$a\alpha+b\beta+c\gamma=2\Delta ABC,$$

where ΔABC is the area and a, b, c the lengths of the sides of ΔABC.

The *areal co-ordinates* (x, y, z) of P are

$$x=\frac{\Delta PBC}{\Delta ABC},\quad y=\frac{\Delta PCA}{\Delta ABC},\quad z=\frac{\Delta PAB}{\Delta ABC},$$

where ΔABC is positive, and ΔPBC is positive or negative according as P is or is not on the same side of BC as A is, and so on. Areal co-ordinates satisfy the identity

$$x+y+z=1.$$

Rectangular homogeneous Cartesian co-ordinates (x, y, z) describe the point whose rectangular Cartesian co-ordinates are x, y.

General homogeneous co-ordinates. A point is defined as the number trio (x, y, z), where $(\lambda x, \lambda y, \lambda z)$ is the same point as (x, y, z) if $\lambda\neq 0$. There is no point $(0, 0, 0)$.

10.12. The *line at infinity* or *non-finite line* is, in trilinear co-ordinates:

$$a\alpha+b\beta+c\gamma=0,$$

where a, b, c are the lengths of the sides of the triangle of reference;

in areal co-ordinates: $x+y+z=0;$

in homogeneous Cartesian co-ordinates: $z=0.$

In trilinear or areal co-ordinates, when the co-ordinates have their *actual* values (i.e. *not* merely ratios), the co-ordinates of a point $P(x, y, z)$ dividing the line P_1P_2, where P_i is the point (x_i, y_i, z_i), in the ratio $m : n$ are

$$x=(mx_2+nx_1)/(m+n),\quad y=(my_2+ny_1)/(m+n),\quad z=(mz_2+nz_1)/(m+n).$$

In general homogeneous co-ordinates P is a point on P_1P_2. If the ratios $x : y : z$ of the homogeneous co-ordinates of a point are known, the point is determined. The only purpose for which it is necessary to use the actual areal or trilinear co-ordinates is to find the co-ordinates of a point dividing a line in a given ratio. Otherwise the ratios $x : y : z$ only are used. All the equations are homogeneous.

10.2. The equation of a line is

$$lx+my+nz=0.$$

The line joining $P_1(x_1, y_1, z_1)$, $P_2(x_2, y_2, z_2)$ is

$$\begin{vmatrix} x & y & z \\ x_1 & y_1 & z_1 \\ x_2 & y_2 & z_2 \end{vmatrix}=0.$$

The equation of any line through the point of intersection of

$$L_i \equiv l_ix+m_iy+n_iz=0, \quad i=1, 2,$$

is

$$L_1+\lambda L_2=0.$$

The points $P_i(x_i, y_i, z_i)$, $i=1, 2, 3$, are collinear if, and only if,

$$\begin{vmatrix} x_1 & y_1 & z_1 \\ x_2 & y_2 & z_2 \\ x_3 & y_3 & z_3 \end{vmatrix}=0.$$

The lines $L_i=0$, $i=1, 2, 3$, are concurrent if, and only if,

$$\begin{vmatrix} l_1 & m_1 & n_1 \\ l_2 & m_2 & n_2 \\ l_3 & m_3 & n_3 \end{vmatrix}=0.$$

Then there are constants λ_i, $i=1, 2, 3$, not all zero, such that

$$\lambda_1L_1+\lambda_2L_2+\lambda_3L_3 \equiv 0.$$

10.3. Homogeneous tangential co-ordinates

So far we have considered the point as the fundamental element. The line can be taken instead of the point as the fundamental element in the plane. Then a line has co-ordinates (l, m, n) and a point has an equation satisfied by the co-ordinates of every line through it. The line $(\lambda l, \lambda m, \lambda n)$ is the same line as (l, m, n), if $\lambda \neq 0$. There is no line $(0, 0, 0)$. All equations are homogeneous. The tangential co-ordinates of the line whose point equation is $lx+my+nz=0$ are (l, m, n). The equation $al+bm+cn=0$ is the condition that the line (l, m, n) passes through the point whose point co-ordinates are (a, b, c), and is the equation of this point in tangential co-ordinates.

The equation $F(l, m, n)=0$, where $F(l, m, n)$ is a homogeneous polynomial of degree **m** in l, m, n, is the *tangential equation* of a curve of *class* **m**, i.e. it is the equation satisfied by the co-ordinates of the tangents of the curve. The class of the curve is the number of its tangents which pass through a general point in its plane.

A *projective* property is a property which is unaltered by a non-singular linear transformation of the co-ordinates (see § 4.2).

10.31. The *Principle of Duality* states that if a theorem T can be stated and proved by equations in point co-ordinates, then the theorem T' obtained by interpreting the equations in tangential co-ordinates is also valid. The theorems T and T' are said to be duals of each other.

In Plane Geometry the principle may be stated thus: If T is any theorem valid in the projective geometry of the plane, then the theorem T', obtained from T by interchanging the words 'point' and 'line' and making the necessary consequent linguistic interchanges, is also valid.

Necessary linguistic adjustments are, e.g. the interchange of

point	line
point of intersection	line joining
lies on	passes through
collinear	concurrent
$f(x, y, z)=0$ is the equation of a curve, locus of a point $P(x, y, z)$	$f(l, m, n)$ is the equation of a curve, envelope of a line $p(l, m, n)$
tangent at a point P	point of contact of a tangent p
order of a curve	class of a curve.

If (ξ, η, ζ), (ξ_i, η_i, ζ_i) are considered as

point co-ordinates,	tangential co-ordinates,

$$a\xi+b\eta+c\zeta=0$$

is the equation of a line;	is the equation of a point;

$$\begin{vmatrix} \xi_1 & \eta_1 & \zeta_1 \\ \xi_2 & \eta_2 & \zeta_2 \\ \xi_3 & \eta_3 & \zeta_3 \end{vmatrix} = 0$$

is the condition that the three

points	lines

$$(\xi_i, \eta_i, \zeta_i), \quad i=1, 2, 3,$$

are collinear;	are concurrent;

$$(\xi_1+\lambda\xi_2, \eta_1+\lambda\eta_2, \zeta_1+\lambda\zeta_2)$$

are the co-ordinates of a

point on a line joining the points	line through the point of intersection of the lines

$$(\xi_1, \eta_1, \zeta_1) \text{ and } (\xi_2, \eta_2, \zeta_2).$$

$$\begin{vmatrix} a_1 & b_1 & c_1 \\ a_2 & b_2 & c_2 \\ a_3 & b_3 & c_3 \end{vmatrix} = 0$$

is the necessary and sufficient condition that the

lines	points

$$a_i\xi+b_i\eta+c_i\zeta=0, \quad i=1, 2, 3,$$

are concurrent.	are collinear.
$f_1(x, y, z)+\lambda f_2(x, y, z)=0$,	$f_1(l, m, n)+\lambda f_2(l, m, n)=0$,

where f_1 and f_2 are homogeneous polynomials of degree n, is the equation of the

pencil of curves through the points of intersection of $f_1(x, y, z)=0$, $f_2(x, y, z)=0$.	tangential pencil of curves touching the common tangents of $f_1(l, m, n)=0$, $f_2(l, m, n)=0$.

10.4. Cross-ratio, homography, involution

The *cross-ratio* of four numbers $\lambda_1, \lambda_2, \lambda_3, \lambda_4$ is denoted by $(\lambda_1, \lambda_2, \lambda_3, \lambda_4)$ or $(\lambda_1\lambda_2\lambda_3\lambda_4)$ or $(\lambda_1, \lambda_3;\ \lambda_2, \lambda_4)$, and is

$$(\lambda_1\lambda_2\lambda_3\lambda_4)=(\lambda_1-\lambda_2)(\lambda_3-\lambda_4)/\{(\lambda_1-\lambda_4)(\lambda_3-\lambda_2)\}. \quad . \quad . \quad (1)$$

That of four ratio numbers $\lambda_1:\mu_1, \lambda_2:\mu_2, \lambda_3:\mu_3, \lambda_4:\mu_4$ is

$$(\lambda_1\mu_2-\lambda_2\mu_1)(\lambda_3\mu_4-\lambda_4\mu_3)/\{(\lambda_1\mu_4-\lambda_4\mu_1)(\lambda_3\mu_2-\lambda_2\mu_3)\}. \quad . \quad (2)$$

The twenty-four arrangements of $\lambda_1, \lambda_2, \lambda_3, \lambda_4$ lead to six distinct cross-ratios, since

$$(\lambda_1\lambda_2\lambda_3\lambda_4)=(\lambda_2\lambda_1\lambda_4\lambda_3)=(\lambda_3\lambda_4\lambda_1\lambda_2)=(\lambda_4\lambda_3\lambda_2\lambda_1).$$

If

$$(\lambda_1\lambda_2\lambda_3\lambda_4)=\rho,$$

then

$$(\lambda_1\lambda_3\lambda_2\lambda_4)=1-\rho, \ (\lambda_1\lambda_3\lambda_4\lambda_2)=1-\frac{1}{\rho}=\frac{\rho-1}{\rho},$$

$$(\lambda_1\lambda_4\lambda_3\lambda_2)=1/\rho, \ (\lambda_1\lambda_4\lambda_2\lambda_3)=1/(1-\rho), \ (\lambda_1\lambda_2\lambda_4\lambda_3)=\rho/(\rho-1).$$

In the following cases the six cross-ratios are not all different:

$$\rho=\tfrac{1}{2},\ \rho=1,\ \rho=-1,\ \rho=0,\ \rho=-\omega,\ \rho=-\omega^2,$$

where $\omega^3=1$ and ω is not real.
If $\rho=-1$, the cross-ratio is said to be harmonic and if $\rho=-\omega$, to be equi-anharmonic.

The *cross-ratio* $(ABCD)$ of four collinear points A, B, C, D, whose homogeneous co-ordinates (x, y) on the line are (x_r, y_r), $r=1, 2, 3, 4$, is defined to be the cross-ratio of these four ratio numbers, i.e. $\left(\frac{x_1}{y_1}, \frac{x_2}{y_2}, \frac{x_3}{y_3}, \frac{x_4}{y_4}\right)$ as given in (2).
It is independent of the base points on the line and of the system of co-ordinates. The cross-ratio of the points P_r which divide AB in the ratio $\lambda_r : 1$, $(r=1, 2, 3, 4)$ is $(P_1P_2P_3P_4)=(\lambda_1\lambda_2\lambda_3\lambda_4)$. The cross-ratio does not exist if three of the points coincide.

In Cartesian co-ordinates the cross-ratio $(ABCD)$ of four collinear points A, B, C, D is that of their one-dimensional co-ordinate x_1, x_2, x_3, x_4 measured from a fixed point O on the line. Thus

$$(ABCD)=(x_1-x_2)(x_3-x_4)/\{(x_1-x_4)(x_3-x_2)\}$$
$$=\frac{BA\,.\,DC}{DA\,.\,BC}=\frac{AB\,.\,CD}{AD\,.\,CB}.$$

It is independent of the position of the origin and of the unit point on the line. If one of the points is at infinity, write $x=\lambda/\mu$, write the x co-ordinate of the point at infinity as $1/0$, and use the expression (2) for the cross-ratio.

For homogeneous co-ordinates (x, y, z) in the plane the *cross-ratio* of the four collinear points $P_r(\lambda_r x_1+\mu_r x_2,\ \lambda_r y_1+\mu_r y_2,\ \lambda_r z_1+\mu_r z_2)$, $r=1, 2, 3, 4$, is $\left(\frac{\lambda_1}{\mu_1}, \frac{\lambda_2}{\mu_2}, \frac{\lambda_3}{\mu_3}, \frac{\lambda_4}{\mu_4}\right)$. This is independent of the base points (x_1, y_1, z_1) and (x_2, y_2, z_2) on the line and of the system of co-ordinates used. Cross-ratio is invariant for linear transformations of co-ordinates.

The cross-ratio of the four points A, B, C, D in which any straight line meets four concurrent and co-planar straight lines a, b, c, d is constant, and is called the cross-ratio of a, b, c, d, written (a, b, c, d).

In the Euclidean plane

$$(a, b, c, d)=\sin \overset{\frown}{(a, b)} \sin \overset{\frown}{(c, d)}/\{\sin \overset{\frown}{(a, d)} \sin \overset{\frown}{(c, b)}\},$$

where $\overset{\frown}{(a, b)}$ denotes the angle between the lines a and b measured in the anti-clockwise sense. If a is the line $A'OA$, where O is the point of concurrence, it is immaterial whether the segment OA or OA' is considered, provided that the same segment is used throughout.

If $L_1=0$, $L_2=0$ are the equations of two lines, the cross-ratio of the four concurrent lines $p_r \equiv \lambda_r L_1 + \mu_r L_2 = 0$, $r=1, 2, 3, 4$, is

$$(\lambda_1/\mu_1, \lambda_2/\mu_2, \lambda_3/\mu_3, \lambda_4/\mu_4)$$

It is independent of the base lines and of the co-ordinate system.

If (l_1, m_1, n_1), (l_2, m_2, n_2) are the tangential co-ordinates of two lines, the cross-ratio of the four lines

$$(\lambda_r l_1 + \mu_r l_2, \lambda_r m_1 + \mu_r m_2, \lambda_r n_1 + \mu_r n_2), \quad r=1, 2, 3, 4,$$

is
$$(\lambda_1/\mu_1, \lambda_2/\mu_2, \lambda_3/\mu_3, \lambda_4/\mu_4).$$

The cross-ratio of the four lines L_1, L_1+kL_2, L_2, $L_1+k'L_2$, and of the four points P_1, P_1+kP_2, P_2, $P_1+k'P_2$, is k/k'.

The points of a line form a *range*. The lines through a point and lying in a plane form a *pencil*.

10.41. Harmonic ratio

Four collinear points A, B, C, D form a *harmonic range* if

$$(ABCD) = -1.$$

Then $(ADCB) = -1$, and B and D are said to *divide* A, C *harmonically*, or to be *harmonic conjugates* with respect to A and C. The points B and D divide AC internally and externally in ratios of the same absolute value. The harmonic conjugate of B with respect to A and C is unique. The harmonic conjugate of the mid-point of AC with respect to A and C is the point at infinity on AC.

If M is the mid-point of AC and $(ABCD) = -1$, then

$$MB \,.\, MD = MC^2.$$

Four concurrent and coplanar lines a, b, c, d form a *harmonic pencil* if $(a, b, c, d) = -1$. The harmonic conjugate of the bisector of an angle with respect to the arms of the angle is the perpendicular bisector.

A line parallel to the line a of a harmonic pencil (a, b, c, d) cuts b, c, d in B, C, D, where C is the mid-point of BD. Conversely, if three lines of a pencil cut equal segments on a line parallel to the fourth line, the pencil is harmonic.

The equations of the lines of a harmonic pencil (a, b, c, d) can be written in the form

$$L=0, \; L+\lambda M=0, \; M=0, \; L-\lambda M=0.$$

The four lines $L+\lambda_r M=0$, $r=1, 2, 3, 4$, form a harmonic pencil if, and only if,

$$2(\lambda_1\lambda_3+\lambda_2\lambda_4) = (\lambda_1+\lambda_3)(\lambda_2+\lambda_4).$$

The necessary and sufficient condition for the line pair

$$aL^2+2hLM+bM^2=0$$

to separate the line pair

$$a'L^2+2h'LM+b'M^2=0$$

harmonically is

$$ab'+a'b=2hh'.$$

10.42. Correspondences

Two variables x_1 and x_2 are said to be in *algebraic* (m, n) *correspondence* if they are connected by a relation

$$f(x_1, x_2)=0, \quad . \quad . \quad . \quad . \quad . \quad (3)$$

where f is a polynomial of degree m in x_1 and n in x_2.

Let the ratio of the homogeneous co-ordinates of a point P of a given line be $x : 1$. The points P_1 and P_2 of the same or different lines are in (m, n) correspondence if their co-ordinates x_1 and x_2 satisfy a relation of the form (3). If the correspondence is between points of the same line, P_1 is a *united point* or a *coincidence* of the correspondence if one of its corresponding points P_2 coincides with P_1. The united points are given by $f(x_1, x_1)=0$ and are $m+n$ in number.

10.43. An algebraic (1, 1) correspondence is called a *homography*. Thus two variables x and x' are in homographic correspondence if

$$axx'+bx+cx'+d=0, \quad . \quad . \quad . \quad . \quad (4)$$

where a, b, c, d are constants. The homography is *degenerate* if $ad=bc$.

If $x_r, x'_r, r=1, 2, 3, 4$, are corresponding pairs in a homography, then

$$(x_1, x_2, x_3, x_4)=(x_1', x_2', x_3', x_4').$$

There are two (distinct or coincident) *united* or *double* points, H and K, in a homography between points of the same line. Their co-ordinates are given by

$$ax^2+(b+c)x+d=0.$$

If H and K are distinct points,

$$(PHP'K)=\text{constant}$$

for all pairs P, P' of the homography. If the united points coincide at a point O,

$$1/OP-1/OP'=\text{constant}$$

for all pairs P, P'.

10.44. Involution

An *involution* $g_n{}^r$ of *order* n and *freedom* r on a line is a variable set of n points given by a equation

$$\lambda_0 f_0(x)+\lambda_1 f_1(x)+ \ldots +\lambda_r f_r(x)=0, \quad . \quad . \quad . \quad (5)$$

where the λ_i are parameters and the f_i are linearly independent fixed polynomials of degree n in x. One set is given by fixed values of the ratios of the λ_i, and as the λ_i vary we have ∞^r sets. One set of the involution passes through r arbitrary points of the line.

An involution of order two and freedom one is given by the equation

$$\lambda_0(a_0x^2+b_0x+c_0)+\lambda_1(a_1x^2+b_1x+c_1)=0,$$

where λ_0 and λ_1 are parameters.

If (x, x') form a set of this involution, then

$$axx'+b(x+x')+d=0,$$

where a, b and d are constants. Hence if (P, Q) form a pair of this involution, P and Q correspond in a symmetric homography in which Q and P also correspond.

If (P_i, Q_i) are corresponding pairs in this involution,

$$(P_1P_2P_3P_4)=(Q_1Q_2Q_3Q_4).$$

If P and Q coincide, their common point is called a *double point* of the involution. There are two double points which are given by

$$ax^2+2bx+d=0.$$

If the double points H and K are distinct,

$$(PHQK)=-1$$

for every pair (P, Q) of the involution.

If O is the mid-point of HK,

$$OP \,.\, OQ=OH^2=\text{constant}.$$

If the double points are coincident at O,

$$OP+OQ=0.$$

An arbitrary pair of points P, Q, given by

$$lx^2+2mx+n=0,$$

belongs to the involution if

$$an+dl=2bm.$$

If two pairs of the involution are given by

$$s_1\equiv l_1x^2+m_1x+n_1=0$$

$$s_2\equiv l_2x^2+m_2x+n_2=0,$$

the double points are given by

$$\begin{vmatrix} 1 & -x & x^2 \\ l_1 & m_1 & n_1 \\ l_2 & m_2 & n_2 \end{vmatrix}=0.$$

The pair

$$k_1s_1+k_2s_2=0$$

is a pair of the involution for all k_1 and k_2.

Two involutions

$$a_i xx' + b_i(x+x') + d_i = 0$$

have a common pair x, x' given by

$$xx' : x+x' : 1 = \begin{vmatrix} b_1 & d_1 \\ b_2 & d_2 \end{vmatrix} : \begin{vmatrix} d_1 & a_1 \\ d_2 & a_2 \end{vmatrix} : \begin{vmatrix} a_1 & b_1 \\ a_2 & b_2 \end{vmatrix}.$$

The pencils $L+\lambda M=0$, $L+\lambda' M=0$ are in *involution* if

$$a\lambda\lambda' + b(\lambda+\lambda') + c = 0,$$

where a, b and d are constants.

10.5. The statements in the two columns are dual.

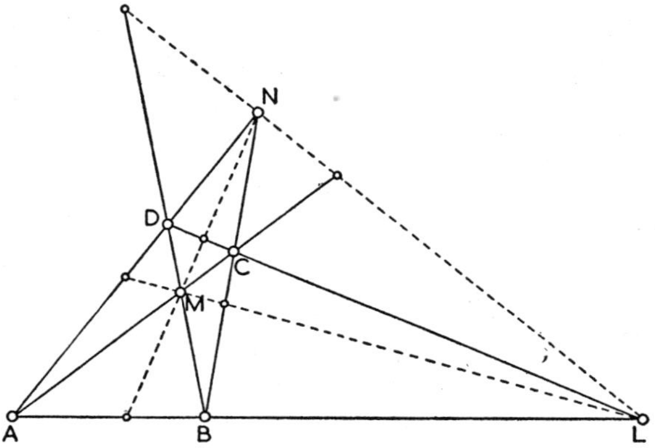

Fig. 10.1

Complete quadrangle

Four coplanar points A, B, C, D, of which no three are collinear, together with their six joins form the vertices and sides of a *complete quadrangle* $ABCD$. The three points of intersection (other than the vertices) of pairs of sides are called the *diagonal points* and their joins form the *diagonal triangle*. (See Fig. 10.1.)

Complete quadrilateral

Four coplanar lines a, b, c, d, of which no three are concurrent, together with their six points of intersection form the sides and vertices of a *complete quadrilateral* a, b, c, d. The three lines (other than the sides) joining pairs of vertices are called the *diagonals* and form the *diagonal triangle*. (See Fig. 10.2.)

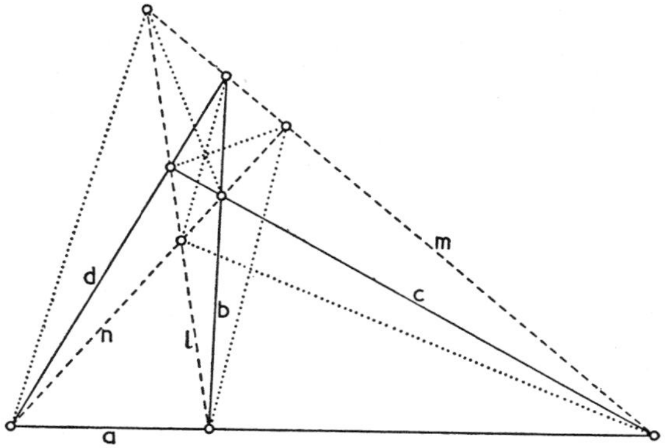

Fig. 10.2

Four harmonic lines meet in each diagonal point of a complete quadrangle. Four harmonic points lie on each side of the complete quadrangle and on each side of the diagonal triangle.

Four harmonic points lie on each side of the diagonal triangle of a complete quadrilateral. Each vertex of the quadrilateral and of the diagonal triangle is the vertex of a harmonic pencil of lines.

If the diagonal triangle LMN of a complete quadrangle $ABCD$ be taken as triangle of reference and the co-ordinates of A are (p, q, r), then the other three points are $(-p, q, r)$, $(p, -q, r)$ and $(p, q, -r)$.

If the diagonal triangle l, m, n of a complete quadrilateral a, b, c, d be taken as triangle of reference and the tangential co-ordinates of a are (P, Q, R), then the tangential co-ordinates of the other three sides are $(-P, Q, R)$, $(P, -Q, R)$, $(P, Q, -R)$.

If the tangential equation of A is $pl+qm+rn=0$, those of the other three points are

$$-pl+qm+rn=0,$$
$$pl-qm+rn=0,$$
$$pl+qm-rn=0.$$

If the point equation of a is $Px+Qy+Rz=0$, those of the other three sides are

$$-Px+Qy+Rz=0,$$
$$Px-Qy+Rz=0,$$
$$Px+Qy-Rz=0.$$

10.6. The conic

In Projective Geometry we define the conic as the locus of a point $P(x, y, z)$ which satisfies the equation

$$S(x, y, z) \equiv ax^2+by^2+cz^2+2fyz+2gzx+2hxy=0.$$

The conic is of order two and also of class two if it is proper and it can be regarded as a conic locus or as a conic envelope, the envelope (q.v.) of its tangents. The points and tangents of a proper conic form a self-dual figure.

Point co-ordinates (x, y, z)

General equation:

$$S(x, y, z) \equiv ax^2+by^2+cz^2 +2fyz+2gzx+2hxy \equiv X'\Gamma X=0,$$

where $X=\begin{bmatrix} x \\ y \\ z \end{bmatrix}$, $\Gamma=\begin{bmatrix} a & h & g \\ h & b & f \\ g & f & c \end{bmatrix}$,

and A, B, etc., are the co-factors of a, b, etc., |in Γ|

Tangential co-ordinates (l, m, n)

$$R(l, m, n) \equiv \begin{vmatrix} a & h & g & l \\ h & b & f & m \\ g & f & c & n \\ l & m & n & 0 \end{vmatrix}$$

$$\equiv Al^2+Bm^2+Cn^2+2Fmn +2Gnl+2Hlm$$

$$\equiv L'(\text{adj } \Gamma)L=0,$$

or $L'\Gamma^{-1}L=0$, if Γ is non-singular,

where $L=\begin{bmatrix} l \\ m \\ n \end{bmatrix}$.

If Γ is of rank two, the conic $S(x, y, z)=0$ degenerates into a pair of distinct lines.

If Γ is of rank one the conic S is a repeated line.

A *conic envelope* $L'ML=0$ is proper if $|M|\neq 0$; it degenerates into a pair of distinct points if M is of rank two and into a repeated point if M is of rank one.

If $|\Gamma|\neq 0$, the conic $S(x, y, z)=0$ is a *proper* or *non-degenerate* conic. The conic envelope $R(l, m, n)=0$ is then also proper.

The locus of a point (x, y, z), where

$$\begin{bmatrix} x \\ y \\ z \end{bmatrix} = \begin{bmatrix} p & q & r \\ p' & q' & r' \\ p'' & q'' & r'' \end{bmatrix} \begin{bmatrix} \theta^2 \\ \theta \\ 1 \end{bmatrix}$$

is a conic.

The envelope of a line (l, m, n), where

$$\begin{bmatrix} l \\ m \\ n \end{bmatrix} = \begin{bmatrix} P & Q & R \\ P' & Q' & R' \\ P'' & Q'' & R'' \end{bmatrix} \begin{bmatrix} \theta^2 \\ \theta \\ 1 \end{bmatrix}$$

is a conic-envelope.

Conic through the vertices of the triangle of reference:

$$fyz+gzx+hxy=0.$$

$$f^2l^2+g^2m^2+h^2n^2-2ghmn -2hfnl-2fglm=0.$$

Conic touching the sides of the triangle of reference:

$u^2x^2+v^2y^2+w^2z^2-2vwyz$
$\quad -2wuzx-2uvxy=0.$

$umn+vnl+wlm=0.$

Conic with respect to which the triangle of reference is self-polar:

$ax^2+by^2+cz^2=0.$

$l^2/a+m^2/b+n^2/c=0.$

Conic touching BC, CA at B and A:

$z^2=kxy,$

$kn^2-4lm=0,$

with parametric representation

$(t^2,\ k,\ tk)$

$(s^2,\ k,\ 2s)$, or $(k,\ t^2,\ -2t)$.

The identities

$$x\frac{\partial S_1}{\partial x_1}+y\frac{\partial S_1}{\partial y_1}+z\frac{\partial S_1}{\partial z_1}\equiv x_1\frac{\partial S}{\partial x}+y_1\frac{\partial S}{\partial y}+z_1\frac{\partial S}{\partial z}\equiv 2P_1 \text{ (say)},$$

where $S_1=S(x_1,\ y_1,\ z_1)$, and

$$l\frac{\partial R_1}{\partial l_1}+m\frac{\partial R_1}{\partial m_1}+n\frac{\partial R_1}{\partial n_1}\equiv l_1\frac{\partial R}{\partial l}+m_1\frac{\partial R}{\partial m}+n_1\frac{\partial R}{\partial n}\equiv 2Q_1 \text{ (say)},$$

are useful.

Polar of $(x_1,\ y_1,\ z_1)$ is

$$x\frac{\partial S_1}{\partial x_1}+y\frac{\partial S_1}{\partial y_1}+z\frac{\partial S_1}{\partial z_1}=0,$$

i.e. $X_1'\Gamma X=0$ or $X'\Gamma X_1=0$.

This is also the chord of contact of tangents from $P(x_1, y_1, z_1)$.

If $P(x_1,\ y_1,\ z)$ is on the conic, this is the tangent at P.

Combined equation of the tangents from $(x_1,\ y_1,\ z_1)$ is $SS_1-P_1{}^2=0$.

Pole of $(l_1,\ m_1,\ n_1)$ is

$$l\frac{\partial R_1}{\partial l_1}+m\frac{\partial R_1}{\partial n_1}+n\frac{\partial R_1}{\partial n_1}=0,$$

i.e. $L_1'\Gamma^{-1}L=0$ or $L'\Gamma^{-1}L_1=0$.

This is also the point of intersection of the tangents at the points of intersection of $(l_1,\ m_1,\ n_1)$ with the conic.

If $p(l_1,\ m_1,\ n_1)$ is a tangent, this is the equation of its point of contact.

Combined equation of points of intersection of $(l_1,\ m_1,\ n_1)$ with the curve is $RR_1-Q_1{}^2=0$.

10.7. A conic is an *ellipse, hyperbola* or *parabola* according as it meets the line at infinity in real distinct or in imaginary points or touches it.

In the complex Cartesian Geometry of the plane every circle passes through the points at infinity on the lines $y = \pm ix$, and in homogeneous complex Cartesian Geometry every circle passes through the points $(1, \pm i, 0)$. These points are called the absolute or circular points I and J. Conversely every conic through the circular points is a circle. The line AI, AJ are called the circular lines through $A(\alpha, \beta)$. Their combined equations is $(x-\alpha)^2+(y-\beta)^2=0$. In homogeneous Cartesians the circular lines through $A(\alpha, \beta, \gamma)$ are $(\gamma x-\alpha z)^2+(\gamma y-\beta z)^2=0$.

Distance and angle may be interpreted projectively as follows. In the Cartesian plane, if O, A, P are collinear and OA is the unit of length, and $OP=x$, and if OAP meets the line at infinity at K, then $x=(P, O, A, K)$.

If AB, AC be two lines $y-\beta=m_i(x-\alpha)$, $i=1, 2$, intersecting at an angle θ (radian measure), then

$$\theta=\frac{1}{2i}\ln\{A(CIBJ)\}=\frac{1}{2i}\ln(m_2, i, m_1, -i),$$

where $A(CIBJ)$ denotes the cross-ratio of the lines AC, AI, AB, AJ.

A right angle forms a harmonic pencil with the circular lines. Any line through a circular point is perpendicular to itself.

A *focus* of a conic is the point of intersection of two tangents, one from each circular point. The *directrices* are the polars of the foci.

In areal co-ordinates the circular points are the points

$$(a\exp\{iC\}, -b, c\exp\{-iA\}), (a\exp\{-iC\}, -b, c\exp\{iA\}),$$

where a, b, c; A, B, C are the sides and angles of the triangle of reference. The tangential combined equation of the circular points is

$$a^2l^2+b^2m^2+c^2n^2-2bc\,mn\cos A-2canl\cos B-2ablm\cos C=0.$$

The *centre* of a conic is the pole of the line at infinity. A *diameter* is the polar of a point on the line at infinity. The diameter of a pencil of parallel lines passes through the points of contact of the tangents which belong to the pencil.

10.71. *Pascal's Theorem*

If A, B, C, D, E, F be six points on a conic, the points (AB, DE), (BC, EF), (CD, FA) are collinear,

Brianchon's Theorem

If a, b, c, d, e, f be six tangents to a conic, the lines $[(a, b), (d, e)]$, $[(b, c), (e, f)]$, $[(c, d), (f, a)]$ are concurrent,

where (a, b) is the intersection of a and b, $[\alpha, \beta]$ is the join of α and β.

The cross-ratio of the chords joining four fixed points A, B, C, D of a conic to a variable point P of the conic is constant and equal to the cross-ratio of the parameters of A, B, C, D.

The cross-ratio of the four points of intersection of a variable tangent to the conic with four fixed tangents a, b, c, d is constant and equal to the cross-ratio of the parameters of a, b, c, d.

The locus of the point of intersection of corresponding rays of two homographic coplanar pencils of lines is a conic through the vertices of the pencils.

The envelope of the line joining corresponding points of two homographic ranges of points on two coplanar lines is a conic touching the two lines.

10.8. Pencils of conics

The equation

$$\lambda S+\mu S'=0,$$

where $S=0$, $S'=0$ are the point equations of two conics,

$$\lambda R+\mu R'=0,$$

where $R=0$ and $R'=0$ are the tangential equations of two conics,

and $\lambda:\mu$ is a variable parameter, represents a conic

through the four points of intersection of $S=0$ and $S'=0$.

touching the four common tangents of $R=0$ and $R'=0$.

Every such conic can have its equation put in the form

$$\lambda S+\mu S'=0$$

$$\lambda R+\mu R'=0$$

for some value of $\lambda:\mu$. This one-parameter family is called

a pencil or a four-point system of conics.

a tangential pencil or a four-line system of conics.

If the four points of intersection are distinct and the diagonal triangle of the complete quadrangle formed by them is taken as triangle of reference, the equations of S and S' are

$$ax^2+by^2+cz^2=0,$$
$$a'x^2+b'y^2+c'z^2=0.$$

If the four common tangents are distinct and the diagonal triangle of the complete quadrilateral formed by them is taken as triangle of reference, the equations of R and R' are

$$Al^2+Bm^2+Cn^2=0,$$
$$A'l^2+B'm^2+C'n^2=0.$$

This triangle is self-conjugate for all conics of the pencil.

This triangle is self-conjugate for all conics of the tangential pencil.

Special cases

If $M=0$, $N=0$ are the equations of straight lines, $S+\lambda MN=0$ is a conic through the points of intersection P, P' of $M=0$ with $S=0$, and the points of intersection Q, Q' of $N=0$ with $S=0$.	If $\mathcal{M}=0$, $\mathcal{N}=0$ are the equations of points, $R+\lambda\mathcal{M}\mathcal{N}=0$ is the tangential equation of a conic touching the tangents p, p' from $\mathcal{M}=0$ to $R=0$, and the tangents q, q' from $\mathcal{N}=0$ to $R=0$.
If $T=0$ is the equation of the tangent to S at A, $S+\lambda MT=0$ is the equation of a conic touching S at A and passing through P and P'.	If $\tau=0$ is the equation of the point of contact of a tangent to R, then $R+\lambda\mathcal{M}\tau=0$ represents a conic touching R at τ and touching the two tangents to R from $\mathcal{M}$.
If $M=0$ and $N=0$ intersect at P on $S=0$ and meet it further in P' and Q', $S+\lambda MN=0$ is a conic touching S at P and passing through P' and Q'.	If the line joining $\mathcal{M}=0$ and $\mathcal{N}=0$ touches R at P, then $R+\lambda\mathcal{M}\mathcal{N}=0$ is a conic touching R at P and touching the remaining tangents from $\mathcal{M}=0$ and $\mathcal{N}=0$ to R.
$S+\lambda M^2=0$ is a conic having double contact with $S=0$ at P and P'.	$R+\lambda\mathcal{M}^2=0$ is a conic having double contact with $R=0$ at the points of contact of the tangents from $\mathcal{M}=0$ to $R=0$.
If $T=0$ and $T'=0$ are tangents to $S=0$ at P and Q, $S+\lambda TT'=0$ is a conic having double contact with $S=0$ at P and Q.	If $\tau=0$ and $\tau'=0$ are points of contact of tangents to $R=0$, then $R+\lambda\tau\tau'=0$ is a conic having double contact with $R=0$ at the points $\tau=0$, $\tau'=0$.
If $M=0$ meets $S=0$ at the point of contact P of $T=0$ and at P', $S+\lambda MT=0$ is a conic having three-point contact with $S=0$ at P and passing through P'.	If $\mathcal{M}=0$ lies on the tangent to $R=0$ at the point $\tau=0$ on $R=0$, then $R+\lambda\mathcal{M}\tau=0$ is a conic having three-point contact with $R=0$ at $\tau=0$ and touching the remaining tangent from $\mathcal{M}=0$ to $R=0$.
$S+\lambda T^2=0$ is a conic having four-point contact with $S=0$ at the point of contact of $T=0$.	$R+\lambda\tau^2=0$ is a conic having four-point contact with $R=0$ at the point $\tau=0$.

10.9. Invariants and covariants of conics

Let $X' \equiv [x \quad y \quad z]$, $L' \equiv [l \quad m \quad n]$ and let **a** and **b** be symmetric matrices of order three. Then

$$S \equiv X'\mathbf{a}X = 0, \quad S' \equiv X'\mathbf{b}X = 0$$

are the equations of two conics. Their tangential equations are

$$R \equiv L'\mathbf{A}L = 0, \quad R' \equiv L'\mathbf{B}L = 0,$$

where $$\mathbf{A} = \text{adj } \mathbf{a}, \ \mathbf{B} = \text{adj } \mathbf{b}.$$

Then $$\text{adj } (\lambda\mathbf{a} + \mu\mathbf{b}) \equiv \lambda^2\mathbf{A} + \lambda\mu\mathbf{C} + \mu^2\mathbf{B},$$
$$|\lambda\mathbf{a} + \mu\mathbf{b}| \equiv \lambda^3\Delta + \lambda^2\mu\Theta + \lambda\mu^2\Theta' + \mu^3\Delta',$$

where **C** is a symmetric matrix and Δ, Θ, Θ', Δ' are polynomials in the elements of **a** and **b**; $\Delta \equiv |\mathbf{a}|$, $\Delta' \equiv |\mathbf{b}|$ are the discriminants of S and S' respectively, and Θ, Θ' are mutual invariants (see § 4.6) of S and S'.

Since

$$(\lambda\mathbf{a} + \mu\mathbf{b}) \,.\, \text{adj } (\lambda\mathbf{a} + \mu\mathbf{b}) \equiv \text{adj } (\lambda\mathbf{a} + \mu\mathbf{b}) \,.\, (\lambda\mathbf{a} + \mu\mathbf{b})$$
$$\equiv |\lambda\mathbf{a} + \mu\mathbf{b}|\mathbf{I},$$

we have

$$\mathbf{aA} = \mathbf{Aa} = \Delta\mathbf{I}, \quad \mathbf{bB} = \mathbf{Bb} = \Delta'\mathbf{I},$$
$$\mathbf{aC} + \mathbf{bA} = \mathbf{Ca} + \mathbf{Ab} = \Theta\mathbf{I}; \quad \mathbf{bC} + \mathbf{aB} \equiv \mathbf{Cb} + \mathbf{Ba} \equiv \Theta'\mathbf{I}.$$

Again $$\text{adj } (\lambda\mathbf{A} + \mu\mathbf{B}) = \lambda^2\Delta\mathbf{a} + \lambda\mu\mathbf{d} + \mu^2\Delta'\mathbf{b},$$

where **d** is a symmetric matrix.

If **a** and **b** are non-singular,

$$\mathbf{A} \equiv \text{adj } \mathbf{a} = \Delta\mathbf{a}^{-1}, \quad \mathbf{B} \equiv \text{adj } \mathbf{b} = \Delta'\mathbf{b}^{-1},$$
$$|\lambda\mathbf{A} + \mu\mathbf{B}| \equiv \lambda^3\Delta^2 + \lambda^2\mu\Delta\Theta' + \lambda\mu^2\Theta\Delta' + \mu^3\Delta'^2$$
$$\mathbf{Ad} + \Delta\mathbf{Ba} \equiv \mathbf{dA} + \Delta\mathbf{aB} \equiv \Delta\Theta'\mathbf{I},$$
$$\mathbf{Bd} + \Delta'\mathbf{Ab} \equiv \mathbf{dB} + \Delta'\mathbf{bA} \equiv \Theta\Delta'\mathbf{I}.$$

The complete system of invariants of S and S' is

$$\Delta, \ \Theta, \ \Theta', \ \Delta'.$$

The complete system of covariants and contravariants of S and S' is

$$S, \ S', \ F \equiv X'\mathbf{d}X, \ \Phi \equiv L'\mathbf{C}L, \ R, \ R',$$

$$G \equiv \tfrac{1}{8}\frac{\partial(S, S', F)}{\partial(x, y, z)}, \quad \Gamma \equiv \tfrac{1}{8}\frac{\partial(R, R', \Phi)}{\partial(l, m, n)} .\dagger$$

All invariants, covariants and contravariants of S and S' can be expressed as polynomials in the above.

† See § 12.9.

Identities

$$\Delta\mathbf{C} \equiv \Theta\mathbf{A} - \mathbf{AbA}, \quad \Delta'\mathbf{C} \equiv \Theta'\mathbf{B} - \mathbf{BaB},$$

$$\mathbf{d} \equiv \Theta'\mathbf{a} - \mathbf{aBa} \equiv \Theta\mathbf{b} - \mathbf{bAb} \equiv \mathbf{aCb} \equiv \mathbf{bCa}.$$

$$\text{adj } \mathbf{C} = \Theta'\mathbf{a} + \Theta\mathbf{b} - \mathbf{d},$$

$$|\mathbf{C}| = \Theta\Theta' - \Delta\Delta'.$$

$$\text{adj } \mathbf{d} = \Theta\Delta'\mathbf{A} + \Delta\Theta'\mathbf{B} - \Delta\Delta'\mathbf{C},$$

$$|\mathbf{d}| = \Delta\Delta'(\Theta\Theta' - \Delta\Delta').$$

If $\quad S \equiv X'\mathbf{a}X \equiv ax^2 + by^2 + cz^2 + 2fyz + 2gzx + 2hxy,$

$\quad R \equiv L'\mathbf{A}L \equiv Al^2 + Bm^2 + Cn^2 + 2Fmn + 2Gnl + 2Hlm,$

where A, B, etc., are the co-factors of a, b, etc., in $|\mathbf{a}|$, with similar expressions for S' and R', then

$$\Delta \equiv aA + hH + gG$$

$$\equiv abc + 2fgh - af^2 - bg^2 - ch^2;$$

$$\Theta \equiv a'A + b'B + c'C + 2f'F + 2g'G + 2h'H;$$

$$\Theta' \equiv aA' + bB' + cC' + 2fF' + 2gG' + 2hH'.$$

Geometrical interpretation

$\Delta = 0$ if, and only if, S is degenerate. The following interpretations are for the case $\Delta \neq 0$, $\Delta' \neq 0$.

$\Theta = 0$ if, and only if, there is a triangle inscribed in S' which is self-polar with respect to S. Then the property is poristic and so there are an infinite number of such triangles, every point of S' being a vertex of such a triangle. There are then also an infinite number of triangles circumscribed to S and self-polar with respect to S'. S' is said to be out-polar to S.

$\Theta' = 0$ if, and only if, S is out-polar to S'. If $\Theta = \Theta' = 0$, the two conics are said to be mutually apolar.

$\Theta'^2 - 4\Theta\Delta' = 0$ if, and only if, a triangle can be inscribed in S and circumscribed to S'. The property is poristic.

$\Theta^2 - 4\Theta'\Delta = 0$ if, and only if, a triangle can be inscribed in S' and circumscribed to S. The property is poristic.

$\Theta'^3 = 4\Delta'(\Theta\Theta' - 2\Delta\Delta')$ if, and only if, a quadrilateral exists whose sides AB, BC, CD, DA touch S', while A, B, C, D lie on S. The property is poristic.

The covariant $F \equiv X'\mathbf{d}X = 0$ is the locus of a point P such that the pairs of tangents from P to S and S' separate each other harmonically. It is a conic known as the harmonic locus of S and S'. The tangential equation of F is

$$\Theta\Delta'R + \Delta\Theta'R' - \Delta\Delta'\Phi = 0.$$

The contravariant $\Phi \equiv \mathbf{L}'\mathbf{C}\mathbf{L} = 0$ is the envelope of a line cut harmonically by S and S'. It is a conic envelope called the harmonic envelope of S and S'. The point equation of Φ is $\Theta' S + \Theta S' - F = 0$.

The tangential equation of the common points of S and S' is

$$\Phi^2 - 4RR' = 0.$$

The equation of the common tangents of S and S' is

$$F^2 - 4\Delta\Delta' SS' = 0.$$

In the general case in which S and S' meet in four distinct points, $G = 0$ is the equation of the three sides of the common self-polar triangle of S and S'. $\Gamma = 0$ is the tangential equation of the three vertices of this triangle.

CHAPTER 11

THREE-DIMENSIONAL ANALYTICAL GEOMETRY

11.1. As in a plane, so in space, Geometry may be based on a set of axioms concerning undefined entities called points, lines and planes, or a point may be defined as a trio (x, y, z) of real or complex or of some other kind of number. The numbers obey certain laws of Algebra. We follow the second method and assume that the numbers obey the laws of Algebra given in § 1.1. In applications of this abstract Geometry to physical space it is assumed that such a trio of real numbers (x, y, z) corresponds to each finite point of the Euclidean space considered.

11.11. Rectilinear co-ordinates

Take three mutually perpendicular concurrent lines Ox, Oy, Oz as x, y and z axes. The axes are called right-handed or left-handed according as a right-handed screw turning from Ox to Oy would move forward or backward along Oz. We use a right-handed rectilinear system (Figs. 11.1 and 11.2). The Cartesian co-ordinates of a point P are (x, y, z), where $x=LP$, $y=MP$, $z=NP$ and L, M, N are the feet of the perpendiculars from P on the planes yOz, zOx, xOy respectively. A length along a line parallel to Ox is positive if measured in the direction Ox and negative if in the direction xO. To each finite point P in space corresponds this trio of finite numbers (x, y, z) and conversely.

Oblique axes. Three concurrent non-coplanar lines Ox, Oy, Oz making angles of less than 180° with one another are taken as axes. The co-ordinates (x, y, z) of P are $x=AP$, $y=BP$, $z=CP$, where PA, PB, PC are lines parallel to the axes meeting the planes yOz, zOx, xOy at A, B, C.

The formulae given in this chapter are for rectangular axes.

Spherical polar co-ordinates (r, θ, ϕ). See Fig. 11.1.

The planes POz and xOy intersect along ON.

$r=OP$, $\theta=P\hat{O}z$, $\phi=N\hat{O}x$.

$r=|(x^2+y^2+z^2)^{\frac{1}{2}}|$, $\cos\theta=z/r$, $\cos\phi=x/|(x^2+y^2)^{\frac{1}{2}}|$, $\sin\phi=y/|(x^2+y^2)^{\frac{1}{2}}|$.

$x=r\sin\theta\cos\phi$, $y=r\sin\theta\sin\phi$, $z=r\cos\theta$.

The *projection* of a line P_1P_2 on a line l or on a plane p is the interval $P_1'P_2'$ between the feet of the perpendiculars from P_1 and P_2 on the line or on the plane.

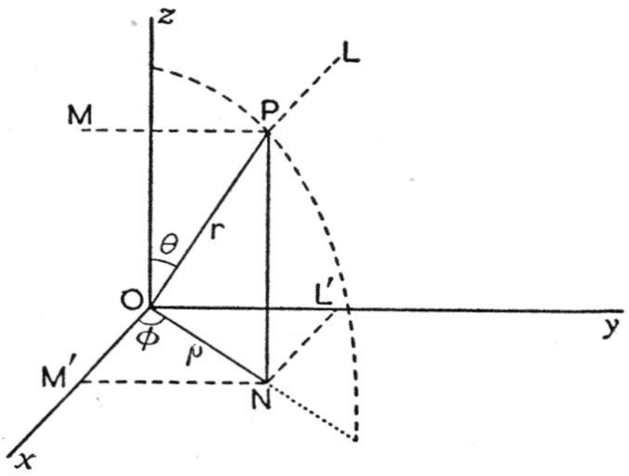

Fig. 11.1

Cylindrical co-ordinates (ρ, ϕ, z)

ρ is the projection ON of OP on the plane xOy, $\phi = N\hat{O}x$, $z = NP$. See Fig. 11.1.

$$\rho = |(x^2+y^2)^{\frac{1}{2}}|, \ \cos\phi = x/|(x^2+y^2)^{\frac{1}{2}}|, \ \sin\phi = y/|(x^2+y^2)^{\frac{1}{2}}|.$$

$$x = \rho\cos\phi, \ y = \rho\sin\phi, \ z = z.$$

11.2. Loci

A *surface* is the locus of a point whose co-ordinates are given parametrically in terms of two *independent* parameters u and v

$$x = \phi_1(u, v), \ y = \phi_2(u, v), \ z = \phi_3(u, v),$$

where ϕ_1, ϕ_2, ϕ_3 are algebraic functions (q.v.).

The locus of a point $P(x, y, z)$, where x, y, z satisfy one equation $F(x, y, z) = 0$ and $F(x, y, z)$ is a polynomial of degree n, is an algebraic surface of *order n*.

A *curve* is the locus of a point P whose co-ordinates are differentiable functions of one parameter

$$x = \phi(t), \ y = \psi(t), \ z = \chi(t),$$

whose derivates do not simultaneously vanish.

The equations $F_1(x, y, z) = 0$, $F_2(x, y, z) = 0$ define a curve which is the complete intersection of two surfaces. Not every curve is the complete intersection of two surfaces.

The *order* of an algebraic curve is the number of points in which it is met by a general plane.

11.21. The straight line

The *distance* between two points (x_1, y_1, z_1), (x_2, y_2, z_2) is

$$|\{|x_2-x_1|^2+|y_2-y_1|^2+|z_2-z_1|^2\}^{\frac{1}{2}}|.$$

If α, β, γ are the angles POx, POy, POz, and $r=OP$, which is reckoned positive,

$$x=r\cos\alpha,\ y=r\cos\beta,\ z=r\cos\gamma, \qquad r=|(x^2+y^2+z^2)^{\frac{1}{2}}|,$$
$$\cos^2\alpha+\cos^2\beta+\cos^2\gamma=1.$$

The *angle* between two non-intersecting lines is the angle between one line and a parallel to the second through a point on the first.

The *direction cosines* of a line are the cosines of the angles α, β, γ between the line and the positive directions of the axes Ox, Oy and Oz. They satisfy

$$\cos^2\alpha+\cos^2\beta+\cos^2\gamma=1.$$

The *direction ratios* $l:m:n$ of the line are numbers satisfying $l:m:n=\cos\alpha:\cos\beta:\cos\gamma$.

The *equations of the line* through $A(x_1, y_1, z_1)$ with direction cosines $\cos\alpha$, $\cos\beta$, $\cos\gamma$ are

$$\frac{x-x_1}{\cos\alpha}=\frac{y-y_1}{\cos\beta}=\frac{z-z_1}{\cos\gamma}.$$

Each ratio$=AP=r$ (say), where P is the point (x, y, z) on the line. The line is given in terms of a parameter r by

$$x=x_1+r\cos\alpha,\ y=y_1+r\cos\beta,\ z=z_1+r\cos\gamma.$$

The line through $A(x_1, y_1, z_1)$ with direction ratios l, m, n is

$$\frac{x-x_1}{l}=\frac{y-y_1}{m}=\frac{z-z_1}{n} \quad . \quad . \quad . \quad . \quad (1)$$

in real Geometry. This is also a line in complex Geometry. Each ratio$=r/\sqrt{(\Sigma l^2)}=\lambda$ (say). The co-ordinates of the point P on the line, where $AP=r$, are

$$x=x_1+lr/\sqrt{(\Sigma l^2)},\ y=y_1+mr/\sqrt{(\Sigma l^2)},\ z=z_1+nr/\sqrt{(\Sigma l^2)}.$$
or $x=x_1+\lambda l, \qquad y=y_1+\lambda m, \qquad z=z_1+\lambda n.$

The line joining (x_1, y_1, z_1), (x_2, y_2, z_2) is

$$\frac{x-x_1}{x_2-x_1}=\frac{y-y_1}{y_2-y_1}=\frac{z-z_1}{z_2-z_1}.$$

The line through (x_1, y_1, z_1) perpendicular to the plane

$$ax+by+cz+d=0$$

is
$$(x-x_1)/a=(y-y_1)/b=(z-z_1)/c.$$

The angle θ between two lines with direction ratios l_1, m_1, n_1; l_2, m_2, n_2 is given by

$$\cos\theta=(l_1l_2+m_1m_2+n_1n_2)/\sqrt{\{(l_1^2+m_1^2+n_1^2)(l_2^2+m_2^2+n_2^2)\}}.$$

Real lines are perpendicular if

$$l_1 l_2 + m_1 m_2 + n_1 n_2 = 0.$$

The co-ordinates of a point $P(x, y, z)$ on the line joining $P_1(x_1, y_1, z_1)$, $P_2(x_2, y_2, z_2)$ such that $P_1P : PP_2 = \lambda : \mu$ are

$$x = (\lambda x_2 + \mu x_1)/(\lambda + \mu),\ y = (\lambda y_2 + \mu y_1)/(\lambda + \mu),\ z = (\lambda z_2 + \mu z_1)/(\lambda + \mu).$$

11.22. The plane

General equation: $ax + by + cz + d = 0$ . . . . . . (2)

Intercept form. The plane which makes intercepts a, b and c on the axes is

$$x/a + y/b + z/c = 1.$$

Plane through the points $P_1(x_1, y_1, z_1)$, $P_2(x_2, y_2, z_2)$, $P_3(x_3, y_3, z_3)$:

$$\begin{vmatrix} x & y & z & 1 \\ x_1 & y_1 & z_1 & 1 \\ x_2 & y_2 & z_2 & 1 \\ x_3 & y_3 & z_3 & 1 \end{vmatrix} = 0.$$

This also gives the necessary and sufficient condition that four points $P(x, y, z)$, P_1, P_2, P_3 be coplanar.

Perpendicular form. The plane on which the perpendicular from the origin is of length p and has direction cosines l, m, n is

$$lx + my + nz = p. \qquad (3)$$

Plane through the point (x_0, y_0, z_0):

$$a(x - x_0) + b(y - y_0) + c(z - z_0) = 0.$$

Plane through (x_0, y_0, z_0) parallel to the two lines whose direction ratios are l, m, n; l', m', n':

$$\begin{vmatrix} x - x_0 & y - y_0 & z - z_0 \\ l & m & n \\ l' & m' & n' \end{vmatrix} = 0,$$

or parametrically

$$x = x_0 + l\lambda + l'\mu,\quad y = y_0 + m\lambda + m'\mu,\quad z = z_0 + n\lambda + n'\mu.$$

The plane through (x_0, y_0, z_0) perpendicular to the line with direction ratios l, m, n:

$$l(x - x_0) + m(y - y_0) + n(z - z_0) = 0.$$

The direction cosines of any normal to (2) are

$$a/\sqrt{(\Sigma a^2)},\ b/\sqrt{(\Sigma a^2)},\ c/\sqrt{(\Sigma a^2)}.$$

The perpendicular distance p_1 of $P_1(x_1, y_1, z_1)$ from the plane $x\cos\alpha+y\cos\beta+z\cos\gamma=p$ or $ax+by+cz+d=0$ is

$$p_1=x_1\cos\alpha+y_1\cos\beta+z_1\cos\gamma-p$$
$$=(ax_1+by_1+cz_1+d)/_+\sqrt{(a^2+b^2+c^2)}.$$

The sign of p_1 is the same or different from the sign of d according as (x_1, y_1, z_1) lies on the same or opposite side of the plane as the origin.

The angle θ between the real planes

$$L_r\equiv a_rx+b_ry+c_rz+d_r=0, \quad r=1, 2, \quad . \quad . \quad . \quad (4)$$

is given by

$$\cos\theta=(a_1a_2+b_1b_2+c_1c_2)/_+\sqrt{\{(a_1^2+b_1^2+c_1^2)(a_2^2+b_2^2+c_2^2)\}}.$$

The planes are perpendicular if $a_1a_2+b_1b_2+c_1c_2=0$.

The planes are parallel if $a_1/a_2=b_1/b_2=c_1/c_2$, and identical if each of these quotients is equal to d_1/d_2.

The planes intersect in a line whose equations are (4), and whose direction cosines are

$$(b_1c_2-b_2c_1)/N, \; (c_1a_2-c_2a_1)/N, \; (a_1b_2-a_2b_1)/N,$$

where $$N^2=(b_1c_2-b_2c_1)^2+(c_1a_2-c_2a_1)^2+(a_1b_2-a_2b_1)^2,$$

the positive root being taken.

11.23. Pencil of planes

The equation $$\lambda L_1+\mu L_2=0$$

is the equation of a plane through the line of intersection of the planes $L_1=0$ and $L_2=0$, and every such plane can have its equation put in this form for one value of $\lambda:\mu$. If $L_1=0$ and $L_2=0$ are parallel, their line of intersection lies at infinity and $\lambda L_1+\mu L_2=0$ is a plane parallel to both $L_1=0$ and $L_2=0$. Every parallel plane can have its equation put in this form for some $\lambda:\mu$.

The planes bisecting the angles between $L_1=0$ and $L_2=0$ are

$$(a_1x+b_1y+c_1z+d_1)/\sqrt{(a_1^2+b_1^2+c_1^2)}$$
$$=\pm(a_2x+b_2y+c_2z+d_2)/\sqrt{(a_2^2+b_2^2+c_2^2)}.$$

11.24. Star of planes

The planes $$L_r\equiv a_rx+b_ry+c_rz+d_r=0, \quad r=1, 2, 3,$$

intersect in a point if the matrix

$$B=\begin{bmatrix} a_1 & b_1 & c_1 & d_1 \\ a_2 & b_2 & c_2 & d_2 \\ a_3 & b_3 & c_3 & d_3 \end{bmatrix}$$

is of rank 3; in a line if B is of rank 2, and are coincident if the rank of B is unity.

If the rank of B is 3 and A is non-singular, where

$$A=\begin{bmatrix} a_1 & b_1 & c_1 \\ a_2 & b_2 & c_2 \\ a_3 & b_3 & c_3 \end{bmatrix}, \quad X=\begin{bmatrix} x \\ y \\ z \end{bmatrix}, \quad D=\begin{bmatrix} d_1 \\ d_2 \\ d_3 \end{bmatrix},$$

the equations are

$$AX=-D,$$

and the planes intersect in the point $X=-A^{-1}D$.

The equation

$$\lambda_1 L_1+\lambda_2 L_2+\lambda_3 L_3=0 \quad . \quad . \quad . \quad . \quad (5)$$

represents a plane through this point of intersection. Every plane through this point can have its equation put in the form (5) for some value of $\lambda_1 : \lambda_2 : \lambda_3$. The planes through a point form a *star* and intersect one another in a *star of lines* through the point.

If the ranks of B and A are 3 and 2 respectively, the planes intersect in pairs in parallel lines. They form a triangular prism.

If the matrix B is of rank 2, constants λ_1, λ_2, λ_3 exist such that

$$\lambda_1 L_1+\lambda_2 L_2+\lambda_3 L_3\equiv 0,$$

and the equation (5) represents the pencil of planes through the *line* $L_1=L_2=L_3=0$. The planes are *line-concurrent.*

If the ranks of B and A are 2 and 1 respectively, the planes are parallel.

Four planes

$$L_r\equiv a_r x+b_r y+c_r z+d_r=0, \quad r=1, 2, 3, 4,$$

are concurrent in a point if the matrix

$$\Delta=\begin{bmatrix} a_1 & b_1 & c_1 & d_1 \\ a_2 & b_2 & c_2 & d_2 \\ a_3 & b_3 & c_3 & d_3 \\ a_4 & b_4 & c_4 & d_4 \end{bmatrix}$$

is of rank 3. The planes are line-concurrent if Δ is of rank 2, and coincident if Δ is of unit rank. If Δ is of rank 3, and $|A|\neq 0$, the point of intersection is $X=-A^{-1}D$.

11.3. A unique line intersects at right angles two given skew lines. The SHORTEST DISTANCE between the lines is the distance between the feet of this common perpendicular. The shortest distance between the lines

$$\frac{x-x_r}{l_r}=\frac{y-y_r}{m_r}=\frac{z-z_r}{n_r}, \quad r=1, 2, \quad . \quad . \quad . \quad (6)$$

is

$$d=\begin{vmatrix} x_1-x_2 & y_1-y_2 & z_1-z_2 \\ l_1 & m_1 & n_1 \\ l_2 & m_2 & n_2 \end{vmatrix} \Big/ \sqrt{\{(m_1n_2-n_1m_2)^2+(n_1l_2-l_1n_2)^2+(l_1m_2-m_1l_2)^2\}}.$$

The lines intersect or are parallel if the determinant on the right is zero.

The equations of the line of shortest distance are

$$\begin{vmatrix} x-x_1 & y-y_1 & z-z_1 \\ l_1 & m_1 & n_1 \\ \lambda & \mu & \nu \end{vmatrix}=0, \quad \begin{vmatrix} x-x_2 & y-y_2 & z-z_2 \\ l_2 & m_2 & n_2 \\ \lambda & \mu & \nu \end{vmatrix}=0,$$

where $\lambda/(m_1n_2-n_1m_2)=\mu/(n_1l_2-l_1n_2)=\nu/(l_1m_2-m_1l_2)$.

Alternatively, the line of shortest distance is the line joining the points

$$(x_r+l_rk_r,\ y_r+m_rk_r,\ z_r+n_rk_r), \quad r=1, 2,$$

where k_1 and k_2 are given by

$$\sum_{\substack{l,\,m,\,n \\ x,\,y,\,z}} l_1(x_1+l_1k_1-x_2-l_2k_2)=0, \quad \sum_{\substack{l,\,m,\,n \\ x,\,y,\,z}} l_2(x_1+l_1k_1-x_2-l_2k_2)=0.$$

The plane through the first line (6), parallel to the second is

$$\begin{vmatrix} x-x_1 & y-y_1 & z-z_1 \\ l_1 & m_1 & n_1 \\ l_2 & m_2 & n_2 \end{vmatrix}=0.$$

If the lines intersect, this is the equation of their plane.

The LENGTH OF THE PROJECTION on the line

$$(x-\alpha)/l=(y-\beta)/m=(z-\gamma)/n \quad . \quad . \quad . \quad (7)$$

of the line P_1P_2, where P_1, P_2 are the points (x_1, y_1, z_1), (x_2, y_2, z_2) is

$$\{l(x_2-x_1)+m(y_2-y_1)+n(z_2-z_1)\}/\sqrt{\{\Sigma l^2\}}.$$

The PERPENDICULAR DISTANCE of a point $P_1(x_1, y_1, z_1)$ from the line (7) is p, where

$$p^2=\Sigma\{m(z_1-\gamma)-n(y_1-\beta)\}^2/(\Sigma l^2).$$

The angle θ between the line (7) and the plane (2) is given by

$$\sin\theta=(al+bm+cn)/\sqrt{\{(l^2+m^2+n^2)(a^2+b^2+c^2)\}}.$$

The line is parallel to the plane if

$$al+bm+cn=0. \quad . \quad . \quad . \quad . \quad (8)$$

It lies in the plane if (8) holds, and also

$$a\alpha+b\beta+c\gamma+d=0.$$

The line is perpendicular to the plane if $a:b:c=l:m:n$.

The AREA OF THE PROJECTION on a plane p of a plane area A, lying in a plane q, is $A\cos\theta$, where θ is the angle between the planes p and q.

The areas A_1, A_2, A_3 of the projections on the co-ordinate planes of an area A in a plane whose normal has direction ratios l, m, n are

$$A_1=Al/\sqrt{(\Sigma l^2)},\ A_2=Am/\sqrt{(\Sigma l^2)},\ A_3=An/\sqrt{(\Sigma l^2)}.$$

Moreover, $$A=(A_1l+A_2m+A_3n)/\sqrt{(\Sigma l^2)}.$$

The AREA A OF A TRIANGLE with vertices (x_1, y_1, z_1), (x_2, y_2, z_2), (x_3, y_3, z_3) is given by

$$A^2=A_1^2+A_2^2+A_3^2,$$

where

$$A_1=\tfrac{1}{2}\begin{vmatrix} y_1 & z_1 & 1\\ y_2 & z_2 & 1\\ y_3 & z_3 & 1\end{vmatrix},\quad A_2=\tfrac{1}{2}\begin{vmatrix} z_1 & x_1 & 1\\ z_2 & x_2 & 1\\ z_3 & x_3 & 1\end{vmatrix},\quad A_3=\tfrac{1}{2}\begin{vmatrix} x_1 & y_1 & 1\\ x_2 & y_2 & 1\\ x_3 & y_3 & 1\end{vmatrix},$$

or by

$$A=\frac{1}{2p}\begin{vmatrix} x_1 & y_1 & z_1\\ x_2 & y_2 & z_2\\ x_3 & y_3 & z_3\end{vmatrix}$$

in numerical value, where p is the distance of the origin from the plane of the triangle.

VOLUME OF THE TETRAHEDRON vertices (x_r, y_r, z_r), $r=1, 2, 3, 4$, is

$$\tfrac{1}{6}\begin{vmatrix} x_1 & y_1 & z_1 & 1\\ x_2 & y_2 & z_2 & 1\\ x_3 & y_3 & z_3 & 1\\ x_4 & y_4 & z_4 & 1\end{vmatrix}.$$

Volume of the tetrahedron bounded by the four planes

$$a_{i1}x+a_{i2}y+a_{i3}z+a_{i4}=0,\quad i=1, 2, 3, 4,$$

is $$\tfrac{1}{6}|\Delta|/\{A_{14}A_{24}A_{34}A_{44}\},$$

where Δ is the matrix $[a_{ij}]$ and A_{ij} is the co-factor of a_{ij} in $|\Delta|$.

11.4. Relations between the direction cosines of three mutually perpendicular lines

If OX, OY, OZ are three mutually perpendicular lines whose direction *cosines* are l_1, m_1, n_1; l_2, m_2, n_2; l_3, m_3, n_3, then

$$\left.\begin{aligned} l_1^2+m_1^2+n_1^2=1\\ l_2^2+m_2^2+n_2^2=1\\ l_3^2+m_3^2+n_3^2=1\end{aligned}\right\} \quad . \quad . \quad (9) \qquad \left.\begin{aligned} l_2l_3+m_2m_3+n_2n_3=0\\ l_3l_1+m_3m_1+n_3n_1=0\\ l_1l_2+m_1m_2+n_1n_2=0\end{aligned}\right\} \quad . \quad . \quad (10)$$

i.e. the matrix

$$\begin{bmatrix} l_1 & m_1 & n_1 \\ l_2 & m_2 & n_2 \\ l_3 & m_3 & n_3 \end{bmatrix}$$

is orthogonal. Hence

$$\left.\begin{aligned} l_1^2+l_2^2+l_3^2=1 \\ m_1^2+m_2^2+m_3^2=1 \\ n_1^2+n_2^2+n_3^2=1 \end{aligned}\right\} \quad . \quad . \ (11) \qquad \left.\begin{aligned} m_1n_1+m_2n_2+m_3n_3=0 \\ n_1l_1+n_2l_2+n_3l_3=0 \\ l_1m_1+l_2m_2+l_3m_3=0 \end{aligned}\right\} \quad . \quad . \ (12)$$

Equations (11) and (12) are not independent of (9) and (10). They follow since the directions cosines of Ox, Oy, Oz referred to OX, OY, OZ as axes of reference are l_1, l_2, l_3; m_1, m_2, m_3; n_1, n_2, n_3.

Further

$$\begin{aligned} l_1&=m_2n_3-m_3n_2, & m_1&=n_2l_3-n_3l_2, & n_1&=l_2m_3-l_3m_2; \\ l_2&=m_3n_1-m_1n_3, & m_2&=n_3l_1-n_1l_3, & n_2&=l_3m_1-l_1m_3; \\ l_3&=m_1n_2-m_2n_1, & m_3&=n_1l_2-n_2l_1, & n_3&=l_1m_2-l_2m_1. \end{aligned}$$

11.41. Change of axes

If $O'x'$, $O'y'$, $O'z'$ be new axes through a point $O'(\alpha, \beta, \gamma)$, parallel to the original axes Ox, Oy, Oz, and the co-ordinates of P referred to the old and new axes are (x, y, z), (x', y', z') respectively, then

$$x=\alpha+x', \ y=\beta+y', \ z=\gamma+z'.$$

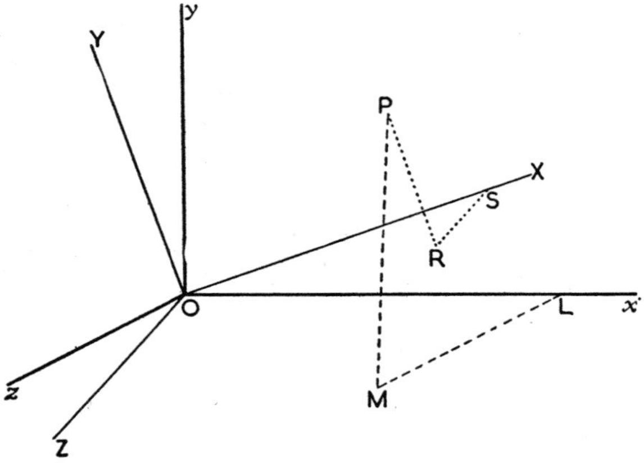

Fig. 11.2

If OX, OY, OZ be three mutually perpendicular lines through the origin O whose direction *cosines* referred to Ox, Oy, Oz as axes are l_1, m_1, n_1; l_2, m_2, n_2; l_3, m_3, n_3; and the co-ordinates of P referred to

Ox, Oy, Oz and OX, OY, OZ as axes are (x, y, z) and (X, Y, Z) respectively, then

$$\begin{aligned} X &= l_1x+m_1y+n_1z, & x &= l_1X+l_2Y+l_3Z, \\ Y &= l_2x+m_2y+n_2z, & y &= m_1X+m_2Y+m_3Z, \\ Z &= l_3x+m_3y+n_3z, & z &= n_1X+n_2Y+n_3Z. \end{aligned}$$

These may be read off from the following table in an obvious manner

	x	y	z
X	l_1	m_1	n_1
Y	l_2	m_2	n_2
Z	l_3	m_3	n_3

In the table, the cosine of the angle between, e.g., OY and Oz is written in the square opposite Y and z.

11.5. The quadric

A *quadric* is the surface given, in Cartesian co-ordinates, by

$$S(x, y, z) \equiv ax^2+by^2+cz^2+2fyz+2gzx+2hxy$$
$$+2ux+2vy+2wz+d=0, \quad . \quad . \quad . \quad (13)$$

i.e.

$$X'\Gamma X=0,$$

where

$$X=\begin{bmatrix} x \\ y \\ z \\ 1 \end{bmatrix}, \quad \Gamma=\begin{bmatrix} a & h & g & u \\ h & b & f & v \\ g & f & c & w \\ u & v & w & d \end{bmatrix}.$$

Notation. Write $\dfrac{\partial S}{\partial t}$ for the result of the following operations:

(i) Make $S(x, y, z)$ homogeneous of degree two by introducing t.

(ii) Differentiate partially with respect to t.

(iii) Put $t=1$.

The identities

$$x\frac{\partial S}{\partial x}+y\frac{\partial S}{\partial y}+z\frac{\partial S}{\partial z}+\frac{\partial S}{\partial t}\equiv 2S(x, y, z),$$

$$x_1\frac{\partial S}{\partial x}+y_1\frac{\partial S}{\partial y}+z_1\frac{\partial S}{\partial z}+\frac{\partial S}{\partial t}\equiv x\frac{\partial S_1}{\partial x_1}+y\frac{\partial S_1}{\partial y_1}+z\frac{\partial S_1}{\partial z_1}+\frac{\partial S_1}{\partial t_1}\equiv 2P_1 \text{ (say)},$$

where $S_1\equiv S(x_1, y_1, z_1)$, are useful.

A *tangent line* at a point P on the surface is a tangent to a curve on the surface through P. The locus of the tangent lines at a point P is a plane called the *tangent plane* at P (unless the surface is a cone and P is its vertex). The locus of the points Q on the quadric, such that the tangent plane at Q passes through a fixed point P in space, is the curve of intersection of S with a plane called the *plane of contact* of the tangent planes from P. The locus of a point R, such that the plane of contact of the tangent planes from R passes through a fixed point P, lies in a plane called the *polar plane* of P. The locus of a point C, on a variable chord PAB through P, such that $(PACB)=-1$ lies in the polar plane of P.

The plane of contact of the tangent planes from P is the polar plane of P.

The line (1) meets the quadric (13) in the points Q and R,

$$\{x_1+lr/\sqrt{(\Sigma l^2)},\ y_1+mr/\sqrt{(\Sigma l^2)},\ z_1+nr/\sqrt{(\Sigma l^2)}\},$$

where r is a root of

$$S(x_1, y_1, z_1)+\frac{r}{\sqrt{(\Sigma l^2)}}\left(l\frac{\partial S_1}{\partial x_1}+m\frac{\partial S_1}{\partial y_1}+n\frac{\partial S_1}{\partial z_1}\right)$$
$$+\frac{1}{2!}\frac{r^2}{\Sigma l^2}\left(l\frac{\partial}{\partial x_1}+m\frac{\partial}{\partial y_1}+n\frac{\partial}{\partial z_1}\right)^{(2)}S(x_1, y_1, z_1)=0 \quad . \ (14)$$

(see §§ 12.5 and 12.8). The roots r_1 and r_2 are the distances PQ and PR.

The quadric is met by a line in at most two points unless it contains the line. It is of order two and intersects a plane in a conic.

The line (1) touches S if (14) has equal roots. It touches it AT $P(x_1, y_1, z_1)$ if $S(x_1, y_1, z_1)=0$ and

$$l\frac{\partial S_1}{\partial x_1}+m\frac{\partial S_1}{\partial y_1}+n\frac{\partial S_1}{\partial z_1}=0. \quad . \quad . \quad . \ (15)$$

The tangent plane AT $P(x_1, y_1, z_1)$ on S has either of the forms (16) or (17) below, where $S(x_1, y_1, z_1)=0$.

The equation of the polar plane of any point $P(x_1, y_1, z_1)$ is

$$x\frac{\partial S_1}{\partial x_1}+y\frac{\partial S_1}{\partial y_1}+z\frac{\partial S_1}{\partial z_1}+\frac{\partial S_1}{\partial t_1}=0, \quad \text{i.e. } X'\Gamma X_1=0, \ . \quad . \ (16)$$

i.e.

$$x_1\frac{\partial S}{\partial x}+y_1\frac{\partial S}{\partial y}+z_1\frac{\partial S}{\partial z}+\frac{\partial S}{\partial t}=0, \quad \text{i.e. } X'_1\Gamma X=0. \ . \quad . \ (17)$$

P is called the pole of the plane (16). The pole of the plane (3) is obtained by identifying (3) with (16).

If the polar plane of B passes through A, then that of A passes through B. The points A and B are said to be *conjugate* with respect to the quadric. Two planes are *conjugate* if each contains the pole of the other. If a point P lies in a plane α its polar plane passes through a fixed point A, the pole of the plane α. If a plane p passes through a fixed point A, its pole P lies in the polar plane of A.

If a point P lies on a fixed line l, given by (1), its polar plane passes through a fixed line l', called the *polar line* of l. The equations of l' are (17) and

$$l\frac{\partial S}{\partial x}+m\frac{\partial S}{\partial y}+n\frac{\partial S}{\partial z}=0.$$

Moreover, l is the polar line of l'.

The tangent lines from a point $P(x_1, y_1, z_1)$ to S generate a quadric cone which touches S along the curve of intersection of S with the polar plane of P. This cone is called the *tangent cone* from P. Its equation is

$$SS_1-P_1^2=0.$$

The *normal* at P is the line through P perpendicular to the tangent plane at P. Its equations are

$$(x-x_1)\bigg/\frac{\partial S_1}{\partial x_1}=(y-y_1)\bigg/\frac{\partial S_1}{\partial y_1}=(z-z_1)\bigg/\frac{\partial S_1}{\partial z_1}.$$

The condition that P be the mid-point of the chord QR is that $r_1+r_2=0$, i.e. that (15) holds.

The locus of the mid-points of a system of parallel chords, direction ratios l, m, n, is the plane

$$l\frac{\partial S}{\partial x}+m\frac{\partial S}{\partial y}+n\frac{\partial S}{\partial z}=0, \quad . \quad . \quad . \quad . \quad (18)$$

which is called the *diametral plane* of the direction l, m, n. It passes through the centre of the quadric. (See § 11.7.)

The chords bisected at $P(x_1, y_1, z_1)$ lie in the plane

$$(x-x_1)\frac{\partial S_1}{\partial x_1}+(y-y_1)\frac{\partial S_1}{\partial y_1}+(z-z_1)\frac{\partial S_1}{\partial z_1}=0. \quad . \quad . \quad (19)$$

The section of S by this plane is a conic whose centre is $P(x_1, y_1, z_1)$. The centre of the section by the plane (3) is obtained by identifying (3) with (19).

The locus of the centres of the system of parallel sections

$$lx+my+nz=\lambda \quad . \quad . \quad . \quad . \quad (20)$$

(λ variable) is the line

$$\frac{\partial S}{\partial x}\bigg/l=\frac{\partial S}{\partial y}\bigg/m=\frac{\partial S}{\partial z}\bigg/n,$$

which passes through the centre of the quadric, and is called a *diameter*. Its diametral plane is the plane of the system (20) through the centre of the quadric. Two diameters are *conjugate* if each lies in the diametral plane of the other.

A line on a surface is a *generator* if it belongs to a system of lines on the surface, one line of which passes through every point on the surface.

The condition that the line (1) shall be a generator of S is that (14) is an identity in r, i.e. that $S_1=0$, (15) holds and

$$\left(l\frac{\partial}{\partial x_1}+m\frac{\partial}{\partial y_1}+n\frac{\partial}{\partial z_1}\right)^{(2)}S_1=0. \quad . \quad . \quad . \ (21)$$

If Γ is non-singular, two generators, real or imaginary, pass through each point on the quadric. Their direction ratios are given by (15) and (21). If $|\Gamma|=0$, one generator passes through each point of the quadric.

11.6. The condition that the plane

$$Ux+Vy+Wz+T=0$$

shall touch the quadric is

$$\mathbf{U}'(\text{adj }\Gamma)\mathbf{U}=0,$$

where $\mathbf{U}'=[U\ V\ W\ T]$. The surface is of class (q.v.) two.

A quadric surface can in general be found to pass through r arbitrary points and to touch $9-r$ arbitrary planes $(r=0, 1, \ldots, 9)$.

The curve of intersection of two quadrics is of order four. If it is not degenerate, it is called a skew quartic of the second kind. It meets each generator of either quadric in two points. It may break up into a skew cubic curve and a chord of the cubic, or into two conics which intersect in two (distinct or coincident) points, or into two line-pairs AB, BC and AD, DC.

11.7. Metrical classification of quadrics

The quadric is given by equation (13), i.e. by

$$S(x, y, z)\equiv X'\Gamma X=0, \text{ where}$$

$$X=\begin{bmatrix} x \\ y \\ z \\ 1 \end{bmatrix}, \quad \Gamma=\begin{bmatrix} a & h & g & u \\ h & b & f & v \\ g & f & c & w \\ u & v & w & d \end{bmatrix}, \quad G=\begin{bmatrix} a & h & g \\ h & b & f \\ g & f & c \end{bmatrix}, \quad Z=\begin{bmatrix} x' \\ y' \\ z' \end{bmatrix}.$$

$$|\Gamma|=\Delta,\ |G|=D,\ A=bc-f^2,\ B=ca-g^2,\ C=ab-h^2.$$

The *centre* of a quadric is the mid-point of every chord through it. Its co-ordinates satisfy

$$\frac{\partial S}{\partial x}=\frac{\partial S}{\partial y}=\frac{\partial S}{\partial z}=0.$$

If $D\neq 0$, the centre is a finite point and the quadric is said to be a *central quadric*. The equation of the quadric referred to parallel axes through the centre is $Z'GZ+\Delta/D=0$.

A *principal diameter* or *axis* of the quadric is a diameter which is perpendicular to its diametral plane.

The direction ratios (l, m, n) of the principal diameters satisfy

$$\left.\begin{aligned}(a-\lambda)l+hm+gn&=0,\\ hl+(b-\lambda)m+fn&=0,\\ gl+fm+(c-\lambda)n&=0,\end{aligned}\right\} \qquad (22)$$

where λ is a root of

$$\begin{vmatrix} a-\lambda & h & g \\ h & b-\lambda & f \\ g & f & c-\lambda \end{vmatrix}=0,$$

or $$\lambda^3-\lambda^2(a+b+c)+\lambda(A+B+C)-D=0, \qquad (23)$$

i.e. λ is a latent root of the matrix G. All the roots of this equation are real if the coefficients in S are real. The expressions Δ, D, $A+B+C$, $a+b+c$ are invariants of the quadric for any change of *rectangular* axes.

If (α, β, γ) is the centre of the quadric and $\lambda_1, \lambda_2, \lambda_3$ are the roots of equation (23), the lengths of the principal semi-axes of the quadric are $\{-(u\alpha+v\beta+w\gamma+d)/\lambda_r\}^{\frac{1}{2}}=\{-\Delta/(\lambda_r D)\}^{\frac{1}{2}}$, $r=1, 2, 3$. Corresponding to each root λ_r of (23), equations (22) give a set of values of $l:m:n$, the direction ratios of a principal axis. The equation of the corresponding principal plane containing the other two principal axes is

$$\lambda_r(l_r x+m_r y+n_r z)+ul_r+vm_r+wn_r=0.$$

If $D=0$, A, B and C do not differ in sign.

		$\Delta>0$	$\Delta<0$	$\Delta=0$
$D\neq0$	$(a+b+c)D>0$ $A+B+C>0$	Virtual quadric	Ellipsoid	Virtual cone
	$(a+b+c)D$ and $A+B+C$ not both >0	Hyperboloid of one sheet	Hyperboloid of two sheets	Real cone

$\Delta<0$, $D=0$; $A+B+C>0$: Elliptic paraboloid.

$\Delta>0$, $D=0$; $A+B+C<0$: Hyperbolic paraboloid.

Γ of rank 3, $D=0$; $A+B+C>0$: Elliptic cylinder.

Γ of rank 3, $D=0$; $A+B+C<0$: Hyperbolic cylinder.

Γ of rank 3, $D=0$; $A+B+C=0$: Parabolic cylinder.

Γ of rank 2 and $A+B+C<0$: Pair of real distinct planes.

Γ of rank 2, $A+B+C>0$: Pair of imaginary planes.

Matrix

$$E \equiv \begin{bmatrix} a & h & g & u \\ h & b & f & v \\ g & f & c & w \end{bmatrix}$$

of rank 1 and Γ of rank 2: Pair of parallel planes.

$a=b=c=f=g=h=0$: Plane at infinity and another plane.

Γ of rank 1: Repeated plane.

Γ of rank 0: Plane at infinity, repeated.

11.8. Special quadrics

11.81. The quadric cone

The necessary and sufficient condition that the quadric $S(x, y, z)=0$ be a cone is $\Delta=0$.

{This cone may be a cylinder (vertex at infinity) or a pair of planes.}

The vertex is given by

$$\frac{\partial S}{\partial x}=\frac{\partial S}{\partial y}=\frac{\partial S}{\partial z}=\frac{\partial S}{\partial t}=0.$$

The general equation of a cone vertex the origin is homogeneous in x, y, z:

$$f(x, y, z) \equiv ax^2+by^2+cz^2+2fyz+2gzx+2hxy=0 \quad . \quad . \; (24)$$

If the principal planes are taken as co-ordinate planes the equation is

$$\lambda_1x^2+\lambda_2y^2+\lambda_3z^2=0.$$

The polar plane of every point in space passes through the vertex. Conversely, if the polar plane with respect to a quadric of every point in space passes through a fixed point A, then the quadric is a cone vertex A.

The necessary and sufficient condition that a cone contains a trio of mutually perpendicular generators is

$$a+b+c=0.$$

The property is poristic, i.e. if there is one such trio, there are an infinite number of such trios. Every generator then belongs to such a trio.

The angle between the lines in which the plane $px+qy+rz=0$ cuts the cone (24) is θ, where

$$(\cos\theta)/\{(a+b+c)(p^2+q^2+r^2)-f(p, q, r)\}=(\sin\theta)/\{\pm 2(p^2+q^2+r^2)^{\frac{1}{2}}P\},$$

where

$$P^2 = \begin{vmatrix} a & h & g & p \\ h & b & f & q \\ g & f & c & r \\ p & q & r & 0 \end{vmatrix}.$$

Reciprocal cone. The normals (q.v.) to a proper cone through its vertex generate a quadric cone called the reciprocal cone. The reciprocal cone of $f(x, y, z) = 0$, i.e. of $Y'GY = 0$, where $Y' = [x\ y\ z]$, is

$$\begin{vmatrix} a & h & g & x \\ h & b & f & y \\ g & f & c & z \\ x & y & z & 0 \end{vmatrix} = 0, \qquad . \quad . \quad . \ (25)$$

i.e.

$$Y' . (\text{adj } G) . Y = 0 \text{ or } Y'G^{-1}Y = 0.$$

The reciprocal of (25) is the original cone $f(x, y, z) = 0$.

The equations of a cone, vertex the origin, with its principal axes as axes of reference is either

$$x^2/a^2 + y^2/b^2 + z^2/c^2 = 0 \quad \text{(Imaginary cone)},$$

or

$$x^2/a^2 + y^2/b^2 - z^2/c^2 = 0 \quad \text{(Real cone)}.$$

The latter surface contains one system of real generators given by the equations:

$$x/a + z/c = y/(b\lambda), \quad x/a - z/c = -\lambda y/b.$$

The tangent plane at any point on any given generator is the same plane and contains the generator.

The surface is cut by a plane not passing through the vertex in a hyperbola, parabola or an ellipse according as the plane is parallel to two, to one or to no real generator.

11.82. Cylinder

The cylinder (see § 20.8) has an axis or line of centres which is the line of concurrence of the planes

$$\frac{\partial S}{\partial x} = \frac{\partial S}{\partial y} = \frac{\partial S}{\partial z} = 0.$$

Referred to principal axes, the equation reduces to one of the forms

(*a*) Elliptic cylinder: $x^2/a^2 + y^2/b^2 = 1$.

(*b*) Hyperbolic cylinder: $x^2/a^2 - y^2/b^2 = 1$.

} The (x, z) and (y, z) planes are planes of symmetry.

(*c*) Parabolic cylinder: $x^2/a^2-2y/b=0$. The (y, z) plane is the plane of symmetry, the (x, z) plane is a tangent plane which touches the surface along the z axis.

Any plane parallel to the z-axis cuts the surfaces (*a*), (*b*), (*c*) in line-pairs. Any other plane cuts them in an ellipse, hyperbola or parabola respectively.

The cylinder contains one system of generators. The tangent plane at every point on the same generator is the same plane and contains the generator.

11.83. Non-singular quadrics

The equation of a non-singular central quadric referred to its principal axes is

$$ax^2+by^2+cz^2=1. \qquad (26)$$

In particular,

Ellipsoid:	$x^2/a^2+y^2/b^2+z^2/c^2=1$,
Hyperboloid of one sheet:	$x^2/a^2+y^2/b^2-z^2/c^2=1$,
Hyperboloid of two sheets:	$x^2/a^2-y^2/b^2-z^2/c^2=1$.

The equation of a non-central quadric referred to suitable axes is

$$ax^2+by^2=2cz. \qquad (27)$$

In particular,

Elliptic paraboloid:	$x^2/a^2+y^2/b^2=2z/c$.
Hyperbolic paraboloid:	$x^2/a^2-y^2/b^2=2z/c$.

Central quadric	*Paraboloid*	
Surface: $ax^2+by^2+cz^2=1$.	$ax^2+by^2=2cz$.	
Tangent plane at (x_1, y_1, z_1): $ax_1x+by_1y+cz_1z=1$.	$ax_1x+by_1y=c(z+z_1)$	(28)
Polar plane of (x_1, y_1, z_1): $ax_1x+by_1y+cz_1z=1$.	$ax_1x+by_1y=c(z+z_1)$	(29)

The condition that the plane (3) touches the surface, obtained by identifying (3) and (28):

$l^2/a+m^2/b+n^2/c=p^2$.	$l^2/a+m^2/b+2np/c=0$.

Locus of the point of intersection of three mutually perpendicular tangent planes is the

director sphere:	director plane:
$x^2+y^2+z^2=1/a+1/b+1/c$.	$2z/c+1/a+1/b=0$.

Condition that the chord (1) is bisected at (x_1, y_1, z_1) is

$ax_1l+by_1m+cz_1n=0.$	$ax_1l+by_1m-cn=0.$

Plane section, centre (x_1, y_1, z_1):

$ax_1(x-x_1)+by_1(y-y_1)$ $+cz_1(z-z_1)=0$	$ax_1(x-x_1)+by_1(y-y_1)$ $=c(z-z_1)$. . . . (30)

Centre, (x_1, y_1, z_1), of the section by the plane (3), obtained by identifying (3) and (30), is given by

$ax_1/l=by_1/m=cz_1/n$	$ax_1/l=by_1/m=-c/n$

and $lx_1+my_1+nz_1=p$.

Diametral plane of the direction $l:m:n$ is

$alx+bmy+cnz=0.$	$alx+bmy-cn=0.$

The lengths of the axes of the conic section of the surface $ax^2+by^2+cz^2=1$ by the plane

$$lx+my+nz=0 \quad . \quad . \quad . \quad . \quad (31)$$

are r_1 and r_2, the roots of

$$l^2/(ar^2-1)+m^2/(br^2-1)+n^2/(cr^2-1)=0. \quad . \quad . \quad (32)$$

The equations of the axes are

$$x(ar_i^2-1)/l=y(br_i^2-1)/m=z(cr_i^2-1)/n, \quad i=1, 2. \quad . \quad . \quad (33)$$

The lengths of the axes of the section by the plane (3) are

$$r_i\{1-p^2/(l^2/a+m^2/b+n^2/c)\}^{\frac{1}{2}}, \quad i=1, 2,$$

where r_i is a root of (32). The axes are the lines through the centre of the section and parallel to the lines (33).

The lengths of the axes of the section of the paraboloid (27) by the plane (3) are given by

$$l^2/\{an^2r^2-ck\}+m^2/\{bn^2r^2-ck\}-n^2/(ck)=0, \quad . \quad . \quad . \quad (34)$$

where $k=cl^2/a+cm^2/b+2np$.

The equations of the axes are

$$(x-\alpha)(an^2r_i^2-ck)/l=(y-\beta)(bn^2r_i^2-ck)/m=(z-\gamma)kc/(-n),$$

where (α, β, γ) is the centre of the section by the plane (3) and r_i is a root of (34).

A central quadric has a system, of freedom three, of trios of *mutually conjugate diameters*, each of which lies in the diametral plane of the other two of the trio. If $P_1(x_1, y_1, z_1)$, $P_2(x_2, y_2, z_2)$, $P_3(x_3, y_3, z_3)$ are the extremities of three mutually conjugate radii of the ellipsoid

$x^2/a^2+y^2/b^2+z^2/c^2=1$, then x_1/a, y_1/b, z_1/c; x_2/a, y_2/b, z_2/c; x_3/a, y_3/b, z_3/c are the direction *cosines* of three mutually perpendicular lines, i.e. the matrix

$$\begin{bmatrix} x_1/a & y_1/b & z_1/c \\ x_2/a & y_2/b & z_2/c \\ x_3/a & y_3/b & z_3/c \end{bmatrix}$$

is orthogonal.

Every plane cuts an ellipsoid in an ellipse, real or virtual.

If two principal axes of an ellipsoid are equal, the ellipsoid is a *spheroid* with the third principal axis as axis of revolution.

If $a=b>c$, the surface is a *planetary* or *oblate* spheroid.

If $a>b=c$, it is an *ovary* or *prolate* spheroid.

11.84. Sphere

The equation of a sphere, centre (α, β, γ) and radius r, is

$$(x-\alpha)^2+(y-\beta)^2+(z-\gamma)^2=r^2.$$

The general equation of a quadric (13) represents a sphere if, and only if,

$$a=b=c, \quad f=g=h=0.$$

The general equation of a sphere is

$$f(x, y, z) \equiv x^2+y^2+z^2+2ux+2vy+2wz+d=0.$$

$$\text{Centre } (-u, -v, -w), \qquad \text{radius}=(u^2+v^2+w^2-d)^{\frac{1}{2}}.$$

If PQR is any secant through $P(x_1, y_1, z_1)$, the product $PQ \,.\, PR$ is constant and equal to $f(x_1, y_1, z_1)$ and to k^2, where k is the length of a tangent from P to the sphere.

11.85. Hyperboloid of one sheet

$$x^2/a^2+y^2/b^2-z^2/c^2=1.$$

Asymptotic cone: $x^2/a^2+y^2/b^2-z^2/c^2=0$.

The surface contains two systems of real generators or two *reguli*:

(1) $$x/a+z/c=\lambda(1+y/b), \quad x/a-z/c=(1-y/b)/\lambda;$$

(2) $$x/a-z/c=\mu(1+y/b), \quad x/a+z/c=(1-y/b)/\mu.$$

Two generators, one of each system, intersect in the point

$$a(\lambda+\mu)/(1+\lambda\mu),\ b(1-\lambda\mu)/(1+\lambda\mu),\ c(\lambda-\mu)/(1+\lambda\mu).$$

No two generators of the same regulus intersect.

Through each point P on the surface pass two generators, one of each system. Their plane is the tangent plane at P. Every plane through a generator is the tangent plane at some point on the generator.

The generators through the point $(a \cos \alpha, b \sin \alpha, 0)$ on the principal elliptic section are

$$(x-a \cos \alpha)/(a \sin \alpha)=(y-b \sin \alpha)/(-b \cos \alpha)=z/(\pm c).$$

If $a=b$, the surface is a surface of revolution with the z-axis as axis of revolution.

11.86. Hyperboloid of two sheets

$$x^2/a^2-y^2/b^2-z^2/c^2=1.$$

Asymptotic cone: $x^2/a^2-y^2/b^2-z^2/c^2=0$.

The generators are unreal lines. If $b=c$, the surface is a surface of revolution with the x-axis as axis of revolution.

11.87. Elliptic paraboloid

$$x^2/a^2+y^2/b^2=2z/c.$$

The generators are unreal. If $a=b$, the surface is a paraboloid of revolution.

11.88. Hyperbolic paraboloid

$$x^2/a^2-y^2/b^2=2z/c.$$

The surface contains two reguli or systems of real generators:

(1) $$x/a-y/b=2\lambda/c, \quad x/a+y/b=z/\lambda;$$

(2) $$x/a+y/b=2\mu/c, \quad x/a-y/b=z/\mu.$$

Two generators, one of each system, intersect in the point

$$a(\mu+\lambda)/c, \quad b(\mu-\lambda)/c, \quad 2\lambda\mu/c.$$

The plane of the generators is the tangent plane at the point. Every plane through a generator is the tangent plane at some point on the generator.

The equations of the generators through the point (α, β, γ) on the surface are

$$\frac{x-\alpha}{a}=\frac{y-\beta}{\pm b}=\frac{z-\gamma}{c\left(\dfrac{\alpha}{a}\mp\dfrac{\beta}{b}\right)} \quad \left\{\equiv\frac{(z-\gamma)(\alpha/a\pm\beta/b)}{2\gamma}\right\}.$$

CHAPTER 12

DIFFERENTIAL CALCULUS

12.1. Functions of a real variable

A *closed interval* (a, b) consists of the aggregate of values of x which satisfy $a \leqslant x \leqslant b$. An *open** interval $)a, b($ consists of the values satisfying $a < x < b$.

Definition. y is a *function* of x if to some values of x correspond values of y.

We write $y = f(x)$, $y = \phi(x)$ and so on. If to every value of x in an interval corresponds a value or values of y, y is defined in the interval. If to each value of x in (a, b) corresponds one value or n values of y, then y is respectively a *one-valued* or an *n-valued* function of x. A function may be infinitely many-valued, e.g. $y = \sin^{-1} x$ in $(-1, 1)$. x is called the *independent* and y the *dependent* variable. It is not necessary that a mathematical equation connecting x and y should be known, e.g. y might be the gross tonnage of the ships in the Pool of London at time x.

If y is given by an equation $\psi(x, y) = 0$ connecting x and y, y is an *implicit* function of x. If $y = \phi(x)$, y is an *explicit* function of x.

Classification of elementary functions

In the following a, b, a_1, . . ., are constant, n and k are constant integers.

A *polynomial* is a function formed by the processes of addition, subtraction and multiplication on x.

$$y \equiv a_0 x^n + a_1 x^{n-1} + \ldots + a_n$$

is a polynomial of degree n, $(a_0 \neq 0)$.

A *rational function* is formed by addition, subtraction, multiplication and division on x. It can be expressed as the quotient of two polynomials.

An *algebraic function* y of x is defined implicitly by an equation

$$y^n P_0(x) + y^{n-1} P_1(x) + \ldots + P_n(x) \equiv \sum_{\mu=0}^{k} \sum_{v=0}^{n} a_{\mu v} x^\mu y^v = 0,$$

where the $P_i(x)$ are polynomials in x.

The function may be given explicitly, e.g. $y = +(x^2 + 3x + 7)^{\frac{1}{2}}$. A rational function is a special case of an algebraic function.

* Some authors denote a closed interval by $[a, b]$, and an open one by (a, b).

A *transcendental function* is a function which is not algebraic. The trigonometrical or circular functions, $\sin x$, $\cos x$, etc., the inverse trigonometrical functions, $\sin^{-1} x$, etc., and the functions $\ln x$, $\exp x$ are transcendental.

Bounded functions

The function $f(x)$ is said to be *bounded* in (a, b) if two constants h and K exist, such that $h \leqslant f(x) \leqslant K$ for all x satisfying $a \leqslant x \leqslant b$. Such a number K is called a *superior number* or an *upper bound.* Among the upper bounds there is a least, M, with the property that

(1) $f(x) \leqslant M$ for all x in (a, b).

(2) If ϵ is any positive number, then there is at least one point c satisfying $a \leqslant c \leqslant b$ at which $f(c) > M - \epsilon$.

The *inferior numbers* h have a greatest, m, such that

(1) $f(x) \geqslant m$ for all x in (a, b).

(2) If ϵ is any positive number, there is at least one point d satisfying $a \leqslant d \leqslant b$, at which $f(d) < m + \epsilon$.

M and m are called the *least upper bound* and the *greatest lower bound* of $f(x)$ in (a, b).

A *neighbourhood* of the point a is defined as the aggregate of points x satisfying $|x-a| < \delta$, where δ is some positive number.

In the following, unless the contrary is stated, the functions referred to are one-valued.

12.2. Behaviour of a function in the neighbourhood of a point *a*

When we consider the behaviour of $f(x)$ near a, two questions arise, viz.:

(1) By how much does $f(x)$ change as x increases through the value a?

(2) At what rate is $f(x)$ changing as x increases through the value a?

Consideration of the first of these questions leads to the concept of continuity and of the second to that of differentiability.

Limits as x tends to a (written $x \to a$)

Definition. $f(x)$ tends to a limit l as $x \to a$ if, given any positive number ϵ, however small, we can find a positive number δ, such that $|f(x) - l| < \epsilon$ for all x satisfying $0 < |x-a| < \delta$.

E.g.
$$\lim_{x \to 0} \frac{\sin x}{x} = 1.$$

The concepts of a limit and of a value of the function are quite distinct. The limit as $x \to a$ may or may not be equal to the value $f(a)$.

It may happen that $f(x)$ tends to a limit as $x \to a$ from one side but not from the other.

If $|f(x)-l_L|<\epsilon$ for all x satisfying $0<a-x<\delta'$, we say that $f(x) \to l_L$ as $x \to a$ through values less than a or as $x \to a-0$.

If $|f(x)-l_R|<\epsilon$ for all x satisfying $0<x-a<\delta''$, then $f(x) \to l_R$ as $x \to a$ through values greater than a or as $x \to a+0$.

The notation $f(a-0)$ and $f(a+0)$ is used for l_L and l_R.

$f(x) \to l$ as $x \to +\infty$ if, given $\epsilon>0$, there exists a number X, such that $|f(x)-l|<\epsilon$ for all $x>X$.

$f(x) \to +\infty$ as $x \to a$ if, given any positive number G, however great, we can find a positive number δ, such that $f(x)>G$ for all x satisfying $0<|x-a|<\delta$.

Example. Tan $x \to +\infty$ as $x \to \frac{1}{2}\pi-0$ and to $-\infty$ as $x \to \frac{1}{2}\pi+0$.

$f(x)$ need not tend to a limit or to $+\infty$ or to $-\infty$ as $x \to a+0$.

E.g. $\sin \frac{1}{x}$ oscillates finitely as $x \to 0$.

If these limits l_L and l_R exist, then together with $f(a)$ they form a first criterion for measuring the amount by which $f(x)$ increases as x increases through a.

$f(x)$ is said to be infinite of order n written $f(x)=O(x^n)$ if $|f(x)/x^n|<K$ for all $x \geqslant x_0$, where K is a fixed constant.

If $f(x)/x^n \to 0$ as $x \to \infty$, we write $f(x)=o(x^n)$.

If $f(x)/\phi(x) \to l$ as $x \to \infty$, $f(x)$ is said to be *asymptotic* to $\phi(x)$, written $f(x) \sim \phi(x)$. If $f(x)/\phi(x) \to 1$ as $x \to \infty$, $f(x)$ is *asymptotically equal* to $\phi(x)$, written $f(x) \simeq \phi(x)$.

Similarly $f(x)=O(x^n)$ as $x \to 0$ if $K>|f(x)/x^n|>k>0$ for all x such that $0<|x|<\delta$.

12.21. Continuity

Definition. The function $f(x)$ is *continuous* at the point a if, given any positive number ϵ, we can find a positive number δ, such that $|f(x)-f(a)|<\epsilon$ whenever $|x-a|<\delta$.

It follows that $f(x)$ is continuous at a if, and only if, $f(x) \to f(a)$ as $x \to a$, i.e. if $\lim_{x \to a-0} f(x)=\lim_{x \to a+0} f(x)=f(a)$. If $\lim_{x \to a+0} f(x)=f(a)$, $f(x)$ is *continuous from the right* at a. Similarly if $\lim_{x \to b-0} f(x)=f(b)$, then $f(x)$ is *continuous from the left* at b.

$f(x)$ is continuous throughout the closed interval (a, b) if (i) it is continuous at every point x satisfying $a<x<b$, (ii) $\lim_{x \to a+0} f(x)=f(a)$ and $\lim_{x \to b-0} f(x)=f(b)$.

If $f(x)$ and $\phi(x)$ are continuous at a, so are the functions $f(x) \pm \phi(x)$, $\{f(x) \, . \, \phi(x)\}$. If also $\phi(a) \neq 0$, $f(x)/\phi(x)$ is continuous at a.

If $f(x)$ is a function of x, continuous at a, and if $x=\phi(t)$ is a function of t, continuous at c where $a=\phi(c)$, then $\psi(t)\equiv f\{\phi(t)\}$ is continuous at $t=c$.

If $f(x)$ is continuous in the closed interval (a, b), then it is bounded in (a, b).

If M and m are the least upper and greatest lower bounds of the continuous function $f(x)$ in (a, b), then there is at least one point c and one point d satisfying $a\leqslant c\leqslant b$, $a\leqslant d\leqslant b$, such that $f(c)=M$, $f(d)=m$, i.e. $f(x)$ actually takes the values M and m at some points in (a, b).

If $f(x)$ is continuous in (a, b), and if $f(a)=y_0$ and $f(b)=y_1$, and if γ is any number such that $y_0\leqslant\gamma\leqslant y_1$ or $y_0\geqslant\gamma\geqslant y_1$, then there is a point c, satisfying $a\leqslant c\leqslant b$, such that $f(c)=\gamma$.

12.3. Differentiation

Definition. The *derivate* or *differential coefficient* $f'(x)$ of $f(x)$ at the point x is defined by

$$f'(x)=\lim_{h\to 0}\frac{f(x+h)-f(x)}{h}.$$

The function $f(x)$ is said to be *differentiable* at the point x if $f'(x)$ exists as a unique finite limit.

If $y=f(x)$ and if the increment h of x is denoted by Δx, and the corresponding increment $f(x+\Delta x)-f(x)$ of y by Δy, then

$$\lim_{\Delta x\to 0}\frac{f(x+\Delta x)-f(x)}{\Delta x}=\lim_{\Delta x\to 0}\frac{\Delta y}{\Delta x}=f'(x).$$

The derivate is also denoted by $\dfrac{dy}{dx}$, $\dfrac{df(x)}{dx}$ or y'. It is a measure of the rate of increase of $f(x)$ at the point x.

The curve (Fig. 12.1) represents $y=f(x)$ in Cartesian co-ordinates,

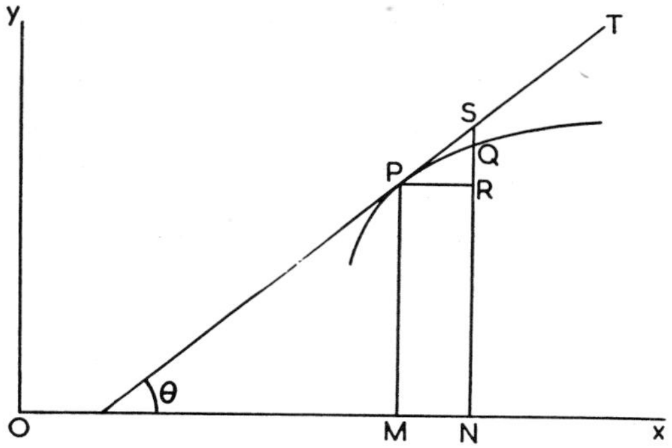

Fig. 12.1

and the tangent at $P(x, y)$ meets the ordinate QN through Q at S. PR is perpendicular to QN.

Then $\tan Q\hat{P}R = \dfrac{RQ}{PR} = \dfrac{RQ}{MN} = \dfrac{\Delta y}{\Delta x}$.

As $\Delta x \to 0$, $Q \to P$ along the curve, and if the chord PQ tends to a limiting position PT, then PT is the tangent at P, and

$$\lim_{Q\to P} \tan Q\hat{P}R = \lim_{\Delta x\to 0} \frac{\Delta y}{\Delta x} = f'(x) = \tan T\hat{P}R = \tan \theta$$
$$= \text{gradient of the tangent at } P.$$

A function which is differentiable at a point a is continuous at a, but a function may be continuous at a and yet not be differentiable at a. There are continuous functions which are not differentiable at isolated points and others which are not differentiable at any point.

If $y \equiv \phi(x)$ is differentiable at the point x and $z \equiv \psi(y)$ is differentiable at the point y, then the function $z \equiv \psi\{\phi(x)\} \equiv f(x)$ is differentiable at the point x and

$$\frac{dz}{dx} = \frac{dz}{dy} \cdot \frac{dy}{dx}, \text{ i.e. } f'(x) = \psi'(y) \cdot \phi'(x).$$

If x is given as a differentiable function of y and if $\dfrac{dx}{dy} \neq 0$, then

$$\frac{dy}{dx} = 1 \bigg/ \frac{dx}{dy}.$$

If x and y are functions of t, then y is a function of x defined parametically. If x and y are differentiable functions of t and if $\dfrac{dx}{dt} \neq 0$, then

$$\frac{dy}{dx} = \frac{dy}{dt} \bigg/ \frac{dx}{dt} = y'/x',$$

where dashes denote differentiation with respect to t.

Function	*Derivate*
$u, v, \ldots$ functions of x; C is a constant	
C	0
$u \pm v$	$u' \pm v'$
$u \pm C$	u'
uv	$uv' + u'v$
Cu	Cu'
$u \cdot v \cdot w \ldots$	$u \cdot v \cdot w \ldots (u'/u + v'/v + w'/w + \ldots)$
u/v	$(vu' - v'u)/v^2$.

To differentiate $y=uvw\ldots$, $y=u^v$, $y=u^{v^w}$, take logarithms (q.v.) and then differentiate, e.g.

$$y=u^v \qquad\qquad y'/y=vu'/u+v'\ln u.$$

The derivate $f'(x)$ of a function $f(x)$ is itself a function of x which may be differentiable. If $f'(x)$ is differentiable, its derivate is called the second derivate of $f(x)$, and so on. We write

$$\frac{d}{dx}\left(\frac{dy}{dx}\right)=\frac{d^2y}{dx^2}\equiv y''\equiv f''(x),\ \frac{d^3y}{dx^3}\equiv y'''\equiv f'''(x),\ \ldots,$$

$$\frac{d^ny}{dx^n}=\frac{d}{dx}\left(\frac{d^{n-1}y}{dx^{n-1}}\right)\equiv y^{(n)}\equiv f^{(n)}(x).$$

Leibniz' theorem gives an expression for the nth derivate of a product $u\,.\,v$ when the derivates of all orders up to the nth of u and v are known.

$$(u\,.\,v)^{(n)}=\binom{n}{0}u^{(n)}v+\binom{n}{1}u^{(n-1)}v'+\binom{n}{2}u^{(n-2)}v^{(2)}$$

$$+\ldots+\binom{n}{r}u^{(n-r)}v^{(r)}+\ldots+\binom{n}{n-1}u'v^{(n-1)}+\binom{n}{n}uv^{(n)}.$$

Provided the linear factors of the denominator are known, the nth derivate of any rational function of x can be found by splitting the function into a polynomial plus a sum of partial fractions (q.v.) in which every fraction is of the form $A/(x-a)^k$, where A is a constant and k a positive integer.

12.31. Differentials

If $y=f(x)$ is differentiable,

$$\Delta y\equiv f(x+\Delta x)-f(x)=f'(x)\,.\,\Delta x+\eta\,.\,\Delta x, \qquad (1)$$

where $\eta\to 0$ as $\Delta x\to 0$.

Definition. The *differential dy* of the dependent variable y is defined by

$$dy=f'(x)\Delta x. \qquad (2)$$

The differential dx of the independent variable x is defined by

$$dx=\Delta x.$$

Hence

$$dy=f'(x)dx \qquad (3)$$

The relation (3) between the differentials holds whether x is the independent variable or not, provided $f'(x)\neq 0$.

In Fig. 12.1, $PR=\Delta x=dx$ and the corresponding increment $\Delta y=RQ$. The corresponding differential $dy=RS$.

The approximation

$$\Delta y \simeq f'(x)\Delta x.$$

is often used in calculations concerning small errors of measurement.

The second differential of the dependent variable is defined as

$$d(dy) \equiv d^2y = f''(x)dx^2.$$

12.4. Function of two real variables

A *continuous plane curve* or *path* is the locus of a point (x, y), where $x=\phi(t)$, $y=\psi(t)$ are functions of t in the range $t_0 \leqslant t \leqslant t_1$, such that $\phi'(t)$ and $\psi'(t)$ exist, are continuous and do not simultaneously vanish except at, at most, a finite number of points of the range. If $\phi(t_0)=\phi(t_1)$, $\psi(t_0)=\psi(t_1)$ the curve is said to be *closed*. If the equations $\phi(t')=\phi(t'')$, $\psi(t')=\psi(t'')$ hold for no pair of points of the range other than t_0, t_1, the curve is *simple*. We call a curve obeying the above conditions a simple closed *contour*.

A *neighbourhood* of a point $P_1(x_1, y_1)$ is the set of points $P(x, y)$ for which

$$(x-x_1)^2+(y-y_1)^2 < r^2$$

for a positive number r.

An *open domain* of the plane is a set of points such that (i) if $P_1(x_1, y_1)$ is any point of the set then there is a neighbourhood of P_1 composed entirely of points of the set, (ii) any two points of the set can be joined by a simple continuous curve composed entirely of points of the set.

A set of points satisfying (i) is called an *open set.*

A domain is *bounded* if it can be enclosed in a square of side k, centre the origin. Otherwise it is unbounded. A point is a boundary point if (i) it does not belong to the open domain, and (ii) it has points of the open domain in every neighbourhood. A bounded open domain together with its boundary forms a *closed domain.*

A domain D is *simply connected* if any path D joining two points P and Q can be deformed into any other path joining P and Q without going outside D.

Definition. V is a *function* of x and y in a domain D, if to each ordered pair of values of (x, y) in D corresponds a value or values of V.

We write $V=f(x, y)$, $V=\phi(x, y)$, etc. x and y are the independent variables and V is the dependent variable.

Similarly we define a function V of three or more independent variables $x, y, z, \ldots$, written $V=f(x, y, z, \ldots)$.

$f(x, y)$ *tends to a limit* l as $(x, y)\rightarrow(a, b)$ if, given any positive number ϵ, we can find a positive number δ, such that

$$|f(x, y)-l| < \epsilon$$

for all points (x, y) such that $|x-a| < \delta$ and $|y-b| < \delta$ except (a, b).

$f(x, y)$ is a *continuous function of x and y* at the point (a, b) if, given any positive number ϵ, we can find a positive number δ such that

$$|f(x, y)-f(a, b)|<\epsilon, \qquad (4)$$

for all points (x, y) satisfying $|x-a|<\delta$, $|y-b|<\delta$.

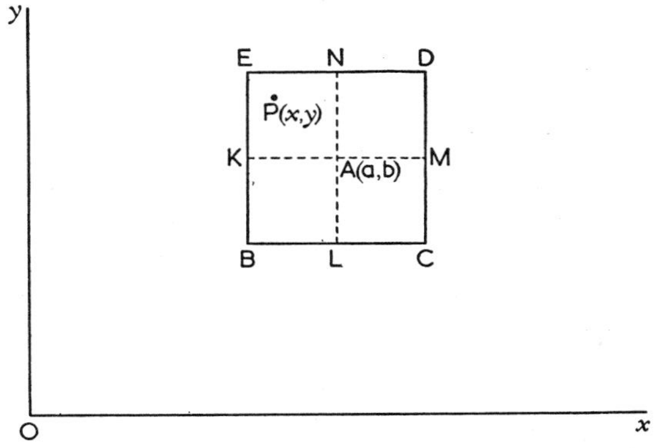

Fig. 12.2

Then $f(x, y)\to f(a, b)$ as $P(x, y)\to A(a, b)$ by any path, and we can find a square $BCDE$, centre $A(a, b)$, of side 2δ, such that the inequality (4) holds for every point $P(x, y)$ within the square (see Fig. 12.2). This is much more than continuity with respect to x alone and with respect to y alone. In the latter case the inequality (4) need hold only for points P on the lines KM and LN.

12.5. Partial differentiation

Let $V=f(x, y)$ be a function of the *independent* variables x and y. The *partial derivate* of V with respect to x is

$$\frac{\partial V}{\partial x}\equiv f_x=\lim_{h\to 0}\frac{f(x+h, y)-f(x, y)}{h}.$$

It is the derivate with respect to x, the other variable y being kept constant.

Similarly $$\frac{\partial V}{\partial y}\equiv f_y=\lim_{k\to 0}\frac{f(x, y+k)-f(x, y)}{k}.$$

The ordinary rules for differentiating products, etc., continue to hold.

Partial derivates of the second order are defined by

$$\frac{\partial}{\partial x}\left(\frac{\partial f}{\partial x}\right)=\frac{\partial^2 f}{\partial x^2}\equiv f_{xx},$$

$$\frac{\partial}{\partial y}\left(\frac{\partial f}{\partial x}\right)=\frac{\partial^2 f}{\partial y\partial x}\equiv f_{xy},^* \quad . \quad . \quad . \quad . \quad (5)$$

$$\frac{\partial}{\partial x}\left(\frac{\partial f}{\partial y}\right)=\frac{\partial^2 f}{\partial x\partial y}\equiv f_{yx}, \text{ etc.} \quad . \quad . \quad . \quad (6)$$

In (5), f is differentiated partially with respect to x, then $\frac{\partial f}{\partial x}$ is differentiated partially with respect to y. In (6) f is differentiated first with respect to y and then $\frac{\partial f}{\partial y}$ with respect to x.

If f_x, f_y and f_{xy} exist in the neighbourhood of the point (x, y) and if f_{xy} is continuous at the point (x, y), then f_{yx} also exists at this point and

$$f_{yx}=f_{xy}.$$

The partial derivates of order n are defined by

$$f_{x^n}\equiv\frac{\partial^n f}{\partial x^n}=\frac{\partial}{\partial x}\left(\frac{\partial^{n-1}f}{\partial x^{n-1}}\right), f_{x^{n-1}y}\equiv\frac{\partial^n f}{\partial y\partial x^{n-1}}=\frac{\partial}{\partial y}\left(\frac{\partial^{n-1}f}{\partial x^{n-1}}\right), \ldots$$

and so on.

In repeated partial differentiation of a function of two independent variables, the order of the differentiations may be changed provided that the derivates in question are continuous functions.

12.51. Total differential

If the partial derivates f_x, f_y of $V=f(x, y)$ exist in the neighbourhood of the point (x, y) and if one of them is continuous in the neighbourhood, then the increment

$$\Delta V\equiv f(x+\Delta x, y+\Delta y)-f(x, y)=f_x\,.\,\Delta x+f_y\,.\,\Delta y+\eta\,.\,\rho,$$

where $\rho^2\equiv\Delta x^2+\Delta y^2$ and $\eta\to 0$ as $\rho\to 0$.

The differentials dx, etc., of the independent variables are defined to be equal to the arbitrary increments:

$$dx=\Delta x,\; dy=\Delta y;$$

and the differential dV or *complete differential* is defined as

$$dV=f_x.dx+f_y.dy \quad . \quad . \quad . \quad . \quad (7)$$

i.e. as the sum of its partial differentials $f_x.dx$, etc.

* Some authors use the opposite convention.

Moreover, if x and y are independent variables and a relation

$$dV = \alpha dx + \beta dy$$

holds, then

$$f_x = \alpha, \ f_y = \beta.$$

If V is a function of u and v, which are themselves functions of the independent variables x and y, then

$$dV = V_u . du + V_v . dv,$$

where $V_u = \left(\frac{\partial V}{\partial u}\right)_{v=\text{constant}}$. This relation is of the form (7).

If the second partial derivates are continuous in the neighbourhood of (x, y), the second differential is defined to be

$$d(dV) = d^2V = f_{xx} . dx^2 + 2f_{xy} . dx\, dy + f_{yy} . dy^2. \quad . \quad . \quad (8)$$

In terms of the variables u and v, which are themselves functions of the independent variables x and y,

$$d^2V = f_{uu} . du^2 + 2f_{uv} . du\, dv + f_{vv} . dv^2 + f_u . d^2u + f_v . d^2v.$$

The form (8) is written symbolically as

$$d^2V = \left(\frac{\partial V}{\partial x} dx + \frac{\partial V}{\partial y} dy\right)^{(2)},$$

where the bracketed index denotes that the expression is to be formally expanded on the understanding that $\frac{\partial V^2}{\partial x^2}$ is to be replaced by $\frac{\partial^2 V}{\partial x^2}$ after expansion.

The total differential of the nth order is defined to be

$$d^nV = f_{x^n} dx^n + \binom{n}{1} f_{x^{n-1}y} dx^{n-1} dy + \ldots$$

$$+ \binom{n}{r} f_{x^{n-r}y^r} dx^{n-r} dy^r + \ldots + f_{y^n} dy^n$$

$$\equiv \left(\frac{\partial V}{\partial x} dx + \frac{\partial V}{\partial y} dy\right)^{(n)}$$

in the symbolic notation.

12.6. Functions of several variables

The concepts can be generalized for functions $V=f(x, y, z, \ldots)$ of any finite number of independent variables $x, y, z, \ldots$.

$$\frac{\partial V}{\partial x} \equiv f_x = \lim_{h\to 0} \frac{f(x+h, y, z, \ldots)-f(x, y, z, \ldots)}{h},$$

all the variables except x being kept constant.

A neighbourhood of $(x_1, y_1, z_1, \ldots)$ is the set of points $(x, y, z, \ldots)$ satisfying

$$\Sigma(x-x_1)^2 < r^2,$$

where r is a positive number.

If all the first partial derivates exist and all, or all except one, are continuous in the neighbourhood of $(x, y, z, \ldots)$, then

$$\Delta V \equiv f(x+\Delta x,\ y+\Delta y,\ z+\Delta z,\ \ldots)-f(x, y, z, \ldots)$$
$$= f_x\ \Delta x + f_y\ \Delta y + f_z\ \Delta z + \ldots + \eta\rho,$$

where $\rho^2 = \Sigma\Delta x^2$ and $\eta\to 0$ as $\rho\to 0$.

The total differential dV is defined as before as

$$dV = f_x dx + f_y dy + f_z dz + \ldots,$$

where $dx=\Delta x$, $dy=\Delta y$, etc., and $\Delta x, \Delta y, \ldots$ are arbitrary increments.

Moreover, if

$$dV = \alpha dx + \beta dy + \gamma dz + \ldots,$$

then

$$f_x=\alpha,\ f_y=\beta,\ f_z=\gamma, \ldots$$

If $V=f(r)$, a function of r, and r is a function of $x, y, z \ldots$, then

$$\frac{\partial V}{\partial x}=f'(r)\frac{\partial r}{\partial x},\quad \frac{\partial V}{\partial y}=f'(r)\frac{\partial r}{\partial y}, \ldots,$$

where $f'(r)=\dfrac{df(r)}{dr}$, the dash denoting ordinary differentiation with respect to the variable in the bracket.

If $V=f(x, y, z, \ldots)$ and $x, y, z, \ldots$ are each functions of the independent variable t, so that V is a function of t, then

$$\frac{dV}{dt}=\frac{\partial V}{\partial x}\frac{dx}{dt}+\frac{\partial V}{\partial y}\frac{dy}{dt}+\ldots \qquad (9)$$

12.61. Implicit functions

Let y be a function of x, implicitly and uniquely defined in some domain D by the equation $f(x, y)\equiv 0$.

Then if $V \equiv f(x, y)$, $V \equiv 0$ so that by (9)

$$0 \equiv \frac{dV}{dx} = f_x + f_y \frac{dy}{dx}, \quad . \quad . \quad . \quad . \quad (10)$$

giving $\dfrac{dy}{dx}$.

Differentiating (10) similarly,

$$0 = f_{xx} + 2f_{xy}\frac{dy}{dx} + f_{yy}\left(\frac{dy}{dx}\right)^2 + f_y \frac{d^2y}{dx^2},$$

provided $f_{xy} = f_{yx}$, giving $\dfrac{d^2y}{dx^2}$.

Partial differentiation of implicit functions

Suppose z is implicitly defined as a function of the two independent variables x and y by the equation $f(x, y, z) = 0$. If $V \equiv f(x, y, z)$, then, as x varies, z varies in such a way that V remains constant. Therefore

$$0 = \left(\frac{\partial V}{\partial x}\right)_{y=\text{const.}} \equiv \left(\frac{\partial f}{\partial x}\right)_{\substack{y=\text{const.}\\ z=\text{const.}}} + \left(\frac{\partial f}{\partial z}\right)_{\substack{y=\text{const.}\\ x=\text{const.}}} \times \left(\frac{\partial z}{\partial x}\right)_{y=\text{const.}} \quad . \quad . \quad (11)$$

giving $\dfrac{\partial z}{\partial x}$.

Similarly,

$$0 = \left(\frac{\partial V}{\partial y}\right)_{x=\text{const.}} \equiv \frac{\partial f}{\partial y} + \frac{\partial f}{\partial z}\frac{\partial z}{\partial y}, \quad . \quad . \quad . \quad (12)$$

giving $\dfrac{\partial z}{\partial y}$.

If the second partial derivates are continuous, differentiating (11) and (12) partially with respect to x and y we get equations for $\dfrac{\partial^2 z}{\partial x^2}$, $\dfrac{\partial^2 z}{\partial x \partial y}$, $\dfrac{\partial^2 z}{\partial y^2}$, viz.:

$$\frac{\partial^2 f}{\partial x^2} + 2\frac{\partial^2 f}{\partial z \partial x}\frac{\partial z}{\partial x} + \frac{\partial^2 f}{\partial z^2}\left(\frac{\partial z}{\partial x}\right)^2 + \frac{\partial f}{\partial z}\frac{\partial^2 z}{\partial x^2} = 0,$$

and two similar expressions.

12.7. Change of the variables

If $V \equiv f(x, y)$ has continuous partial derivates and if the variables are functions of new *independent* variables u and v, given by

$$x = x(u, v), \quad y = y(u, v),$$

where $x(u, v)$, $y(u, v)$ have continuous partial derivates with respect to u and v, then

$$V=f(x, y)=f[x(u, v), y(u, v)]=\phi(u, v),$$

$$dV=V_x\, dx+V_y\, dy,$$

$$dx=x_u du+x_v dv,\quad dy=y_u du+y_v dv,$$

yielding

$$dV=(V_x x_u+V_y y_u)du+(V_x x_v+V_y y_v)dv.$$

Since V is a function of the *independent* variables u and v,

$$V_u=V_x x_u+V_y y_u,\quad V_v=V_x x_v+V_y y_v. \qquad . \quad . \quad . \quad . \quad (13)$$

Note. In V_x we regard V as a function of x and y and differentiate with respect to x keeping y constant, while in x_u we regard x as a function of u and v and differentiate with respect to u keeping v constant. A chain rule similar to (13) applies for functions of any finite number of independent variables.

If the partial derivates of the second order exist and are continuous, equations (13) can be applied to V_u in place of V, giving

$$V_{uu}=V_{xx}x_u^2+2V_{xy}x_u y_u+V_{yy}y_u^2+V_x x_{uu}+V_y y_{uu},$$

$$V_{uv}=V_{xx}x_u x_v+V_{xy}(x_u y_v+x_v y_u)+V_{yy}y_u y_v+V_x x_{uv}+V_y y_{uv}.$$

Similarly

$$V_{vv}=V_{xx}x_v^2+2V_{xy}x_v y_v+V_{yy}y_v^2+V_x x_{vv}+V_y y_{vv}.$$

The Cartesian co-ordinates are changed to polars by the equations

$$x=r\cos\theta,\quad y=r\sin\theta.$$

If $V=f(x, y)=\phi(r, \theta)$ has continuous second order partial derivates,

$$dV=V_x\, dx+V_y\, dy=V_r\, dr+V_\theta\, d\theta.$$

$$dx=\cos\theta\, dr-r\sin\theta\, d\theta,\quad dy=\sin\theta\, dr+r\cos\theta\, d\theta.$$

Therefore

$$dV=(V_x\cos\theta+V_y\sin\theta)dr+(-V_x\, r\sin\theta+V_y\, r\cos\theta)d\theta,$$

whence

$$V_x=V_r\cos\theta-\frac{1}{r}V_\theta\sin\theta,\quad V_y=V_r\sin\theta+\frac{1}{r}V_\theta\cos\theta.$$

Applying these results to the functions V_x and V_y, we have

$$V_{xx}=\frac{1}{2}\left(V_{rr}+\frac{1}{r^2}V_{\theta\theta}+\frac{1}{r}V_r\right)$$

$$+\frac{1}{2}\left(V_{rr}-\frac{1}{r^2}V_{\theta\theta}-\frac{1}{r}V_r\right)\cos 2\theta-\frac{1}{r}\left(V_{r\theta}-\frac{1}{r}V_\theta\right)\sin 2\theta,$$

$$V_{xy}=\frac{1}{2}\left(V_{rr}-\frac{1}{r^2}V_{\theta\theta}-\frac{1}{r}V_r\right)\sin 2\theta+\frac{1}{r}\left(V_{r\theta}-\frac{1}{r}V_\theta\right)\cos 2\theta.$$

$$V_{yy}=\frac{1}{2}\left(V_{rr}+\frac{1}{r^2}V_{\theta\theta}+\frac{1}{r}V_r\right)$$

$$-\frac{1}{2}\left(V_{rr}-\frac{1}{r^2}V_{\theta\theta}-\frac{1}{r}V_r\right)\cos 2\theta+\frac{1}{r}\left(V_{r\theta}-\frac{1}{r}V_\theta\right)\sin 2\theta.$$

Whence

$$V_x^2+V_y^2=V_r^2+\frac{1}{r^2}V_\theta^2;\quad \nabla^2 V\equiv V_{xx}+V_{yy}=V_{rr}+\frac{1}{r^2}V_{\theta\theta}+\frac{1}{r}V_r.$$

12.8. Euler's theorem on homogeneous functions

Definition. The function $f(x, y, z)$ is said to be homogeneous of degree n in the variables x, y, z if it satisfies the identity

$$f(tx, ty, tz)\equiv t^n f(x, y, z).$$

We suppose that the partial derivates of order r are continuous. Then

$$x\frac{\partial f}{\partial x}+y\frac{\partial f}{\partial y}+z\frac{\partial f}{\partial z}\equiv nf(x, y, z),$$

and

$$\left(x\frac{\partial}{\partial x}+y\frac{\partial}{\partial y}+z\frac{\partial}{\partial z}\right)^{(r)} f\equiv n(n-1)\ldots(n-r+1)f(x, y, z),$$

where the symbolic notation with the index (r) in brackets denotes the result of multiplying out the operator formally and then operating on f.* The result holds for homogeneous functions of any finite number of variables. The degree n need not be an integer.

12.9. Jacobian

If $u_1, u_2, \ldots, u_n$ are n functions of the n independent variables $x_1, x_2, \ldots, x_n$, their *Jacobian* is the determinant

$$J\equiv\frac{\partial(u_1, u_2, \ldots, u_n)}{\partial(x_1, x_2, \ldots, x_n)}\equiv\left\|\frac{\partial u_i}{\partial x_j}\right\|.$$

A relation $\phi(u_1, u_2, \ldots, u_n)=0$, which does not involve any of the variables $x_1, x_2, \ldots, x_n$ explicitly, holds between $u_1, u_2, \ldots, u_n$ if, and only if, their Jacobian is identically zero.

* Thus $$\left(x\frac{\partial}{\partial x}+y\frac{\partial}{\partial y}\right)^{(2)} f\equiv x^2\frac{\partial^2 f}{\partial x^2}+2xy\frac{\partial^2 f}{\partial x\partial y}+y^2\frac{\partial^2 f}{\partial y^2},$$

whereas $$\left(x\frac{\partial}{\partial x}+y\frac{\partial}{\partial y}\right)^2 f\equiv\left(x\frac{\partial}{\partial x}+y\frac{\partial}{\partial y}\right)\left(x\frac{\partial f}{\partial x}+y\frac{\partial f}{\partial y}\right)$$

$$=\left(x\frac{\partial}{\partial x}+y\frac{\partial}{\partial y}\right)^{(2)} f+x\frac{\partial f}{\partial x}+y\frac{\partial f}{\partial y},$$

provided $\dfrac{\partial^2 f}{\partial x\partial y}=\dfrac{\partial^2 f}{\partial y\partial x}$.

If $u_1, \ldots, u_n$ are functions of the n independent variables $x_1, \ldots, x_n$, and if $x_1, \ldots, x_n$ are themselves functions of the n independent variables $y_1, \ldots, y_n$, then

$$\frac{\partial(u_1, u_2, \ldots, u_n)}{\partial(y_1, y_2, \ldots, y_n)} = \frac{\partial(u_1, u_2, \ldots, u_n)}{\partial(x_1, x_2, \ldots, x_n)} \cdot \frac{\partial(x_1, x_2, \ldots, x_n)}{\partial(y_1, y_2, \ldots, y_n)}.$$

In particular

$$\frac{\partial(u_1, u_2, \ldots, u_n)}{\partial(x_1, x_2, \ldots, x_n)} \cdot \frac{\partial(x_1, x_2, \ldots, x_n)}{\partial(u_1, u_2, \ldots, u_n)} = 1.$$

12.91. The functions $u_i(x)$, $(i=1, 2, \ldots, n)$ are *linearly dependent* if a relation

$$c_1u_1 + c_2u_2 + \ldots + c_nu_n \equiv 0 \quad . \quad . \quad . \quad (14)$$

holds for some set of constants c_i not all zero. They are *linearly independent* if (14) implies $c_i=0$, $(i=1, 2, \ldots, n)$.

The *Wronskian* of n functions $u_1, u_2, \ldots, u_n$ of x is

$$W \equiv \begin{vmatrix} u_1 & u_2 & \ldots & u_n \\ u'_1 & u'_2 & \ldots & u'_n \\ \cdot & \cdot & \cdot & \cdot \\ \cdot & \cdot & \cdot & \cdot \\ u_1^{(n-1)} & u_2^{(n-1)} & \ldots & u_n^{(n-1)} \end{vmatrix}$$

The necessary and sufficient condition that the functions $u_1(x), \ldots, u_n(x)$ be linearly dependent is that

$$W \equiv 0.$$

CHAPTER 13

MEAN VALUE THEOREMS. MAXIMA AND MINIMA

13.1. Rolle's theorem and the mean value theorems

Rolle's theorem. If (i) $f(x)$ is differentiable in $)a, b($, (ii) $f(x)$ is continuous in (a, b), (iii) $f(a)=f(b)$, then there is at least one point c satisfying $a<c<b$ for which $f'(c)=0$. The result of course holds if $f(x)$ is differentiable in (a, b) and $f(a)=f(b)$.

First mean value theorem. If $f(x)$ is differentiable in $)a, b($ and continuous in (a, b), then there is at least one point c satisfying $a<c<b$ for which

$$f(b)-f(a)=(b-a)f'(c).$$

Or, if $f(x)$ is differentiable in $(x, x+h)$ then there is a number θ_1, such that

$$f(x+h)=f(x)+hf'(x+\theta_1 h) \quad (0<\theta_1<1).$$

The geometrical interpretation of this is that between A and B on the curve $y=f(x)$, there is at least one point C at which the tangent is parallel to the chord AB.

Second mean value theorem. If $f''(x)$ exists in the interval $(x, x+h)$ then there is a number θ_2 satisfying $0<\theta_2<1$, such that

$$f(x+h)=f(x)+hf'(x)+\frac{h^2}{2!}f''(x+\theta_2 h).$$

Taylor's theorem for real variable is an nth mean value theorem. It states that if the derivates of $f(x)$ of all orders up to and including the nth exist throughout $(x, x+h)$, then

$$f(x+h)=f(x)+hf'(x)+\frac{h^2}{2!}f''(x)+\ldots+\frac{h^{n-1}}{(n-1)!}f^{(n-1)}(x)+R_n,$$

where

$$R_n=\frac{h^n}{n!}f^{(n)}(x+\theta_n h) \qquad (0<\theta_n<1)\text{—Lagrange's form},$$

$$R_n=\frac{h^n(1-\theta'_n)^{n-1}}{(n-1)!}f^{(n)}(x+\theta'_n h) \quad (0<\theta'_n<1)\text{—Cauchy's form},$$

$$R_n=\frac{h^n(1-\theta''_n)^{n-p}}{(n-1)!p}f^{(n)}(x+\theta''_n h) \quad (0<\theta''_n<1)\text{—Schölmich-Roche form.}$$

Maclaurin's theorem is obtained by taking $x=0$:

$$f(x)=f(0)+xf'(0)+\frac{x^2}{2!}f''(0)+\ldots+\frac{x^{n-1}}{(n-1)!}f^{(n-1)}(0)+\frac{x^n}{n!}f^{(n)}(\theta_n x)$$

$$(0<\theta_n<1),$$

with similar forms for the other remainders ($x=0$, $h=x$).

Taylor's theorem enables us to expand a function in an infinite series (q.v.) of powers of x if the derivates of all orders of $f(x)$ exist in the interval and if $R_n \to 0$ as $n\to\infty$. In practice it is usually easier to treat the corresponding function $f(z)$ of the complex variable z and find its Taylor expansion (see § 17.1), or to find the radius of convergence of the power series $\Sigma x^n f^{(n)}(0)/n!$ (see § 18.6). If this radius is r, and if $R_n\to 0$ as $n\to\infty$ when $x=\pm r$, then the expansion holds for the points $x=\pm r$ respectively.

Cauchy's mean value theorem. If (i) $f(x)$ and $\phi(x)$ are differentiable in (a, b), (ii) $f'(x)$ and $\phi'(x)$ do not vanish simultaneously in (a, b), (iii) $\phi(a)\neq\phi(b)$, then there is a point c satisfying $a<c<b$ for which

$$\frac{f(b)-f(a)}{\phi(b)-\phi(a)}=\frac{f'(c)}{\phi'(c)}.$$

The result holds if $f(x)$ and $\phi(x)$ are differentiable in (a, b) and $\phi'(x)\neq 0$ in (a, b).

13.2. Indeterminate forms. De l'Hospital's rule

A function $f(x)/\phi(x)$, $f(x)\phi(x)$, $f(x)-\phi(x)$, $f(x)^{\phi(x)}$ which for $x=a$ takes one of the forms $0/0$, ∞/∞, $0.\infty$, $\infty-\infty$, ∞^0, 0^0, 1^∞ is called an indeterminate form. The values of

$$\lim_{x\to a}\{f(x)/\phi(x)\},\ \lim_{x\to a}\{f(x)\phi(x)\},\ \lim_{x\to a}\{f(x)-\phi(x)\},\ \lim_{x\to a}\{f(x)^{\phi(x)}\}$$

can sometimes be evaluated by applying de l'Hospital's rule to a QUOTIENT.

De l'Hospital's rule. If (i) $f(a)=\phi(a)=0$ and (ii) $f'(x)$ and $\phi'(x)$ exist and are not simultaneously zero in some neighbourhood of $x=a$ except at a, then

$$\lim_{x\to a}\frac{f(x)}{\phi(x)}=\lim_{x\to a}\frac{f'(x)}{\phi'(x)},\text{ if this limit exists.} \qquad (1)$$

The result holds also if (i) $f(x)\to\infty$ and $\phi(x)\to\infty$ as $x\to a$ and (ii) holds.

If all the derivates of $f(x)$ and $\phi(x)$ up to the nth exist in the neighbourhood of a and if $f^{(n)}(a)$ and $\phi^{(n)}(a)$ are the lowest derivates that are not both zero at the point a, then, subject to analogous conditions on the vanishing of the derivatives,

$$\lim_{x\to a}\frac{f(x)}{\phi(x)}=\frac{f^{(n)}(a)}{\phi^{(n)}(a)}.$$

If (i) $f(x) \to 0$ and $\phi(x) \to 0$ as $x \to +\infty$, (ii) $f'(x)$ and $\phi'(x)$ exist and are not simultaneously zero for $x >$ some x_0, then (1) holds with a replaced by ∞.

An analogous result also holds if $f(x) \to \infty$ and $\phi(x) \to \infty$ as $x \to +\infty$.

De l'Hospital's rule applies only to a quotient, so the function considered must be written as a quotient.

E.g. if $f(x) \to 0$ and $\phi(x) \to \infty$ as $x \to a$, then $f(x) \, . \, \phi(x) = f(x) \Big/ \left\{ \dfrac{1}{\phi(x)} \right\}$ is a quotient of the form 0/0.

If $f(x) - \phi(x)$ is of the form $\infty - \infty$ when $x = a$, arrange it as
$f(x) - \phi(x) = \left\{ \dfrac{1}{\phi(x)} - \dfrac{1}{f(x)} \right\} \Big/ \left\{ \dfrac{1}{\phi(x) f(x)} \right\}$, a quotient of the form 0/0.

If $f(x)^{\phi(x)}$ is of the form 0^0, ∞^0, 1^∞, then

$$\ln \{f(x)^{\phi(x)}\} = \phi(x) \ln f(x) = \{\ln f(x)\} \Big/ \frac{1}{\phi(x)},$$

a quotient of the form ∞/∞ or 0/0.

Evaluate the quotient by de l'Hospital's rule and then take the exponential (q.v.).

13.3. Mean value theorem and Taylor's theorem for functions of two variables

If the partial derivates of the first order of $z = f(x, y)$ exist in a domain which includes the rectangle whose vertices are (x, y), $(x+h, y)$, $(x, y+k)$, $(x+h, y+k)$, then

$$f(x+h, y+k) = f(x, y) + h f_x(x+\theta_1 h, y+\theta_1 k) + k f_y(x+\theta_1 h, y+\theta_1 k), \quad (0 < \theta_1 < 1).$$

Taylor's theorem. If the partial derivates of $z = f(x, y)$ of all orders up to the nth exist and are continuous in the closed rectangle, then

$$f(x+h, y+k) = f(x, y) + \frac{1}{r!} \sum_{r=1}^{n-1} \left(h \frac{\partial}{\partial x} + k \frac{\partial}{\partial y} \right)^{(r)} f(x, y) + R_n,$$

where

$$R_n = \frac{1}{n!} \left(h \frac{\partial}{\partial x} + k \frac{\partial}{\partial y} \right)^{(n)} f(x, y)_{(x+\theta_n h,\, y+\theta_n k)} \quad (0 < \theta_n < 1),$$

where the notation indicates that the derivates in R_n are evaluated at the point $(x+\theta_n h, y+\theta_n k)$ (see § 12.8).

If $z = f(x, y)$ has partial derivates of all orders and if $\lim_{n \to \infty} R_n = 0$ throughout the rectangle, the function can be expanded in the convergent Taylor series:

$$f(x+h, y+k) = \sum_{n=0}^{\infty} \frac{1}{n!} \left(h \frac{\partial}{\partial x} + k \frac{\partial}{\partial y} \right)^{(n)} f(x, y).$$

Similar theorems hold for functions of three or more variables.

13.4. Maxima and minima

Definition. The function $f(x)$ has (i) a *true* (or *strict*) *maximum* value at the point a if there is a positive number δ such that $f(x) < f(a)$ for all x satisfying $0 < |x-a| \leqslant \delta$; (ii) a *true minimum* value at a if $f(x) > f(a)$ for all x satisfying $0 < |x-a| \leqslant \delta$.

In either case $f(x)$ is said to have an *extremum* at a.

The function $f(x)$ has a *semi-maximum* at a if $f(x) \leqslant f(a)$ for all x satisfying $0 < |x-a| \leqslant \delta$.

These maxima and minima are relative, not absolute. There may be a maximum at a although at points b outside the interval $(a-\delta, a+\delta)$, $f(b) > f(a)$.

Theorem I. If (i) $f(x)$ has an extremum at $x=a$,
(ii) $f'(x)$ exists in $(a-\delta, a+\delta)$ for some positive δ,
then $f'(a)=0$.

I.e. a necessary condition for an extremum at a is that $f'(a)=0$ or does not exist. This condition is not sufficient.

Theorem II. If (i) $f'(x) > 0$ in $a-\delta \leqslant x < a$,
(ii) $f'(x) < 0$ in $a < x \leqslant a+\delta$ for some positive δ,
(iii) $f(x)$ is continuous at a,
then $f(x)$ has a true maximum at a.

I.e. a sufficient condition for a maximum of a continuous function at a is that $f'(x)$ changes from positive to negative as x increases through the value a. This condition is not necessary.

Theorem IIa. If the inequality signs in Theorem II, (i) and (ii), are reversed, $f(x)$ has a true minimum at $x=a$.

Theorem III. If (i) $f'(a)=0$,
(ii) $f''(a) < 0$,
then $f(x)$ has a true maximum at $x=a$.

If (i) $f'(a)=0$,
(ii) $f''(a) > 0$,
then $f(x)$ has a true minimum at $x=a$.

Theorem IV. If (i) $f'(a)=f''(a)= \dots =f^{(n-1)}(a)=0, f^{(n)}(a) \neq 0$,
(ii) n is even,
then $f(x)$ has an extremum at $x=a$ which is a true maximum if $f^{(n)}(a) < 0$ and a true minimum if $f^{(n)}(a) > 0$.

If (i) as above, and (ii) n is odd, $f(x)$ has no extremum at $x=a$. The curve $y=f(x)$ has a point of inflexion at $x=a$.

If $f''(a)=0$ and $f'''(a)\neq 0$, the curve $y=f(x)$ has a point of inflexion at $x=a$.

To find the maxima and minima of $f(x)$, find the points at which $f'(x)=0$ and those at which it does not exist. Examine each of these points in turn, using Theorems II, III and IV to determine whether there is a maximum or minimum at each point and, if so, which.

13.5. Maxima and minima of functions of several variables

Two variables. Definition. The function $f(x, y)$ has a *true maximum* at (a, b) if $f(x, y)<f(a, b)$ for all points (x, y) in the neighbourhood of (a, b) except (a, b). The function has a *semi-maximum* at (a, b) if $f(x, y)\leqslant f(a, b)$ for all points in the neighbourhood of (a, b). For a minimum the inequality signs are reversed.

Theorem V. If (i) the partial derivates of the first order exist in the neighbourhood of (a, b),

(ii) $f(x, y)$ has a maximum (minimum) at (a, b),

then
$$\left(\frac{\partial f}{\partial x}\right)_{(a,\,b)}=\left(\frac{\partial f}{\partial y}\right)_{(a,\,b)}=0.$$

These conditions are not sufficient for an extremum.

Theorem VI. If (i) $\left(\frac{\partial f}{\partial x}\right)_{(a,\,b)}=\left(\frac{\partial f}{\partial y}\right)_{(a,\,b)}=0,$

(ii) $\Delta_2\equiv\begin{vmatrix} f_{xx} & f_{xy} \\ f_{yx} & f_{yy}\end{vmatrix}_{(a,\,b)}>0,$

then $z=f(x, y)$ has an extremum at (a, b), which is a maximum or minimum according as $\left(\frac{\partial^2 f}{\partial x^2}\right)_{(a,\,b)}$, $\left(\frac{\partial^2 f}{\partial y^2}\right)_{(a,\,b)}$ are both negative or both positive. These conditions are sufficient but not necessary for an extremum.

n Variables.

Theorem VII. If (i) $f(x_1, x_2, \ldots, x_n)$ has a maximum at $(a_1, a_2, \ldots, a_n)$, (ii) the first order partial derivates exist at $(a_1, a_2, \ldots, a_n)$, then
$$\left(\frac{\partial f}{\partial x_i}\right)_{(a_1,\, a_2,\, \ldots,\, a_n)}=0 \quad (i=1, 2, \ldots, n).$$

Theorem VIII. If (i) the first order partial derivates all vanish at $(a_1, a_2, \ldots, a_n)$, (ii) the quadratic form (q.v.)
$$\left(h_1\frac{\partial}{\partial x_1}+h_2\frac{\partial}{\partial x_2}+\ldots+h_n\frac{\partial}{\partial x_n}\right)^{(2)} f(x_1, x_2, \ldots, x_n),$$
where the partial derivates are evaluated at $(a_1, a_2, \ldots, a_n)$, is negative

(positive) definite, then $f(x_1, x_2, \ldots, x_n)$ has a maximum (minimum) at $(a_1, a_2, \ldots, a_n)$.

13.6. Restricted maxima and minima

(a) *One independent variable*

To find the extrema of $f(x, y)$ subject to the relation $\phi(x, y) \equiv 0$.

Method I. Find a parametric representation $x = x(t)$, $y = y(t)$ of the curve $\phi(x, y) = 0$ and then find the extrema of $f\{x(t), y(t)\}$ as a function of one variable t.

Method II. The extrema of $f(x, y)$, for which the partial derivates exist, are among the solutions of the simultaneous equations

$$\phi(x, y) \equiv 0, \qquad (2)$$

$$\frac{d\phi}{dx} \equiv \frac{\partial\phi}{\partial x} + \frac{\partial\phi}{\partial y}\frac{dy}{dx} \equiv 0,$$

$$\frac{df}{dx} \equiv \frac{\partial f}{\partial x} + \frac{\partial f}{\partial y}\frac{dy}{dx} = 0,$$

and hence are among the solutions of (2) and

$$f_x\phi_y - f_y\phi_x = 0.$$

Test whether these points give maxima or minima.

(b) *Two independent variables*

Necessary conditions, provided the partial derivates exist, for extrema of $u \equiv f(x, y, z)$ subject to $\phi(x, y, z) \equiv 0$ are

$$\frac{f_x}{\phi_x} = \frac{f_y}{\phi_y} = \frac{f_z}{\phi_z} \qquad (3)$$

at an extremum (a, b, c). Solve the equations (3) with $\phi(x, y, z) = 0$ and then examine u at the points found.

(c) *Lagrange's method of undetermined multipliers*

To find the extrema of $u \equiv f(x_1, x_2, \ldots, x_n)$, when there are k identities $\phi_1(x_1, x_2, \ldots, x_n) = \ldots = \phi_k(x_1, x_2, \ldots, x_n) = 0$ between the variables.

If $\lambda_1, \lambda_2, \ldots, \lambda_k$ are unknown constants, we require the extrema of

$$f + \lambda_1\phi_1 + \lambda_2\phi_2 + \ldots + \lambda_k\phi_k.$$

Hence find $x_1, x_2, \ldots, x_n$ satisfying

$$\frac{\partial f}{\partial x_r} + \lambda_1\frac{\partial\phi_1}{\partial x_r} + \ldots + \lambda_k\frac{\partial\phi_k}{\partial x_r} = 0 \quad (r = 1, 2, \ldots, n),$$

$$\phi_1 = \phi_2 = \ldots = \phi_k = 0.$$

If the partial derivates exist, these points give the possible extrema. Examine each point in turn.

CHAPTER 14

INDEFINITE INTEGRATION

14.1. The problem of indefinite integration is:—Given a function $f(x)$, to find a function $\psi(x)$ of which $f(x)$ is the derivate, i.e. such that $\dfrac{d\psi(x)}{dx}=f(x)$. The notation $\psi(x)=\int f(x)\,dx$ is used. If one solution $\psi_1(x)$ is known, then the general solution is $\psi_1(x)+C$, where C is an arbitrary constant.

Methods of Integration

(*a*) Change of variables. Put $x=\phi(t)$. Then

$$\int f(x)\,dx=\int f\{\phi(t)\}\phi'(t)\,dt.$$

(*b*) Integration by parts.

$$\int u\frac{dv}{dx}\,dx=uv-\int v\frac{du}{dx}\,dx.$$

The method used to integrate $f(x)$ depends on the form of $f(x)$. Unless an obvious change of variable can be made to simplify the integral, e.g. $\cos x=u$ in $\displaystyle\int\frac{\sin x\,dx}{a^2+\cos^2 x}$ or $x^2=u$ in $\displaystyle\int\frac{x\,dx}{1+x^4}$, first classify $f(x)$ as either (i) a rational function, (ii) an irrational algebraic function or (iii) a transcendental function. Then apply the method or one of the methods appropriate to that class.

The standard forms, given in Table III, should be learnt. In the remainder of this section we show how to reduce various integrals to these standard forms. The integrals given in Table IV are useful for reference.

14.2. To integrate a rational function $P(x)/Q(x)$ where the coefficients in $Q(x)$ are real, split it up into partial fractions (q.v.) in the form

$$\frac{P(x)}{Q(x)}=C(x)+\Sigma\frac{a_{ij}}{(x-a_i)^j}+\Sigma\frac{b_{ij}x+c_{ij}}{(x^2+p_ix+q_i)^j},$$

where $p_i^2<4q_i$ and the a_i are real and $C(x)$ is a polynomial.

$$\int\frac{bx+c}{x^2+px+q}\,dx=\frac{b}{2}\int\frac{2x+p}{x^2+px+q}\,dx+\frac{2c-bp}{2}\int\frac{dx}{x^2+px+q}.$$

The integrals on the right and that of $a/(x-\alpha)^j$ are given in Tables III and IV.

$$\int \frac{bx+c}{(x^2+px+q)^n}\,dx = \frac{b}{2(1-n)}(x^2+px+q)^{1-n} + \frac{2c-bp}{2}\int \frac{dx}{(x^2+px+q)^n} \quad (n>1).$$

In $u_n = \int \frac{dx}{(x^2+px+q)^n}$, either substitute $x+\frac{p}{2}=t$ and integrate by parts, obtaining the reduction formula

$$2\left(n-1\right)\left(q-\frac{p^2}{4}\right)u_n = \left(2n-3\right)u_{n-1} + \frac{x+p/2}{(x^2+px+q)^{n-1}},$$

or substitute $x+\frac{p}{2} = \sqrt{\left(q-\frac{p^2}{4}\right)}\tan\theta$,

giving
$$u_n = \left(q-\frac{p^2}{4}\right)^{\frac{1}{2}-n}\int \cos^{2n-2}\theta\,d\theta,$$

and use the reduction formula in Table IV.

Thus the integral of any real rational function can be found if the factors of the denominator are known. The result is a polynomial, plus a sum of rational functions, plus a sum of logarithms, plus a sum of inverse tangents.

14.3. Irrational algebraic function $\int z\,dx$, where z is an algebraic function of x.

It is often simpler to regard the integrand as $R(x, y)$, where R is a rational function of x and y, whilst y is an algebraic function of x satisfying $f(x, y)=0$. Here $f(x, y)$ is an irreducible polynomial and we confine our attention to one of its roots y. Classify the integral according to the type of irrational algebraic function y, which is chosen so that this classification is more useful than a classification based on the form of z.

E.g.
$$\int \frac{x-1}{(x-a)^{\frac{1}{2}}+(x-a)^{\frac{1}{3}}}\,dx$$

is considered as a rational function of x and $y \equiv (x-a)^{\frac{1}{6}}$. If a rational parametric representation $x=\phi(t)$, $y=\psi(t)$ of the curve $f(x, y)=0$ can be found, then $\int R(x, y)\,dx$ can be reduced to the integral of a rational function of t. This may not be the best practical method.

The most usual method is, by a substitution, to reduce the integral to one of a rational function or to a standard form.

14.31. $\int \mathbf{R}\left\{\mathbf{x}, \left(\dfrac{\mathbf{ax+b}}{\mathbf{cx+d}}\right)^{\frac{1}{q}}\right\} \mathbf{dx}.$

The substitution $(ax+b)/(cx+d)=t^q$ reduces the integral to that of a rational function of t.

14.32. $\int \mathbf{R_2\{x, \sqrt{(c+bx\pm ax^2)}\}\, dx}$**, where** $\mathbf{a>0}$**.**

Let $X\equiv c+bx\pm ax^2$.

Now $R_2(x, \sqrt{X})\equiv P(x, \sqrt{X})/Q(x, \sqrt{X})$ where P and Q are polynomials,

$$=(A+B\sqrt{X})/(C+D\sqrt{X})=(A+B\sqrt{X})(C-D\sqrt{X})/(C^2-D^2X),$$

where A, B, C, D are polynomials in x.

Hence
$$R_2(x, \sqrt{X})\equiv M+N\sqrt{X},$$
where M and N are rational in x,

and so
$$R_2(x, \sqrt{X})\equiv R_1(x)+R(x)/\sqrt{X},$$
where R_1 and R are rational in x.

The rational function $R_1(x)$ may be integrated by the methods of § 14.2. If the coefficients of $R(x)$ are real and the real linear and quadratic factors of its denominator can be found, $\int \{R(x)/\sqrt{X}\}\, dx$ may be split up into a sum of integrals of the form

$$u_n\equiv\int \frac{x^n\, dx}{\sqrt{X}}, \quad n=\text{a positive integer or zero},$$

$$v_n\equiv\int \frac{dx}{(x-\alpha)^n\sqrt{X}}, \quad n=\text{a positive integer},$$

$$w_n\equiv\int \frac{(px+q)\, dx}{(x^2+\beta x+\gamma)^n\sqrt{X}}, \quad n=\text{a positive integer}, \ \beta^2<4\gamma$$

The reduction formula

$$x^{n-1}\sqrt{(c+bx\pm ax^2)}=(n-1)cu_{n-2}+(n-\tfrac{1}{2})bu_{n-1}\pm nau_n,$$

reduces u_n to u_1 and u_0, the integrals of which are given in Table IV. The substitution $x-\alpha=1/t$ reduces v_n to an integral of the type $\int\{t^{n-1}/\sqrt{(c'+b't\pm a't^2)}\}dt$, which is of the form u_n.

Alternatively, evaluate v_1 by this substitution and deduce v_n by differentiation of v_1 with respect to α under the integration sign (q.v.)

The integral w_1, where $\beta^2 < 4\gamma$, may be evaluated by putting

$$x = \frac{\mu t + \nu}{t+1},$$

where μ and ν are chosen to satisfy

$$\pm 2a\mu\nu + b(\mu+\nu) + 2c = 0, \qquad 2\mu\nu + \beta(\mu+\nu) + 2\gamma = 0,$$

i.e. so that μ and ν are the roots of the equation

$$(\pm a\beta - b)\xi^2 - 2(c \mp a\gamma)\xi + b\gamma - c\beta = 0,$$

which are real and distinct if a, b, c, β, γ are real, as we suppose.*

The integral reduces to

$$H\int\frac{t\,dt}{(lt^2+m)\sqrt{(nt^2+p)}} + K\int\frac{dt}{(lt^2+m)\sqrt{(nt^2+p)}}. \qquad (1)$$

Put $t = \sqrt{(p/n)}\tan\theta$, followed by $\sin\theta = y$. Then w_n can be deduced from w_1 by differentiation with respect to γ.

Or putting $t = 1/v$ in the first of the integrals in (1), it reduces to one of the same type as the second. The latter can be rationalized by putting $t/\sqrt{(nt^2+p)} = u$, which gives

$$\int\frac{dt}{(lt^2+m)\sqrt{(nt^2+p)}} = \int\frac{du}{m+(lp-mn)u^2}.$$

Alternatively $w_1(\beta^2 < 4\gamma)$ may be integrated by Greenhill's substitution

$$y^2 = \frac{c+bx\pm ax^2}{x^2+\beta x+\gamma}.$$

The following method is useful when the integrand involves a quadratic irrationality:

Reduce $\sqrt{(c+bx\pm ax^2)}$ by a linear substitution $x = lt+m$ to one of the following forms and then apply the trigonometrical or hyperbolic substitution indicated.

$\sqrt{(A^2-t^2)}$	$t = A\sin\theta$.
$\sqrt{(A^2+t^2)}$	$t = \sinh\theta$ or $t = A\tan\theta$.
$\sqrt{(t^2-A^2)}$	$t = A\cosh\theta$ or $t = A\sec\theta$.

14.33. Binomial integrals

$\int x^m(a+bx^n)^p\,dx$, where m, n and p are rational numbers. Write $bx^n = at$. The integral reduces to $k\int t^q(1+t)^p dt$, where $q = (m-n+1)/n$, and $k = a^{(np+m+1)/n}b^{-(m+1)/n}n^{-1}$. If p or q is an integer, the integrand

* If $\pm a\beta - b = 0$, the method fails. In this case put $x + \frac{1}{2}\beta = t$.

is a simple linear irrationality. If $p+q$ is an integer, put $\frac{1+t}{t}=u^s$, where s is the denominator of the rational number p. The integral is then rationalized.

Laplace's principle states that an irrationality cannot be removed by differentiation. Hence no irrationality which does not occur in the integrand can appear after integration.

14.4. Transcendental functions

When the integrand is a transcendental function or a mixture of transcendental and algebraic functions, it is usually best to integrate by parts to evaluate the integral or to obtain a reduction formula. If the integrand is a trigonometrical function, a substitution may be better.

Trigonometrical functions

$$\int \cos^n x\,dx, \quad \int \sin^k x\,dx, \quad \int \cos^n x \sin^k x\,dx,$$

where n and k are positive or negative integers.

If $k+n$ is even, put $\tan x=t$, which reduces the integral to that of a rational function of t.

If one or both of n and k is odd, put

$$\cos x=u, \text{ if } k \text{ is odd}$$
$$\sin x=u, \text{ if } n \text{ is odd.}$$

The integral is reduced to that of a rational function of u.

One of the above substitutions enables one to integrate any polynomial in $\sin x$ and $\cos x$, but it is often simpler to use a reduction formula (see Table IV).

$\mathbf{I}=\int \mathbf{R(\tan x)\,dx}$, where R is a rational function of $\tan x$.

Substitute $\tan x=t$, giving

$$I=\int \frac{R(t)dt}{1+t^2}.$$

$\mathbf{I}=\int \mathbf{R(\sin x, \cos x)\,dx}$, where R is a rational function of $\sin x$ and $\cos x$, but not of $\tan x$.

Put $\tan\frac{x}{2}=t$, then $\frac{dx}{dt}=\frac{2}{1+t^2}$, $\sin x=\frac{2t}{1+t^2}$, $\cos x=\frac{1-t^2}{1+t^2}$,

hence
$$I=\int R\left(\frac{2t}{1+t^2}, \frac{1-t^2}{1+t^2}\right)\frac{2dt}{1+t^2}.$$

In some cases it may be simpler to express the integral as a sum of integrals of standard form,

e.g. $$I_1 = \int \frac{dx}{a+b\cos x+c\sin x} = \int \frac{dx}{a+\sqrt{(b^2+c^2)}\cos(x-\alpha)},$$

where $\cos\alpha = b/\sqrt{(b^2+c^2)}$, $\sin\alpha = c/\sqrt{(b^2+c^2)}$, and this is given in Table IV.

Expressing

$$p+q\cos x+r\sin x \equiv \lambda(a+b\cos x+c\sin x) + \mu(-b\sin x+c\cos x)+\nu,$$

we find that

$$\int \frac{p+q\cos x+r\sin x}{a+b\cos x+c\sin x}\,dx = \frac{cr+bq}{c^2+b^2}x + \frac{qc-br}{c^2+b^2}\ln|a+b\cos x+c\sin x| + \{p-(cr+bq)a/(c^2+b^2)\}I_1.$$

It is sometimes useful to express the trigonometrical functions as exponentials (see § 15.4), e.g. if

$$P = \int e^{ax}\cos(bx+c)\,dx,\quad Q = \int e^{ax}\sin(bx+c)\,dx,$$

then $$P+iQ = \int e^{ax+i(bx+c)}\,dx = \frac{a-ib}{a^2+b^2}e^{ax+i(bx+c)},$$

whence the values given in Table IV for P and Q may be found.

These results may also be obtained by integration by parts.

CHAPTER 15

THE DEFINITE RIEMANN INTEGRAL

15.1. The function $\phi(x)$ is one-valued and bounded in the closed interval (a, b). Divide (a, b) into n sub-intervals $(x_{i-1}, x_i), i=1, 2, \ldots, n$, where $a=x_0$, $b=x_n$ and $x_{i-1}<x_i$. Let M, m, M_i, m_i be the least upper and greatest lower bounds of $\phi(x)$ in (a, b) and in (x_{i-1}, x_i) respectively.

To every mode of subdivision $a=x_0, x_1, \ldots, x_n=b$ corresponds a lower sum L_n and an upper sum U_n, where

$$U_n=\sum_{i=1}^{n} M_i(x_i-x_{i-1}),\quad L_n=\sum_{i=1}^{n} m_i(x_i-x_{i-1}).$$

The sums U_n have a greatest lower bound I and the sums L_n a least upper bound J, where $J\leqslant I$. The sums U_n and L_n tend respectively to I and J as the number of sub-intervals tends to infinity in such a way that the length of the longest tends to zero, i.e. given $\epsilon>0$, a number $\delta>0$ exists, such that if the least upper bound of $|x_i-x_{i-1}|$ is less than δ, then $U_n<I+\epsilon$ and $L_n>J-\epsilon$. The function $\phi(x)$ is *Riemann integrable* in (a, b) if $I=J$, and the common value of I and J is written $\int_a^b \phi(x)\,dx$.

A function which in (a, b) is

(i) bounded and continuous,

or (ii) bounded and monotonic,

or (iii) bounded, and its points of discontinuity can be enclosed in a finite set of intervals whose total length is as small as we please,

is integrable in (a, b).

Properties of $\int_a^b \phi(x)\,dx$

$$m(b-a)\leqslant\int_a^b \phi(x)\,dx\leqslant M(b-a).$$

$$\int_a^b \phi(x)\,dx=\lim\sum_{i=1}^{n}\phi(\xi_i)(x_i-x_{i-1}),$$

where ξ_i is any point in (x_{i-1}, x_i), where the limit is to be taken as $n\to\infty$, in such a way that the length of the longest sub-interval $\to 0$.

If a is fixed and b varies, the integral is a function of its upper limit b.

Fundamental theorem of the integral calculus

If $\phi(t)$ is continuous at $t=x$, then

$$\frac{d}{dx}\int_a^x \phi(t)\,dt=\phi(x),$$

i.e. if $$f(x)=\int_a^x \phi(t)\,dt, \text{ then } f'(x)=\phi(x),$$

and hence $$f(x)+C=\int \phi(x)\,dx\equiv F(x),$$

where $F(x)$ is the indefinite integral obtained by the process which is the reverse of differentiation and C is an arbitrary constant.

Since $f(a)=0$,

$$\int_a^b \phi(x)\,dx=F(b)-F(a),$$

where $F(x)$ is any function whose derivate is $\phi(x)$.

This theorem enables one to evaluate a definite integral if the indefinite integral of the integrand is known.

If $a>b$, $\int_a^b \phi(x)\,dx=-\int_b^a \phi(x)\,dx$,

$$\therefore \frac{d}{dx}\int_x^a \phi(t)\,dt=-\phi(x).$$

15.2. Area bounded by plane curves

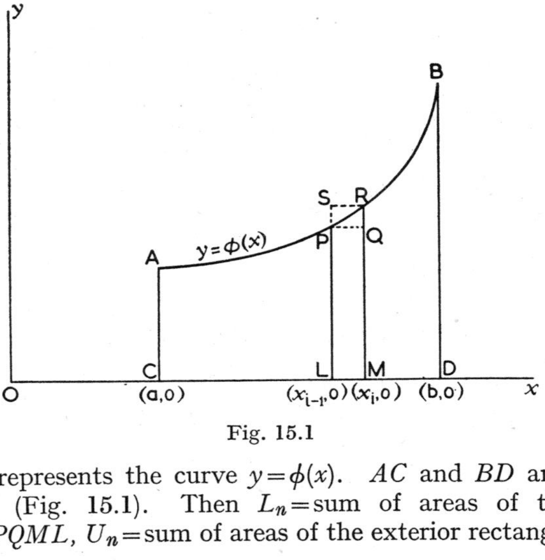

Fig. 15.1

Arc AB represents the curve $y=\phi(x)$. AC and BD are the lines $x=a$, $x=b$ (Fig. 15.1). Then L_n=sum of areas of the interior rectangles $PQML$, U_n=sum of areas of the exterior rectangles $SRML$.

Definition. The *area A* enclosed by the lines $y=0$, $x=a$, $x=b$, and the curve $y=\phi(x)$, where $\phi(x)>0$, is the common limit, if it exists, of the sums of the areas of the interior and exterior rectangles as $n\to\infty$ in such a way that the greatest of $(x_i-x_{i-1})\to 0$.

If $\phi(x)$ is integrable in (a, b), the sums have a common limit, viz. $\int_a^b \phi(x)\,dx$.

If $\phi(x)<0$ in (a, b), area $= -\int_a^b \phi(x)\,dx$.

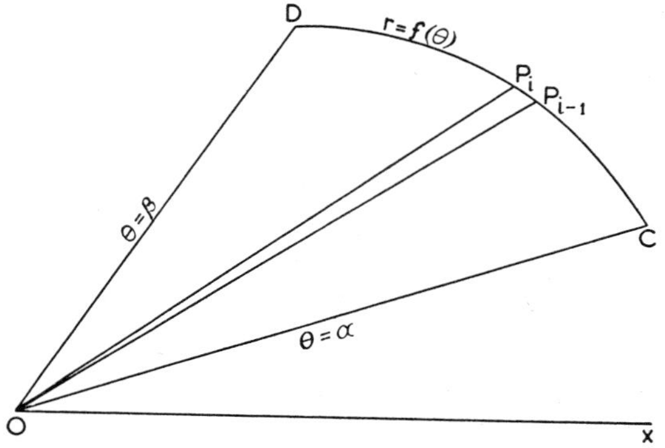

Fig. 15.2

The area B (see Fig. 15.2) bounded by the arc of the curve $r=f(\theta)$ from $\theta=\alpha$ to $\theta=\beta$, and the radii vectores $\theta=\alpha$ and $\theta=\beta$ is given by

$$B=\tfrac{1}{2}\int_\alpha^\beta r^2 d\theta=\tfrac{1}{2}\int_\alpha^\beta [f(\theta)]^2 d\theta.$$

The area of a loop of a curve, given parametrically by $x=\psi(t)$, $y=\chi(t)$, where the point (x, y) encircles the loop as t varies from γ to δ, is

$$\tfrac{1}{2}\int_\gamma^\delta \left(x\frac{dy}{dt}-y\frac{dx}{dt}\right) dt=\tfrac{1}{2}\int_\gamma^\delta \{\psi(t)\chi'(t)-\chi(t)\psi'(t)\}\,dt.$$

Simpson's rule gives an approximation to a definite integral. Divide the interval (a, b) into $2n$ equal parts each of length h by the points $x_0=a, x_1, x_2, \ldots, x_{2n}=b$. Let $y_r=\phi(x_r)$. Then

$$\int_a^b \phi(x)\,dx \simeq \tfrac{1}{3}h\{y_0+y_{2n}+2(y_2+y_4+\ldots+y_{2n-2})$$
$$+4(y_1+y_3+\ldots+y_{2n-1})\}.$$

15.3. Change of variable

If $x=f(t)$ is a single-valued differentiable function of t, $a=f(\alpha)$, $b=f(\beta)$ and, as t varies from α to β, $f(t)$ either increases steadily or decreases steadily from a to b, then

$$\int_a^b \phi(x)\,dx=\int_\alpha^\beta \phi[f(t)]\,f'(t)\,dt.$$

If $a<b$ and $\phi(x)\geqslant 0$ in (a, b),

$$\int_a^b \phi(x)\,dx\geqslant 0.$$

If $\psi(x)\leqslant\phi(x)$ in $a\leqslant x\leqslant b$,

$$\int_a^b \psi(x)\,dx\leqslant\int_a^b \phi(x)\,dx.$$

If $H\leqslant\phi(x)\leqslant K$ in $a\leqslant x\leqslant b$, then

$$H(b-a)\leqslant\int_a^b \phi(x)\,dx\leqslant K(b-a).$$

Mean value theorems for integrals

If $\phi(x)$ is continuous in (a, b),

$$\int_a^b \phi(x)\,dx=(b-a)\,\phi(c),$$

for some value c satisfying $a<c<b$.

If $\phi(x)>0$ and $H\leqslant f(x)\leqslant K$ in (a, b),

$$H\int_a^b \phi(x)\,dx\leqslant\int_a^b f(x)\,\phi(x)\,dx\leqslant K\int_a^b \phi(x)\,dx,$$

and if also $f(x)$ is continuous in (a, b),

$$\int_a^b f(x)\,\phi(x)\,dx=f(c)\int_a^b \phi(x)\,dx,\ \text{where } a<c<b.$$

Second mean value theorem

If $f'(x)$ is continuous and of constant sign throughout (a, b), then

$$\int_a^b f(x)\,\phi(x)\,dx=f(a)\int_a^c \phi(x)\,dx+f(b)\int_c^b \phi(x)\,dx,$$

where $a<c<b$.

Bonnet's form

If $f'(x)$ is of constant sign in (a, b) and if $f(b)$ and $f(a)-f(b)$ have the same sign,

$$\int_a^b f(x)\,\phi(x)\,dx = f(a)\int_a^c \phi(x)\,dx,$$

where $a<c<b$.

15.4. Logarithmic, exponential and hyperbolic functions of a real variable

Definition. If $x>0$, $\ln x = \int_1^x \frac{dt}{t}$.

$$\ln(1/x) = -\ln x.$$

$$\ln x \to +\infty \text{ as } x \to +\infty.$$

$$\ln x \to -\infty \text{ as } x \to +0.$$

$$\ln(xy) = \ln x + \ln y.$$

$$\frac{d}{dx}\ln x = \frac{1}{x}.$$

Definition. e is the number such that $\ln e = 1$.

Definition. The exponential function, $\exp y$, is defined as the inverse of the logarithmic function, i.e. $x=\exp y$ if $y=\ln x$.

$$\text{Exp } 0=1, \quad \exp 1 = e, \quad \exp y \to +\infty \text{ as } y \to +\infty.$$

$$\text{Exp } y \to 0 \text{ as } y \to -\infty.$$

Exp y is a one-valued differentiable function of y.

$$\text{Exp}(y_1+y_2) = \exp y_1 \times \exp y_2.$$

$$\frac{d}{dy}\exp y = \exp y.$$

Definition. $a^y = \exp(y \ln a)$ if $a>0$.

Hence $$e^y = \exp y.$$

The laws of indices hold: $a^y a^z = a^{y+z}$, $(a^y)^z = a^{yz}$.

Definition. $$y = \log_a x \text{ if } x = a^y.$$

$$\log_a e = 1/\log_e a.$$

Hyperbolic functions

Definitions.

$\sinh x = (e^x - e^{-x})/2$, $\cosh x = (e^x + e^{-x})/2$, $\tanh x = \sinh x/\cosh x$.

$\operatorname{cosech} x = 1/\sinh x$, $\operatorname{sech} x = 1/\cosh x$, $\coth x = 1/\tanh x$.

$\cosh x$ is an even function; $\sinh x$ and $\tanh x$ are odd functions.

Identities

$$\cosh^2 x - \sinh^2 x = 1.$$

$$\operatorname{sech}^2 x + \tanh^2 x = 1.$$

$$\coth^2 x - \operatorname{cosech}^2 x = 1.$$

$$\cosh (x+y) = \cosh x \cosh y + \sinh x \sinh y.$$

$$\sinh (x+y) = \sinh x \cosh y + \cosh x \sinh y.$$

$$\cosh 2x = 2 \cosh^2 x - 1 = 2 \sinh^2 x + 1.$$

$$\sinh 2x = 2 \sinh x \cosh x.$$

$$(\cosh x + \sinh x)^n = \exp nx = \cosh nx + \sinh nx.$$

$$(\cosh x - \sinh x)^n = \exp (-nx) = \cosh nx - \sinh nx.$$

These may be remembered by this mnemonic:

Take any standard formula connecting sine and cosine. In it replace sin by i sinh and cos by cosh. The resulting formula is the corresponding hyperbolic formula. This is true also for complex values of the argument.

Inverse hyperbolic functions

Definition.

$$y = \sinh^{-1} x = \operatorname{arc} \sinh x \quad \text{if } x = \sinh y.$$

$$y = \cosh^{-1} x = \operatorname{arc} \cosh x \quad \text{if } x = \cosh y.$$

$$y = \tanh^{-1} x = \operatorname{arc} \tanh x \quad \text{if } x = \tanh y.$$

Then $\sinh^{-1} x = \ln \{x + \sqrt{(x^2+1)}\}$,

$\cosh^{-1} x = \ln \{x \pm \sqrt{(x^2-1)}\}$. Take the $\pm$ sign according as $\cosh^{-1} x$ is positive or negative.

$$\ln \{x + \sqrt{(x^2-1)}\} = \ln [1/\{x - \sqrt{(x^2-1)}\}] = -\ln \{x - \sqrt{(x^2-1)}\}.$$

$$\tanh^{-1} x = \tfrac{1}{2} \ln \frac{1+x}{1-x}, \quad |x| < 1.$$

$$\coth^{-1} x = \tfrac{1}{2} \ln \frac{x+1}{x-1}, \quad |x| > 1.$$

15.5. The Gamma and Beta Functions are defined for real variables as

$$\Gamma(x)=\int_0^\infty t^{x-1}\,e^{-t}\,dt, \qquad x>0. \quad \text{(See § 18.1.)}$$

$$B(x,y)=\int_0^1 t^{x-1}\,(1-t)^{y-1}\,dt, \quad x>0,\ y>0.$$

$$B(x,y)=\Gamma(x)\,\Gamma(y)/\Gamma(x+y), \quad x>0,\ y>0.$$

$$\Gamma(x+1)=x\Gamma(x),$$

$$\Gamma(x)\,\Gamma(1-x)=\pi/\{\sin x\pi\}, \qquad 0<x<1.$$

$$\Gamma(1)=\Gamma(2)=1, \quad \Gamma(\tfrac{1}{2})=\sqrt{\pi}.$$

$\Gamma(n)=(n-1)!$ if n is a positive integer.

$\Gamma(n+\tfrac{1}{2})=1\,.\,3\,.\,5\ldots(2n-1)\sqrt{\pi}/2^n=(2n)!\sqrt{\pi}/(2^{2n}n!)$ (n a positive integer).

$$\Gamma(x)\,\Gamma\left(x+\frac{1}{n}\right)\Gamma\left(x+\frac{2}{n}\right)\ldots\Gamma\left(x+\frac{n-1}{n}\right)=\Gamma(nx)(2\pi)^{\frac{1}{2}(n-1)}n^{\frac{1}{2}-nx}$$

(n a positive integer).

Stirling's formula

$$\Gamma(x+1)\sim x^x e^{-x}\sqrt{(2\pi x)}\left\{1+\frac{1}{12x}+\frac{1}{288x^2}-\frac{139}{51840x^3}-\frac{571}{2488320x^4}+\ldots\right\}$$

if x is large.

$$\ln\Gamma(x+1)\sim\tfrac{1}{2}\ln(2\pi)-x-(x+\tfrac{1}{2})\ln x+\frac{B_1}{1\,.\,2\,.\,x}-\frac{B_2}{3\,.\,4\,.\,x^3}+\frac{B_3}{5\,.\,6\,.\,x^5}-\ldots$$

where B_i are Bernoulli's numbers (q.v.). This is an asymptotic* series. The absolute value of the error is less than the first term neglected.

* A divergent series (q.v.)

$$a_0+\frac{a_1}{x}+\frac{a_2}{x^2}+\ldots$$

is called an asymptotic expansion of a function $f(x)$, which is defined for all sufficiently large positive values of x, if for every *fixed* positive integral or zero value of n,

$$\{f(x)-(a_0+a_1x^{-1}+a_2x^{-2}+\ldots+a_nx^{-n})\}x^n\to 0$$

as $x\to+\infty$. We write

$$f(x)\sim a_0+\frac{a_1}{x}+\frac{a_2}{x^2}+\ldots.$$

$$\ln \Gamma(1+x) = -\gamma x + \tfrac{1}{2}S_2x^2 - \tfrac{1}{3}S_3x^3 + \tfrac{1}{4}S_4x^4 \ldots \quad (x^2<1),$$

where γ = Euler's constant $= \lim_{n\to\infty}\left(1+\frac{1}{2}+\frac{1}{3}+\ldots+\frac{1}{n}-\ln n\right)$

$$=0{\cdot}5772157\ldots.$$

and $S_r = \sum_1^\infty n^{-r}$.

$$\frac{1}{\Gamma(x)} = xe^{\gamma x}\prod_{n=1}^{\infty}\left(1+\frac{x}{n}\right)e^{-x/n}. \quad \text{(See § 18.9.)}$$

$$\Gamma(x) = \lim_{n\to\infty}\frac{1\,.\,2\ldots(n-1)\,n^x}{x(x+1)\ldots(x+n-1)} = \lim_{n\to\infty}\frac{n!\,n^x}{x(x+1)\ldots(x+n)}$$

CHAPTER 16

MULTIPLE, LINE AND SURFACE INTEGRALS

16.1. Double integrals

Let $f(x, y)$ be a function of the two variables x and y which is one-valued and bounded in the closed domain A bounded by a simple closed curve C. Divide the area A into small areas σ_r by a network of curves. An area σ_r is said to be less than b in all its dimensions if it can be enclosed in a circle of diameter b. Let M, m, M_r, m_r be the least upper and greatest lower bounds of $f(x, y)$ in A and σ_r respectively. Form the sums

$$U_n = \sum_{r=1}^{n} M_r \sigma_r, \quad L_n = \sum_{r=1}^{n} m_r \sigma_r.$$

The upper sums U_n have a greatest lower bound I and the lower sums L_n a least upper bound J, and $J \leqslant I$. Moreover, if all the dimensions of σ_r tend to zero, $U_n \to I$ and $L_n \to J$ as $n \to \infty$. If $I = J$, the function $f(x, y)$ is said to be *Riemann integrable* in A and the common limit is the double integral, written

$$\iint_A f(x, y)\, d\sigma \quad \text{or} \quad \iint_A f(x, y)\, (dx\, dy).$$

$f(x, y)$ is said to have *normal discontinuities* in A if its points or curves of discontinuity can be enclosed in a finite set of regions whose total area is as small as we please. If $f(x, y)$ is continuous in A or has only normal discontinuities in A, then it is R-integrable in A.

If the double integral exists, its value may be calculated by expressing it as a repeated integral.

If A is a rectangle, vertices (a, c), (b, c), (b, d), (a, d),

$$\iint_A f(x, y)\, d\sigma = \int_c^d \left(\int_a^b f(x, y)\, dx \right) dy$$

$$\equiv \int_c^d dy \int_a^b f(x, y)\, dx = \int_a^b dx \int_c^d f(x, y)\, dy.$$

In the second and third integrals we integrate first with respect to x, treating y as a constant, and then evaluate $\int_c^d g(y)\, dy$, where

$$g(y) = \int_a^b f(x, y)\, dx.$$

In the fourth integral we integrate first with respect to y treating x as a constant.

If $f(x, y)$ is continuous in A and A is a rectangle, then the repeated integrals exist and are equal.

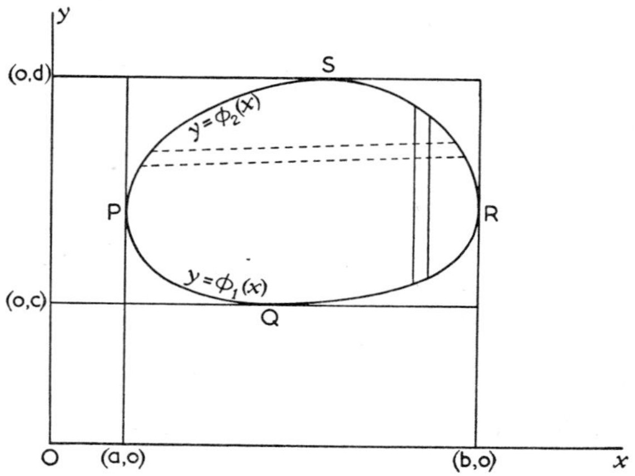

Fig. 16.1

If A is the area bounded by a closed curve C which is not met by any line parallel to either axis in more than two points except when that line forms part of C, the curve C can be divided into two parts, viz. PQR of equation $y=\phi_1(x)$, RSP of equation $y=\phi_2(x)$, where $a \leqslant x \leqslant b$, and each of which is met by a line parallel to the y-axis in only one point. Enclose A in a rectangle with sides $x=a$, $x=b$, $y=c$, $y=d$. Then

$$\iint_A f(x, y)\, d\sigma = \iint_A f(x, y)\, (dx\, dy) = \int_a^b dx \int_{\phi_1(x)}^{\phi_2(x)} f(x, y)\, dy.$$

We may proceed in the reverse order. If the equation of QRS is $x=\psi_2(y)$, and of SPQ is $x=\psi_1(y)$,

$$\iint_A f(x, y)\, dx\, dy = \int_c^d dy \int_{\psi_1(y)}^{\psi_2(y)} f(x, y)\, dx.$$

When expressing a double integral as a repeated integral it is advisable to draw a figure to aid one in inserting the correct limits.

Triple integrals and integrals of higher multiplicity are defined by a straight-forward generalization of double integrals and, if they exist, may be expressed as repeated integrals.

16.2. Differentiation under the integral sign

If $f(x, y)$ and $\dfrac{\partial f}{\partial y}$ are continuous in the rectangle $a \leqslant x \leqslant b$, $c \leqslant y \leqslant d$,

$$\frac{d}{dy}\int_a^b f(x, y)\,dx = \int_a^b \frac{\partial f}{\partial y}\,dx$$

for all points y satisfying $c < y < d$.

If
$$F(y) = \int_{\psi_1(y)}^{\psi_2(y)} f(x, y)\,dx,$$

where $\psi_1(y)$ and $\psi_2(y)$ have continuous derivates with respect to y, and $f(x, y)$ and $\dfrac{\partial f}{\partial y}$ are continuous functions of x and y throughout the region considered, then

$$F'(y) = \psi'_2(y)f\{\psi_2(y), y\} - \psi'_1(y)f\{\psi_1(y), y\} + \int_{\psi_1(y)}^{\psi_2(y)} \frac{\partial f}{\partial y}\,dx.$$

16.3. Change of variables in double and triple integrals

The variables x and y are changed to new variables u and v, where $x = \phi_1(u, v)$, $y = \phi_2(u, v)$. Here ϕ_1 and ϕ_2 are one-valued functions of u and v with continuous partial derivates for all points (u, v) of a region A_1 of the u, v plane bounded by a contour C_1. The equations set up a correspondence between the region A_1 and a region A of the (x, y) plane. If this correspondence is (1, 1) and if the Jacobian

$$J = \begin{vmatrix} x_u & x_v \\ y_u & y_v \end{vmatrix}$$

does not change sign inside C_1, then

$$\iint_A f(x, y)\,dx\,dy = \iint_{A_1} f\{\phi_1(u, v), \phi_2(u, v)\}|J|\,du\,dv.$$

If the variables are changed from Cartesians to polars,

$$\iint_A f(x, y)\,dx\,dy = \iint_{A_1} f(r\cos\theta, r\sin\theta)r\,dr\,d\theta.$$

The equations

$$x = \phi_1(u, v, w),\ y = \phi_2(u, v, w),\ z = \phi_3(u, v, w)$$

give a transformation of the volume V of the (x, y, z) space into a volume V' of the (u, v, w) space. If (i) the partial derivates $\dfrac{\partial \phi_1}{\partial u}, \ldots, \dfrac{\partial \phi_3}{\partial w}$ are continuous at all points in V' and on its boundary surface S', (ii) the correspondence between V and V' is (1, 1), (iii) the Jacobian

$$J=\frac{\partial(\phi_1, \phi_2, \phi_3)}{\partial(u, v, w)}$$

does not change sign in V', then

$$\iiint_V f(x, y, z)\, dx\, dy\, dz=\iiint_{V'} f\{\phi_1, \phi_2, \phi_3\}|J|du\, dv\, dw.$$

The formula for the integral in terms of spherical polar-co-ordinates r, θ, ϕ is

$$\iiint_V f(x, y, z)dx\, dy\, dz=\iiint_{V'} f(r \sin\theta \cos\phi, r \sin\theta \sin\phi, r \cos\theta)r^2 \sin\theta\, dr\, d\theta\, d\phi,$$

and of cylindrical co-ordinates, ρ, ϕ, z is

$$\iiint_V f(x, y, z)dx\, dy\, dz=\iiint_{V'} f(\rho \cos\phi, \rho \sin\phi, z)\rho\ \ d\rho\ \ d\phi\ \ dz.$$

16.4. Volume bounded by a curved surface

Consider a surface $z=f(x, y)$, where $f(x, y)$ is single-valued, continuous and positive when $(x, y, 0)$ lies in an area A in the plane $z=0$ bounded by a closed curve C. A cylinder with generators parallel to Oz can be drawn through the curve C meeting the surface in a curve C'. Then the volume V enclosed between the cylinder, the plane $z=0$ and the part of the surface bounded by the curve C' is given by

$$V=\iint_A f(x, y)\, dx\, dy.$$

If the area of the section of a surface by the plane $x=x_1$ is a function $\phi(x_1)$ of x_1 only, then the volume of the surface between the planes $x=a$ and $x=b$ is

$$V=\int_a^b \phi(x)\, dx.$$

The arc of a continuous plane curve $y=f(x)$, $z=0$, where $f(x)\geqslant 0$, between $x=a$ and $x=b$ is rotated about the axis of x. Then the volume enclosed by the surface of revolution generated and the planes $x=a$ and $x=b$ is

$$\pi\int_a^b y^2\, dx=\pi\int_a^b \{f(x)\}^2\, dx. \qquad (1)$$

If the plane area bounded by the curve $r=f(\theta)$ and the lines $\theta=\alpha$ and $\theta=\beta$ is rotated about the initial line, the volume generated is

$$\tfrac{2}{3}\pi\int_\alpha^\beta r^3 \sin\theta\, d\theta=\tfrac{2}{3}\pi\int_\alpha^\beta \{f(\theta)\}^3 \sin\theta\, d\theta \qquad (2)$$

Note that (1) gives the volume generated by the rotation of the area $APRBDC$ about Ox in Fig. 15.1 and (2) that generated by the rotation of area OCP_iD about Ox in Fig. 15.2.

Pappus' theorem. The volume generated by a plane area, which is rotated about an axis in its plane which does not intersect it, is equal to the area multiplied by the length of the path of the centre of gravity *of the area.*

16.5. The *length* of a curve from A to B is the limit, if it exists, of an inscribed polygon whose vertices follow one another in order when the number of sides tends to infinity in such a way that the length of the greatest tends to zero. The polygon is not closed unless the curve is. Curves which have length in this sense are said to be *rectifiable.*

If $f'(x)$ is continuous in the interval $a \leqslant x \leqslant b$, then the plane curve $y=f(x)$ is rectifiable in $a \leqslant x \leqslant b$ and its length is

$$\int_a^b \left\{1+\left(\frac{dy}{dx}\right)^2\right\}^{\frac{1}{2}} dx.$$

The length of a rectifiable curve, whose equation in polar co-ordinates is $r=f(\theta)$ is

$$S=\int_\alpha^\beta \left\{r^2+\left(\frac{dr}{d\theta}\right)^2\right\}^{\frac{1}{2}} d\theta$$

from $\theta=\alpha$ to $\theta=\beta$.

If the curve is $x=\phi(t)$, $y=\psi(t)$, the length of arc from t_1 to t_2 is

$$\int_{t_1}^{t_2} \left[\left\{\phi'(t)\right\}^2+\left\{\psi'(t)\right\}^2\right]^{\frac{1}{2}} dt.$$

16.6. Curvilinear or line integrals along a plane curve

$P(x, y)$ and $Q(x, y)$ are functions with partial derivates which are continuous in a region A. Let C be a curve $x=\phi(t)$, $y=\psi(t)$ lying within A such that either $\phi'(t)$ and $\psi'(t)$ are continuous in the interval $t_1 \leqslant t \leqslant t_2$, or C is a continuous curve consisting of a finite number of parts in each of which $\phi'(t)$ and $\psi'(t)$ are continuous.

Definition. The curvilinear or line integral

$$\int_C P(x, y)\, dx+Q(x, y)\, dy$$

$$\equiv \int_{t_1}^{t_2} \left[P\left\{\phi(t), \psi(t)\right\}\phi'(t)+Q\left\{\phi(t), \psi(t)\right\}\psi'(t)\right] dt.$$

If $Pdx+Qdy$ is a complete differential, $\frac{\partial P}{\partial y}=\frac{\partial Q}{\partial x}$ and the value of the curvilinear integral depends only on t_1 and t_2 and is independent of the path C, provided C lies within A. If, in this case, the curve C is closed, then the integral is zero.

The *positive* direction along a closed curve C is the direction in which a person moves round the curve if the interior of the curve is on his left.

Gauss' theorem. If $\frac{\partial Q}{\partial x}$, $\frac{\partial P}{\partial y}$ are continuous within and on the boundary C of a region A,

$$\iint_A \left(\frac{\partial Q}{\partial x}-\frac{\partial P}{\partial y}\right) dx\, dy=\int_C (Pdx+Qdy),$$

where the integral is taken in the positive direction along C.

16.7. Area of a surface

Consider a portion of a surface $z=f(x, y)$ bounded by a closed curve C'. Let the projection of C' on the plane $z=0$ be a curve C. If $p=\frac{\partial z}{\partial x}$ and $q=\frac{\partial z}{\partial y}$ exist and are continuous, then the *area* of the surface bounded by C' is given by

$$S\equiv\iint_A \sec\gamma\, dx\, dy=\iint_A \left\{1+\left(\frac{\partial z}{\partial x}\right)^2+\left(\frac{\partial z}{\partial y}\right)^2\right\}^{\frac{1}{2}} dx\, dy,$$

where A is the area in the plane $z=0$ enclosed by C and γ is the angle between Oz and the outward drawn normal to the surface at (x, y, z).

If the surface is

$$x=\phi_1(u, v),\ y=\phi_2(u, v),\ z=\phi_3(u, v),$$

then the area is given by

$$S=\iint_A \{1+p^2+q^2\}^{\frac{1}{2}} dx\, dy$$

$$=\iint_{A_1}\left[\left\{\frac{\partial(y, z)}{\partial(u, v)}\right\}^2+\left\{\frac{\partial(z, x)}{\partial(u, v)}\right\}^2+\left\{\frac{\partial(x, y)}{\partial(u, v)}\right\}^2\right]^{\frac{1}{2}} du\, dv,$$

where A is the projection of the area on the (x, y) plane and A_1 is the corresponding area in the (u, v) plane.

If the surface is given in spherical polar co-ordinates by $r=f(\theta, \phi)$, the area is

$$S=\iint_{A_1}\left\{r^2\left(\frac{\partial r}{\partial\phi}\right)^2+r^2\sin^2\theta\left(\frac{\partial r}{\partial\theta}\right)^2+r^4\sin^2\theta\right\}^{\frac{1}{2}} d\theta\, d\phi$$

over the appropriate field of integration in the (θ, ϕ) plane.

If the surface is $z=f(\rho, \phi)$ in cylindrical co-ordinates, the area is

$$S=\iint_{A_1}\left\{\left(\frac{\partial z}{\partial \phi}\right)^2+\rho^2\left(\frac{\partial z}{\partial \rho}\right)^2+\rho^2\right\}^{\frac{1}{2}} d\rho\, d\phi$$

over the area A_1 in the (ρ, ϕ) plane.

The area between the planes $x=a$, $x=b$ of the surface of revolution generated by rotating the plane curve $y=\phi(x)$, $z=0$ about the axis of x is

$$S=2\pi\int_a^b y\left\{1+\left(\frac{dy}{dx}\right)^2\right\}^{\frac{1}{2}} dx=2\pi\int y\, ds$$

between the appropriate limits of the arc s of the curve.

Pappus' theorem. The area of the surface, generated by revolving an arc of a plane curve about an axis in its plane which does not intersect it, is equal to the length of the arc multiplied by the length of the path of the centre of gravity *of the arc.*

16.8. Surface integrals

S is the portion, bounded by a closed curve C, of a surface $z=f(x, y)$ and is met by any line parallel to Oz in one point only. R is the region of the plane $z=0$ which is the projection of this portion S of the surface. We suppose that the partial derivates f_x, f_y exist and that the surface has two well-defined sides (see § 21.7).

Definition. If $\phi(x, y, z)$ is one-valued and continuous on S, the *surface integral* over the outside of S

$$\iint_S \phi(x, y, z)\, dS=\iint_R \phi[x, y, f(x, y)] \sec\gamma\, dx\, dy$$

$$=\iint_R \phi[x, y, f(x, y)]\sqrt{\{1+f_x^2+f_y^2\}}\, dx\, dy,$$

where γ is the angle between Oz and the positive direction of the normal.

Gauss' theorem. If $P(x, y, z)$, $Q(x, y, z)$, $R(x, y, z)$ are one-valued functions with continuous partial derivates P_x, Q_y, R_z within and on the boundary surface S of a region V of space, then

$$\iiint_V\left(\frac{\partial P}{\partial x}+\frac{\partial Q}{\partial y}+\frac{\partial R}{\partial z}\right) dx\, dy\, dz=\iint_S (P\, dy\, dz+Q\, dz\, dx+R\, dx\, dy),$$

where the surface integral is taken over the outside of the surface S.

See also § 21.7.

CHAPTER 17

ANALYTIC FUNCTIONS OF A COMPLEX VARIABLE

17.1. The function $w=f(z)$ is said to be *analytic* in a domain D if it is differentiable at each point z_0 of D, i.e. if

$$f'(z_0)=\lim_{h\to 0}\frac{f(z_0+h)-f(z_0)}{h}$$

exists, i.e. if, given $\epsilon>0$, numbers $\delta>0$ and $f'(z_0)$ exist such that

$$\left|\frac{f(z_0+h)-f(z_0)}{h}-f'(z_0)\right|<\epsilon$$

for all z satisfying $|z-z_0|<\delta$. The function is *regular* in D if it is analytic and one-valued at every point of D.

A function which is regular in D is continuous in D. Further, if $z=x+i\,y$ and $f(z)\equiv u(x,y)+i\,v(x,y)$, where u and v are real functions of x and y, the partial derivates exist and satisfy the *Cauchy-Riemann equations:*

$$u_x=v_y,\quad v_x=-u_y$$

at all points of D.

Then

$$f'(z)=u_x+i\,v_x=u_x-i\,u_y=v_y+i\,v_x=v_y-i\,u_y.$$

Conversely, if $f(z)=u(x,y)+i\,v(x,y)$, where u and v are real functions of x and y, and if u_x, v_x, u_y, v_y are continuous and satisfy the Cauchy-Riemann equations at all points of a domain D, then $f(z)$ is analytic in D.

A point at which $f(z)$ is not analytic is called a *singularity* of $f(z)$.

If $f(z)$ is one-valued and continuous in a domain D and if z_0 and z_1 are two points of D joined by a simple continuous contour C lying entirely in D, the definite integral

$$\int_{z_0}^{z_1} f(z)\,dz=\int_C f(z)\,dz=\int_C (u\,dx-v\,dy)+i\int_C (u\,dy+v\,dx)$$

exists. (See definition of line integral in § 16.6.)

Cauchy's theorem. If $f(z)$ is regular within and on a simple closed contour C, (see §12·4), then

$$\int_C f(z)\,dz=0.$$

Hence, if $f(z)$ is regular in a simply connected domain D and z_0 and z_1 are any two points in D,

$$\int_{z_0}^{z_1} f(z)\, dz$$

is independent of the path provided the path joining z_0 to z_1 lies entirely in D. The function

$$F(z)=\int_{z_0}^{z} f(z)\, dz$$

taken along any path within D is a function of the upper limit z. $F(z)$ is regular in D and

$$F'(z)=f(z).$$

Cauchy's formula. If $f(z)$ is regular within and on a simple closed contour C and a is a point WITHIN C, then

$$f(a)=\frac{1}{2\pi i}\int_C \frac{f(z)}{(z-a)}\, dz.$$

Moreover, the derivates of $f(z)$ of all orders exist at all points inside C and are given by

$$f^{(n)}(a)=\frac{n!}{2\pi i}\int_C \frac{f(z)}{(z-a)^{n+1}}\, dz.$$

Taylor's theorem states: If $f(z)$ is regular in a domain D and a is any interior point of D, then $f(z)$ can be expanded in a convergent power series (q.v.) (Taylor series):—

$$f(z)\equiv f(a)+(z-a)f'(a)+\ \dots\ +\frac{(z-a)^n}{n!}f^{(n)}(a)+\ \dots \qquad (1)$$

for all points z satisfying $|z-a|<R$, where R is the distance from a to the nearest singular point of $f(z)$. R is the radius of convergence of the series on the right of (1). All the derivates of $f(z)$ may be found by term-by-term differentiation of (1) and all the series so obtained have the same radius of convergence R. All the series so obtained are uniformly convergent (q.v.) in $|z-a|\leqslant R_1$, where $R_1<R$.

Taylor's theorem for an analytic function $f(z)$ is simpler than his theorem for a function $f(x)$ of the real variable x as no remainder after n terms has to be considered. In the proof of the theorem it is shown once for all that, if $|z-a|$ is less than the distance from a to the nearest singularity of $f(z)$, and R_n is the remainder after n terms, then $R_n\to 0$ and the series converges absolutely (q.v.).

If $0<r<R$ and if $M(r)$ is the maximum value of $|f(z)|$ on the circle $|z-a|=r$, then

$$|f^{(n)}(a)|\leqslant n!\ M(r)/r^n.$$

If $f(z)$ has a zero of order n at a, the first non-zero term in the Taylor expansion is $f^{(n)}(a)\,(z-a)^n/n!$
Hence $f(a)=f'(a)=f''(a)=\ldots=f^{(n-1)}(a)=0,\ f^{(n)}(a)\neq 0.$

Laurent's theorem. If $f(z)$ is regular within an open annulus D given by $r<|z-a|<R$, then at all points in D

$$f(z)=\sum_{-\infty}^{\infty} c_n(z-a)^n,$$

where

$$c_n=\frac{1}{2\pi i}\int_{\Gamma}\frac{f(z)}{(z-a)^{n+1}}\,dz$$

and Γ is any circle within the annulus. The series is uniformly convergent within and on the boundary of the closed annulus

$$R_1\leqslant|z-a|\leqslant R_2,\ \text{where } r<R_1<R_2<R.$$

Liouville's theorem. A function $f(z)$, which is regular at all finite points and is bounded, is a constant.

17.2. Singular points of an analytic function

There are three kinds of singular points of a *one-valued* analytic function, viz. (i) removable singularities, (ii) poles, (iii) essential singularities.

(i) The point a is a *removable singularity* for $f(z)$ if $f(z)$ can be made regular at a by altering the value $f(a)$.

E.g. $f(z)=(\sin z)/z$ at the origin. (Put $f(0)=1$.)

Such singularities are trivial.

(ii) The point a is a *pole* of $f(z)$ if it is a singular point for $f(z)$ and a regular point for the function $1/f(z)$.

A pole is an isolated† singularity. In the neighbourhood of a pole a, $f(z)$ can be expanded in a Laurent series which consists of a power series in $(z-a)$ plus a *polynomial* in $1/(z-a)$. If the highest power of $1/(z-a)$ is of degree k, the pole is of order k.

(iii) An *essential singularity* is a singularity which is not a pole nor a removable singularity.

All non-isolated singularities are essential singularities. In the neighbourhood of an isolated essential singularity $f(z)$ can be expanded in a Laurent series in which the terms in $1/(z-a)$ form an infinite series and do not reduce to a polynomial.

† i.e. there is a neighbourhood of the point which contains no other singularity.

17.3. The *residue* of $f(z)$, at an isolated singularity a, is the coefficient of $1/(z-a)$ in the Laurent expansion about the point a.

By the formula for the coefficients in the Laurent expansion the residue b_1 is

$$b_1=\frac{1}{2\pi i}\int_C f(z)\,dz,$$

where C is any circle, centre a, of radius less than the distance from a to the nearest singularity of $f(z)$.

Theorem of residues. If $f(z)$ is regular within and on a simple closed contour C except at a finite number of singularities *within* C,

$$\int_C f(z)\,dz=2\pi i\,\Sigma R,$$

where ΣR stands for the sum of the residues of $f(z)$ at its singularities within C. The integral is taken in the positive sense round C.

Let the function $f(z)$ be regular within and on C except at a finite number of poles $b_1, b_2, \ldots, b_n$ of multiplicities $s_1, s_2, \ldots, s_n$, and let the zeros of $f(z)$ within C be at the points $a_1, a_2, \ldots, a_k$, of multiplicities $r_1, r_2, \ldots, r_k$, and let $f(z)$ have no zeros or poles on C. Let $\phi(z)$ be a function regular within and on C, then

$$\frac{1}{2\pi i}\int_C \frac{\phi(z)\,f'(z)}{f(z)}\,dz=\sum_{i=1}^{k} r_i\phi(a_i)-\sum_{s=1}^{n} s_i\phi(b_i).$$

In particular

$$\frac{1}{2\pi i}\int_C \frac{f'(z)}{f(z)}\,dz=\sum_{i=1}^{k} r_i-\sum_{i=1}^{n} s_i\equiv N-P=\frac{1}{2\pi}\Delta_C \operatorname{amp} f(z),$$

where N and P are the number of zeros and poles, respectively, of $f(z)$ within C, each being counted according to its order, and $\Delta_C \operatorname{amp} f(z)$ is the increment in $\operatorname{amp} f(z)$ as z described C in the positive sense.

Rouché's theorem. If $f(z)$ and $\phi(z)$ are regular within a simple closed contour C and continuous on C and if $|\phi(z)|<|f(z)|$ on C, then the number of zeros of $f(z)+\phi(z)$ within C is equal to the number of zeros of $f(z)$ within C.

The point at infinity. With one exception we say that a function $f(z)$ has a property at the point at infinity if the function $f(1/z)$ has that property at $z=0$. The exception is the residue at the point at infinity. If the point at infinity is a regular point or an isolated singularity, then

$$f(z)=\sum_{-\infty}^{\infty} c_n z^n \text{ for } |z|>R.$$

Definition. The *residue* at the point at infinity is $-c_{-1}$, i.e. the coefficient of $1/z$ with its sign changed.

17.4. Special functions

By definition a rational function is formed by addition, multiplication and division on z and constants.

A function, whose only singularities in the whole plane including the point at infinity are poles, is a rational function.

Definition.
$$\text{Log}\, z=\int_C \frac{dt}{t},$$
where C is any path in the t plane from the point $t=1$ to the point $t=z$, and which does not pass through the origin.

If $\quad z=r(\cos\theta+i\sin\theta),$
$$\text{Log}\, z=\ln r+i(\theta+2k\pi),\quad k=0 \text{ or an integer.}$$

Log z is therefore a many-valued function. The principal value of Log z is written $\ln z$ and defined as $\ln z=\ln r+i\theta$, where θ is the principal value of amp z.

Log z satisfies the equation
$$\text{Log}\, z_1 z_2=\text{Log}\, z_1+\text{Log}\, z_2$$
in the sense that every value of either side is one of the values of the other side.

Definition. $\quad z=\exp w$ if $w=\text{Log}\, z$.

Exp w is a one-valued function of w. If $w=u+i\,v$,
$$\exp w=(\cos v+i\sin v)\exp u.$$
$$\exp w_1\times\exp w_2=\exp(w_1+w_2).$$

Definition.
$$a^z=\exp(z\,\text{Log}\, a).$$
If $\quad a=\rho(\cos\phi+i\sin\phi)$ and $z=x+i\,y$,
$$a^z=(\exp L)(\cos M+i\sin M),$$
where $L=x\ln\rho-y(\phi+2n\pi)$, $M=y\ln\rho+x(\phi+2n\pi)$, and n is an integer or zero.

a^z is an infinitely many-valued function unless z is real and rational.

Definition.
$$\cos z=\tfrac{1}{2}[\exp(iz)+\exp(-iz)],\qquad \sin z=-\tfrac{1}{2}i[\exp(iz)-\exp(-iz)],$$
$$\cosh z=\tfrac{1}{2}[\exp z+\exp(-z)],\qquad \sinh z=\tfrac{1}{2}[\exp z-\exp(-z)].$$

Whence
$$\cos(iz)=\cosh z,\ \sin iz=i\sinh z,$$
$$\cosh(iz)=\cos z,\ \sinh iz=i\sin z.$$

See also § 15.4.

17.5. Branch points of a many-valued function

The function

$$w \equiv z^{1/n} = r^{1/n} [\cos(\theta/n + 2k\pi/n) + i \sin(\theta/n + 2k\pi/n)],$$

where $z = r(\cos\theta + i\sin\theta)$ and $r^{1/n}$ denotes the positive arithmetical root, is an n-valued function of z.

The function $w = \text{Log}\, z = \ln r + i(\theta + 2k\pi)$ is an infinitely many-valued function of z. If k is given a particular value, we obtain a branch of the many-valued function $w \equiv \text{Log}\, z$. If z describes a circuit round the origin, w changes from one branch of the function to another. The origin is a branch point for each of the functions.

A *branch point* of an many-valued function w is a singular point a such that if z makes a circuit about a, w changes from one branch of the function to another.

Many-valued functions may have singular points of the types (i), (ii), (iii) (§ 17.2) in addition to branch points.

CHAPTER 18

INFINITE INTEGRALS, SERIES AND PRODUCTS

18.1. Infinite integrals of the first kind

Definitions.

$$\int_a^\infty \phi(x)\,dx = \lim_{b\to+\infty} \int_a^b \phi(x)\,dx, \quad . \quad . \quad . \quad . \quad (1)$$

$$\int_{-\infty}^\infty \phi(x)\,dx = \lim_{\substack{a\to-\infty \\ b\to+\infty}} \int_a^b \phi(x)\,dx, \quad . \quad . \quad . \quad . \quad (2)$$

where a and b tend to $-\infty$ and $+\infty$ independently. The integrals *converge* if the limits on the right exist.

The integral (1) converges if, and only if, given any positive number ϵ, we can find a number x_0, such that

$$\left| \int_{x_1}^{x_2} \phi(x)\,dx \right| < \epsilon$$

for all $x_2 > x_1 \geqslant x_0$.

If $\int_a^\infty |\phi(x)|dx$ converges, so does $\int_a^\infty \phi(x)\,dx$.

The latter is then said to *converge absolutely*.

If $|\phi(x)| < f(x)$ for $x > a$ and $\int_a^\infty f(x)\,dx$ converges, so does $\int_a^\infty \phi(x)\,dx$.

The *Cauchy principal value* of the integral (2) is

$$P\int_{-\infty}^\infty \phi(x)\,dx = \lim_{a\to\infty} \int_{-a}^a \phi(x)\,dx.$$

This may exist when (2) is not convergent.

18.11. Infinite integrals of the second kind

Definition. If $\phi(x)\to\infty$ as $x\to c$ where $a<c<b$, then

$$\int_a^b \phi(x)\,dx = \lim_{\delta\to 0} \int_a^{c-\delta} \phi(x)\,dx + \lim_{\delta'\to 0} \int_{c+\delta'}^b \phi(x)\,dx, \quad . \quad . \quad (3)$$

where δ and $\delta'\to 0$ independently.

If $\phi(x)\to\infty$ as $x\to a$,

$$\int_a^b \phi(x)\,dx \equiv \lim_{\delta'\to 0}\int_{a+\delta'}^b \phi(x)\,dx$$

is convergent if, and only if, given $\epsilon>0$, we can find $\delta>0$, such that

$$\left|\int_{x_1}^{x_2}\phi(x)\,dx\right|<\epsilon$$

for all x_1 and x_2 such that $a<x_1<x_2\leqslant a+\delta$.

If $\int_a^b |\phi(x)|\,dx$ is convergent, so is $\int_a^b \phi(x)\,dx$. The latter is then said to be *absolutely convergent.*

If $|\phi(x)|<f(x)$ in $a<x<b$ and $\int_a^b f(x)\,dx$ converges, so does $\int_a^b \phi(x)\,dx$.

The *Cauchy principal value* of the integral (3) is

$$P\int_a^b \phi(x)\,dx = \lim_{\delta\to 0}\left\{\int_a^{c-\delta}\phi(x)\,dx+\int_{c+\delta}^b \phi(x)\,dx\right\}.$$

This may exist when (3) is not convergent.

18.2. Convergence of sequences and series

If to every integer n corresponds a number a_n, the numbers a_1, a_2, . . ., a_n, . . . are said to form a *sequence* (a_n).

A real sequence behaves in one of five ways as $n\to\infty$:

(i) $a_n\to l$ as $n\to\infty$ if, given any positive number ϵ, however small, we can find a number $n_0\equiv n_0(\epsilon)$ such that $|a_n-l|<\epsilon$ for all $n\geqslant n_0$.

(ii) $a_n\to+\infty$ (or $\to-\infty$) if, given any positive number G, however great, we can find $n_0\equiv n_0(G)$, such that $a_n>G(a_n<-G)$ for all $n\geqslant n_0$.

(iii) a_n *oscillates* as $n\to\infty$ if it does not tend to a limit or to $+\infty$ or to $-\infty$. Then, if (a_n) is bounded, it oscillates finitely; if unbounded, it oscillates infinitely.

If $a_n\to l$, (a_n) is said to *converge* to the *limit* l, otherwise it *diverges*.

A sequence is *monotonic* increasing (decreasing) if $a_{n+1}\geqslant a_n(a_{n+1}\leqslant a_n)$ for every n.

Theorem. A monotonic increasing (decreasing) sequence either tends to a limit or to $+\infty(-\infty)$. A monotonic bounded sequence is convergent.

Cauchy's necessary and sufficient condition for the convergence of a sequence a_n: (a_n) converges as $n\to\infty$ if, and only if, given any positive number ϵ, we can find an integer $n_0 \equiv n_0(\epsilon)$ such that $|a_{n_1} - a_{n_2}| < \epsilon$ for all $n_2 > n_1 \geqslant n_0$.

Limit points. Definition. The point c is a *limit point* or *point of accumulation* of a set of numbers z if, given any positive number ϵ, there is at least one point z of the set, other than c itself, satisfying $|z-c| < \epsilon$.

There will in fact be an infinite number of points of the set satisfying this inequality.

Weierstrass' theorem. A bounded infinite set possesses at least one limit point.

The *upper limit* μ of a sequence a_n, written $\overline{\lim}\, a_n$, is defined by:—

$$a_n < \mu + \epsilon \text{ for ALL } n \geqslant \text{some } n_0,$$

$$a_n > \mu - \epsilon \text{ for SOME } m > \text{ any given } n, \text{ where } \epsilon > 0 \text{ is arbitrary.}$$

The *lower limit* λ of a sequence a_n, written $\underline{\lim}\, a_n$ is defined by:—

$$\underline{\lim}\, a_n = -(\overline{\lim} - a_n).$$

If $\underline{\lim}\, a_n = \overline{\lim}\, a_n = l$, then (a_n) converges to l. If $\lim\limits_{n \to \infty} a_n = a$, $\lim\limits_{n \to \infty} b_n = b$ (a and b finite), then $\lim\limits_{n \to \infty} (a_n \pm b_n) = a \pm b$, $\lim\limits_{n \to \infty} a_n b_n = ab$, and if $b \neq 0$, $b_n \neq 0$, $\lim\limits_{n \to \infty} \dfrac{a_n}{b_n} = \dfrac{a}{b}$.

The *infinite series*

$$\sum_{n=0}^{\infty} a_n \equiv a_0 + \ldots + a_n + \ldots$$

is merely another symbol for the sequence $s_n = a_0 + a_1 + \ldots + a_n$. It *converges, diverges* to $+\infty$ or to $-\infty$, or *oscillates* according as its partial sum s_n converges to s, diverges to $+\infty$ or to $-\infty$ or oscillates. If the series converges, s is called its *sum*.

Cauchy's necessary and sufficient condition for the convergence of a series: Σa_n is convergent if, and only if, given any positive number ϵ, we can find a number $n_0 \equiv n_0(\epsilon)$ such that

$$|a_{n+1} + a_{n+2} + \ldots + a_{n+p}| < \epsilon$$

for all $n \geqslant n_0$ and all positive integers p.

If Σa_n is convergent, then $a_n \to 0$. The converse is not true.

The series Σa_n is said to be *absolutely* convergent if the series $\Sigma |a_n|$ is convergent. If $\Sigma |a_n|$ is convergent, so is Σa_n. If Σa_n is convergent but $\Sigma |a_n|$ is divergent, Σa_n is said to be *conditionally* convergent.

18.3. Series with positive terms

The sequence s_n of the partial sums is monotonic increasing, and hence the series must converge or diverge to $+\infty$ and cannot oscillate. If s_n is bounded the series converges; if unbounded it diverges.

The question of convergence or divergence can sometimes be settled by comparing the given series Σa_n with another series of positive terms known to converge or known to diverge. Such tests are known as comparison tests and can be applied only to series of positive terms. All such tests give sufficient, not necessary, conditions for convergence.

Comparison tests

Notation. The numbers a_n, c_n, d_n are positive for every n. Σc_n is convergent and Σd_n divergent. K is a positive constant, independent of n. A is a constant. If, in the following, the word lim is written instead of $\overline{\lim}$ or $\underline{\lim}$, the result remains true.

If any one of the following conditions is fulfilled, then the series Σa_n is

	convergent,	divergent.
	General comparison tests	
I	$a_n \leqslant K c_n$ for all $n \geqslant n_0$.	$a_n \geqslant K d_n$ for all $n \geqslant n_0$.
II	$a_n/c_n \to l$ as $n \to \infty$, where l is finite.	$a_n/d_n \to l > 0$ or to $+\infty$ as $n \to \infty$.
III	$\dfrac{a_{n+1}}{a_n} \leqslant \dfrac{c_{n+1}}{c_n}$ for all $n \geqslant n_0$.	$\dfrac{a_{n+1}}{a_n} \geqslant \dfrac{d_{n+1}}{d_n}$ for all $n \geqslant n_0$.
IV	*d'Alembert's ratio test*	
(a)	$\overline{\lim}\, \dfrac{a_{n+1}}{a_n} < 1$.	$\underline{\lim}\, \dfrac{a_{n+1}}{a_n} > 1$.
(b)	$\dfrac{a_{n+1}}{a_n} \leqslant K < 1$ for all $n \geqslant n_0$.	$\dfrac{a_{n+1}}{a_n} \geqslant 1$ for all $n \geqslant n_0$.
V	*Cauchy's root test*	
(a)	$\overline{\lim}\, a_n^{1/n} < 1$.	$\overline{\lim}\, a_n^{1/n} > 1$.
(b)	$a_n^{1/n} \leqslant K < 1$ for all $n \geqslant n_0$.	$a_n^{1/n} \geqslant 1$ for an infinite number of values of n.

VI *Raabe's test*

(*a*) $\overline{\lim}\, n\left(\frac{a_{n+1}}{a_n}-1\right)<-1.$ $\qquad \underline{\lim}\, n\left(\frac{a_{n+1}}{a_n}-1\right)>-1.$

(*b*) $n\left(\frac{a_{n+1}}{a_n}-1\right)\leqslant -K<-1$ $\qquad n\left(\frac{a_{n+1}}{a_n}-1\right)\geqslant -1$ for all $n \geqslant n_0$.

for all $n \geqslant n_0$.

VII *Gauss's test*

$$\frac{a_{n+1}}{a_n}=1-\frac{A}{n}+O\left(\frac{1}{n^{1+\lambda}}\right), \text{ where } \lambda>0, \text{ and}$$

$A>1.$ $\qquad A \leqslant 1.$

VIII *Logarithmic test*

$\overline{\lim}\left\{n\left(\frac{a_{n+1}}{a_n}-1\right)+1\right\}\ln n<-1.$ $\qquad \underline{\lim}\left\{n\left(\frac{a_{n+1}}{a_n}-1\right)+1\right\}\ln n>-1.$

Each of the tests IV-VIII is more delicate than the preceding.

18.31. Tests for series whose terms monotonically decrease

Integral test. If $a_n \to 0$ monotonically and if $\phi(x) \to 0$ monotonically and $\phi(n)=a_n$ for all positive integers, then the series Σa_n and the integral $\int_1^\infty \phi(x)\,dx$ converge or diverge together.

Cauchy's condensation test. If $a_n \to 0$ monotonically, then the series $\sum_{n=1}^{\infty} a_n$ and $\sum_{k=1}^{\infty} 2^k a_{2^k}$ converge or diverge together.

Abel's theorem. If $a_n \to 0$ monotonically and if Σa_n is convergent then $na_n \to 0$. This cannot prove convergence.

18.4. Series whose terms are not all positive

In discussing the convergence of Σa_n, it is advisable to consider first that of $\Sigma|a_n|$, since it is much easier to deal with a series known to be absolutely convergent than with one merely convergent. Moreover, tests for absolute convergence, being tests for convergence of a series of positive terms $\Sigma|a_n|$, are easier to apply than are the tests for conditional convergence.

Tests for conditional convergence

Leibniz' test for alternating series. If $a_n \to 0$ monotonically, then the series $\Sigma(-1)^n a_n$ is convergent.

Dirichlet's test. If Σa_n has bounded partial sums and $b_n \to 0$ monotonically, then $\Sigma a_n b_n$ is convergent.

Abel's test. If Σa_n is convergent and b_n is monotonic and bounded, then $\Sigma a_n b_n$ is convergent.

Dedekind's test. If Σa_n has bounded partial sums, $\Sigma |b_n - b_{n+1}|$ is convergent and $b_n \to 0$, then $\Sigma a_n b_n$ is convergent.

18.5. Derangement and multiplication of absolutely convergent series

The terms of a series are said to be *deranged* if they are rearranged so that every term appears once and once only in the new series.

The terms of an absolutely convergent series may be deranged in any manner and the new series will be absolutely convergent and its sum will be equal to that of the original series.

If the terms of two absolutely convergent series Σa_n and Σb_n, with sums a and b, are multiplied together and arranged in any order as a single series, then the resulting series is absolutely convergent and its sum is $a \,.\, b$.

18.6. Power series

The series

$$P(z) \equiv \sum_0^{\infty} a_n z^n \equiv a_0 + a_1 z + \ldots,$$

where the a_n are constants independent of the variable z, is called a *power series* in z.

Every power series has a non-negative *radius of convergence* R, such that the series is absolutely convergent for all z for which $|z| < R$ and divergent for all z for which $|z| > R$. Its behaviour when $|z| = R$ depends on the particular series. The radius R can be zero or infinite, i.e. there are power series which diverge for all z except $z = 0$ and others which converge for all finite z. The circle $|z| < R$ is called the *circle of convergence*. For a power series in the real variable x the circle of convergence is replaced by an interval of convergence $)-R, R($.

The radius of convergence is

$$R = 1/\{\overline{\lim}\ |a_n|^{1/n}\}.$$

It is also given by

$$R = 1/\lim |a_n|^{1/n}, \text{ and by } R = \lim \left| \frac{a_n}{a_{n+1}} \right|,$$

if these limits exist.

The sum $P(z)$ of a power series is a function of z regular within its circle of convergence. At all interior points of the circle $P(z)$ is continuous and differentiable and its derivate $P'(z)$ is equal to the sum of the series obtaining by differentiating the given series term by term, i.e. $P'(z) = \sum_{n=1}^{\infty} na_n z^{n-1}$. The derivates $P^{(k)}(z)$ of all orders exist at interior points of the circle and are given by

$$P^{(k)}(z) = \sum_{n=k}^{\infty} n(n-1) \ldots (n-k+1)a_n z^{n-k}.$$

These series all have the same radius of convergence R as $P(z)$.

The expansion of a function in a power series in z is unique, i.e. if

$$f(z) = \sum_{0}^{\infty} a_n z^n \text{ and } f(z) = \sum_{0}^{\infty} b_n z^n$$

and the series have non-zero radii of convergence, then $a_n = b_n$ for every n.

18.7. Uniform convergence. Real sequences and series

A sequence $b_n(x)$ *converges uniformly* to $b(x)$ in the closed interval (a, b) if, given any positive number ϵ, a number $N \equiv N(\epsilon)$, independent of x, exists such that

$$|b_n(x) - b(x)| < \epsilon,$$

for all $n \geqslant N$ and all x in (a, b).

A sequence $b_n(x)$ is *uniformly bounded* in (a, b) if a number K, independent of x and n, exists such that $|b_n(x)| < K$ for all n and all x in (a, b).

Consider a series $\Sigma a_n(x)$ of functions $a_n(x)$ of x, which is convergent in an interval J of x. Let

$$s_n(x) = a_1(x) + a_2(x) + \ldots + a_n(x).$$

Definition. The series is said to be *uniformly convergent* in the closed interval (a, b) if $s_n(x)$ is uniformly convergent in (a, b).

$\Sigma a_n(x)$ is uniformly convergent in (a, b) if, and only if, given any positive number ϵ, we can find a number $N = N(\epsilon)$, independent of x, such that

$$|a_{n+1}(x) + a_{n+2}(x) + \ldots + a_{n+p}(x)| < \epsilon$$

for all $n \geqslant N(\epsilon)$, all positive integers p and every x in (a, b).

Tests for uniform convergence

Weierstrass' M-test. If $|a_n(x)| \leqslant M_n$ for every x satisfying $a \leqslant x \leqslant b$ and ΣM_n is convergent, then $\Sigma a_n(x)$ is uniformly convergent in (a, b).

If the partial sums $\sum_{1}^{N} a_n(x)$ are uniformly bounded in (a, b), and if the sequence $b_n(x)\to 0$ uniformly in (a, b) and is monotonic for every fixed x in (a, b), then $\Sigma a_n(x)\, b_n(x)$ is uniformly convergent in (a, b).

If $\Sigma a_n(x)$ is uniformly convergent in (a, b), and if the sequence $b_n(x)$ is uniformly bounded in (a, b) and is monotonic for every fixed x in (a, b) then $\Sigma a_n(x)\, b_n(x)$ is uniformly convergent in (a, b).

If the series $\sum\limits_0^\infty a_n(x)$ converges uniformly to $f(x)$ in (a, b) and if $a_n(x)$ is continuous in (a, b) for all n, then $f(x)$ is continuous in (a, b) and

$$\int_a^b \left\{\sum_0^\infty a_n(x)\right\} dx \equiv \int_a^b f(x)\, dx = \sum_0^\infty \int_a^b a_n(x)\, dx,$$

i.e. term by term integration is allowable.

If $a_n(x)$ is differentiable in (a, b) and if $\sum\limits_0^\infty a_n(x)$ converges at one point of (a, b) and if $\sum\limits_0^\infty a'_n(x)$ converges uniformly to $\phi(x)$ in (a, b), then $\sum\limits_0^\infty a_n(x)$ converges uniformly to $f(x)$ in (a, b) and

$$f'(x) = \phi(x).$$

18.71. Uniform convergence of series of analytic functions

A sequence $a_n(z)$ of analytic functions $a_n(z)$ *converges uniformly* to $a(z)$ in a bounded closed domain D if, given any positive number ϵ, a number $N \equiv N(\epsilon)$, independent of z, exists such that

$$|a_n(z) - a(z)| < \epsilon,$$

for all $n \geqslant N$ and all z in D.

The series $\Sigma a_n(z)$ *converges uniformly* in D if the sequence $s_n(z)$ does.

The series converges uniformly in D if, and only if, given any positive number ϵ, there is a number $n_0 = n_0(\epsilon)$, independent of z, such that

$$|a_{n+1}(z) + \ldots + a_{n+p}(z)| < \epsilon$$

for all $n \geqslant n_0$, all positive integers p, and every z in D.

Tests for uniform convergence

(i) If $|a_n(z)| \leqslant M_n$ for every z in D and ΣM_n is convergent, then $\Sigma a_n(z)$ is uniformly convergent in D.

(ii) If (*a*) the partial sums of the series $\Sigma a_n(z)$ are uniformly bounded in D, (*b*) $\Sigma|b_n(z) - b_{n+1}(z)|$ is uniformly convergent in D, (*c*) $b_n(z)\to 0$ uniformly in D, then $\Sigma a_n(z)\, b_n(z)$ is uniformly convergent in D.

If each term of $\Sigma a_n(z)$ is continuous in a bounded closed domain D

and if the series converges uniformly in D, then the sum $s(z)$ of the series is continuous in D. If L is any simple contour in D,

$$\int_L s(z)\, dz = \sum_{n=0}^{\infty} \int_L a_n(z)\, dz.$$

Weierstrass' theorem. If each term of $\Sigma a_n(z)$ is an analytic function, regular within a closed contour C, and if the series converges uniformly in every closed domain D within C, then the sum $s(z)$ of the series is an analytic function regular within C. Further

$$s'(z) = \Sigma a_n'(z),$$

and the latter series is uniformly convergent in D.

18.8. Fourier series

Definition. The *Fourier series* of a function $f(x)$ is the series

$$\tfrac{1}{2}a_0 + \sum_{n=1}^{\infty} (a_n \cos nx + b_n \sin nx), \quad . \quad . \quad . \quad (4)$$

where

$$a_n = \frac{1}{\pi}\int_{-\pi}^{\pi} f(t) \cos nt\, dt,\ b_n = \frac{1}{\pi}\int_{-\pi}^{\pi} f(t) \sin nt\, dt. \quad . \quad . \quad (5)$$

a_n and b_n are called the *Fourier coefficients* of $f(x)$.

The series (4) need not converge, and if it does its sum $F(x)$ need not equal $f(x)$. If (4) does converge to $f(x)$, the Fourier series of $f(x)$ is said to be *valid* at x.

If $f(x)$ is integrable in $(-\pi, \pi)$, $a_n \to 0$ and $b_n \to 0$ as $n \to \infty$.

The Fourier series of an even function in $(-\pi, \pi)$ is a series of cosines and that of an odd function is a series of sines.

If a trigonometrical series converges uniformly to $f(x)$ in $(-\pi, \pi)$, it is the Fourier series of $f(x)$.

The function $F(x)$ [i.e. the sum of (4)] cannot be represented in $(-\pi, \pi)$ by any trigonometrical series other than (4).

If (*a*) $f(x)$ is periodic of period 2π with Fourier coefficients a_n and b_n:

(*b*) $|f(x)|$ is integrable in $(-\pi, \pi)$,

then

$$\tfrac{1}{2}a_0 + \sum_{n=1}^{\infty} (a_n \cos nx + b_n \sin nx) = \tfrac{1}{2}\{f(x+0) + f(x-0)\}, \quad . \quad . \quad (6)$$

whenever (*c*) the series is convergent,

and (*d*) the limits on the right of equation (6) exist,

i.e. under conditions (*a*) and (*b*) equation (6) holds whenever both sides have a meaning.

If conditions (*a*), (*b*) and (*d*) hold and

$$s_n = \tfrac{1}{2}a_0 + \sum_{r=1}^{n} (a_r \cos rx + b_r \sin rx),$$

where a_r and b_r are given by (5), and

$$\sigma_n = (s_0 + s_1 + \ldots + s_n)/n,$$

then

$$\sigma_n \to \tfrac{1}{2}\{f(x+0) + f(x-0)\}.$$

The behaviour of the Fourier series of $f(x)$ at the point x_0 depends on the behaviour of $f(x)$ in the neighbourhood of x_0 only.

If $f(t)$ is of bounded variation* in the neighbourhood of $t=x$, then the series (4) converges to the sum $\tfrac{1}{2}\{f(x+0)+f(x-0)\}$.

If $f(t)$ is continuous and of bounded variation in the neighbourhood of $t=x$, the expansion is valid at x.

The Fourier series of $f(x)$ converges uniformly to $f(x)$ in any interval interior to an interval in which $f(x)$ is continuous and of bounded variation.

If $f(x)$ has only a finite number of maxima and minima and a finite number of discontinuities in the interval $(-\pi, \pi)$, its Fourier series is convergent to $\tfrac{1}{2}\{f(x+0)+f(x-0)\}$ in $(-\pi, \pi)$.

Dirichlet's integral gives an expression for $s_n(x)$:

$$s_n(x) = \frac{1}{2\pi}\int_0^\pi \left\{ f(x+t) + f(x-t) \right\} \frac{\sin (n+\frac{1}{2})t}{\sin \frac{1}{2}t}\, dt. \qquad (7)$$

If $f(x)$ is integrable in $(-\pi, \pi)$ with period 2π, its Fourier series converges at the point x if, and only if, Dirichlet's integral (7) tends to a finite limit as $n \to \infty$. This limit is then the sum of the Fourier series at the point x. Moreover, the Fourier series of $f(x)$ converges to $s(x)$ at x if, and only if,

$$s_n(x) - s(x) = \frac{1}{2\pi}\int_0^\pi \left\{ f(x+t) - f(x-t) - 2s \right\} \frac{\sin (n+\frac{1}{2})t}{\sin \frac{1}{2}t}\, dt \to 0 \qquad (8)$$

Lipschitz condition

If $f(x)$ is integrable in $(-\pi, \pi)$ and has period 2π, if x_0 is fixed and if two constants $p(>0)$ and M exist such that

$$\left| \frac{f(x_0+t) - f(x_0)}{t^p} \right| < M \qquad (9)$$

for all $t \neq 0$, then the Fourier series for $f(x)$ is valid at x_0.

If the condition (9) holds for each x_0 in (α, β) and if p and M are independent of x_0, then $s_n(x) \to f(x)$ uniformly in (α, β).

* $f(x)$ is of bounded variation if it is the difference of two bounded increasing functions.

18.81. Intervals other than $(-\pi, \pi)$

If the interval is $(0, 2\pi)$, proceed as for $(-\pi, \pi)$.

Corresponding to any integrable function $f(x)$ in (a, b) there is a general Fourier series, a series of sines and a series of cosines corresponding to $f(x)$ in (a, b). To find the general Fourier series write

$$\frac{x-a}{b-a}=\frac{X+\pi}{2\pi} \quad . \quad . \quad . \quad . \quad (10)$$

so that (a, b) of x corresponds to $(-\pi, \pi)$ of X. Let $f(x)\equiv\phi(X)$ where (10) holds, and let

$$\pi a_n=\int_{-\pi}^{\pi}\phi(t)\cos nt\,dt=\frac{2\pi}{b-a}\int_a^b f(\theta)\cos\frac{\pi n(2\theta-a-b)}{b-a}\,d\theta,$$

$$\pi b_n=\int_{-\pi}^{\pi}\phi(t)\sin nt\,dt=\frac{2\pi}{b-a}\int_a^b f(\theta)\sin\frac{\pi n(2\theta-a-b)}{b-a}\,d\theta.$$

Then, if the series is convergent and the limits exist,

$$\tfrac{1}{2}a_0+\sum_{n=1}^{\infty}\left[a_n\cos\left\{\frac{n\pi}{b-a}(2x-a-b)\right\}+b_n\sin\left\{\frac{n\pi}{b-a}(2x-a-b)\right\}\right]$$

represents $\frac{1}{2}[f(x+0)+f(x-0)]$ in $a<x<b$.

For a cosine series, write $\dfrac{x-a}{b-a}=\dfrac{X}{\pi}$ and $f(x)\equiv\phi(X)$ in $0\leqslant X\leqslant\pi$. Let $\phi(X)=\phi(-X)$ in $-\pi\leqslant X\leqslant 0$. Then $\phi(X)$ is even in $(-\pi, \pi)$ and $b_n=0$.

$$\pi a_n=\int_{-\pi}^{\pi}\phi(t)\cos nt\,dt=2\int_0^{\pi}\phi(t)\cos nt\,dt$$

$$=\frac{2\pi}{b-a}\int_a^b f(\theta)\cos\frac{\pi n(\theta-a)}{b-a}\,d\theta.$$

For a sine series, write $\dfrac{x-a}{b-a}=\dfrac{X}{\pi}$, and define $\phi(X)$ by

$\phi(X)=f(x)$ in $0\leqslant X<\pi$, $\phi(X)=-\phi(-X)$ in $-\pi<X<0$, $\phi(0)=0$.

Then $a_n=0$,

$$\pi b_n=\int_{-\pi}^{\pi}\phi(t)\sin nt\,dt=2\int_0^{\pi}\phi(t)\sin nt\,dt$$

$$=\frac{2\pi}{b-a}\int_a^b f(\theta)\sin\frac{n\pi(\theta-a)}{b-a}\,d\theta.$$

18.9. Infinite products

The symbol

$$(1+a_1)(1+a_2)\ldots$$

or

$$\prod_1^{\infty}(1+a_n)$$

is called an *infinite product*. We suppose that $a_n \neq -1$ for all n.

The infinite product is *convergent* if the partial product

$$p_n = \prod_{r=1}^{n}(1+a_r)$$

tends to a finite non-zero limit. If $p_n \to 0$, the product is said to *diverge to zero*.

Theorems. If $a_n \geqslant 0$ and Σa_n is convergent, then the products $\Pi(1+a_n)$, $\Pi(1-a_n)$ converge. If $1 > a_n \geqslant 0$ and Σa_n is divergent, then $\Pi(1+a_n)$ diverges to $+\infty$ and $\Pi(1-a_n)$ diverges to zero.

Definition. The product $\Pi(1+a_n)$ is said to be absolutely convergent if the product $\Pi(1+|a_n|)$ is convergent.

An absolutely convergent product is convergent.

The product $\Pi(1+a_n)$ converges absolutely if, and only if, $\Sigma|a_n|$ is convergent.

$\Pi(1+a_n)$ converges if, and only if, $\Sigma \ln(1+a_n)$ converges. The product converges absolutely if, and only if, the series does. Moreover, if

$$\Pi(1+a_n)=p, \quad \Sigma \ln(1+a_n)=l,$$

then

$$l = \ln p + 2k\pi i,$$

where k is an integer.

If Σa_n^2 converges absolutely, then Σa_n and $\Pi(1+a_n)$ converge or diverge together.

If Σa_n^2 converges absolutely and $|a_n|<1$, then

$$p_n \sim \exp s_n,$$

where $s_n = \sum_1^n a_n$.

Definition. If a_n is a function of a real variable x or of a complex variable z, the product is said to *converge uniformly* in a range of x or domain of z if p_n converges uniformly in that range or domain to a limit which is never zero.

Theorem. The product $\Pi\{1+a_n(z)\}$ is uniformly convergent in any domain in which the series $\Sigma|a_n(z)|$ is uniformly convergent.

If $|a_n(z)| \leqslant M_n$ for all z in a domain D and ΣM_n is convergent, then $\Pi\{1+a_n(z)\}$ converges uniformly in D.

CHAPTER 19

DIFFERENTIAL EQUATIONS

19.1. *Definition.* An *ordinary* differential equation of *order* n is a relation

$$F(x, y, y', y'', \ldots, y^{(n)})=0. \quad . \quad . \quad . \quad (1)$$

A *solution* or *integral* of the equation is a function $y=\phi(x)$ which, together with its first n derivates $y'=\phi'(x), \ldots, y^{(n)}=\phi^{(n)}(x)$, satisfies the given differential equation identically.

The *general* solution of any ordinary equation of order n is of the form

$$y=\phi(x, c_1, c_2, \ldots, c_n), \quad . \quad . \quad . \quad . \quad (2)$$

where $c_1, c_2, \ldots, c_n$ are n arbitrary constants. On differentiating (2) n times with respect to x and eliminating the n constants c_i between (2) and the n equations resulting, the differential equation (1) is obtained.

A *particular* solution is a solution obtained by giving the constants in (2) special values. Solutions, called *singular* solutions, may exist which cannot be obtained by giving the constants special values.

The equation is said to be solved even if y has been obtained only as an implicit function of x by $\psi(x, y, c_1, c_2, \ldots, c_n)=0$, or if the solution has been reduced to quadratures.

The *degree* of a differential equation is the degree of the derivate of highest order when the equation has been made rational and integral in the derivates $y', \ldots, y^{(n)}$.

Throughout this chapter all the functions considered are assumed to be differentiable as many times as is required. The letter c denotes an arbitrary constant.

19.2. Equations of the first order

Existence theorem for equations of the first order and of the first degree: if $f(x, y)$ is an analytic function of the complex variables x and y in the neighbourhood of the point (x_0, y_0), then the equation

$$\frac{dy}{dx}=f(x, y)$$

has a solution $y(x)$ analytic in the neighbourhood of the point x_0 and equal to y_0 when $x=x_0$.

The solution may be found in the form of an infinite series. Certain types of equation can be solved by other methods.

METHODS OF SOLUTION

19.21. Separation of the variables

The general solution of the equation

$$M(x)\,P(y)\,dx+N(x)\,Q(y)\,dy=0,$$

where M and N are functions of x only and P and Q functions of y only is

$$\int\frac{M(x)}{N(x)}\,dx+\int\frac{Q(y)}{P(y)}\,dy=c.$$

19.22. Exact equations

The left-hand side of the equation

$$M(x, y)\,dx+N(x, y)\,dy=0 \quad . \quad . \quad . \quad (3)$$

is the complete differential dU of a function $U(x, y)$ if, and only if,

$$\frac{\partial M}{\partial y}=\frac{\partial N}{\partial x}.$$

Then the general solution is $U+c=0$,

i.e. $$\int M(x, y)\,dx+\int\left\{N(x, y)-\frac{\partial}{\partial y}\int M(x, y)\,dx\right\}dy+c=0.$$

19.23. Integrating factors

It may be possible to transform the equation into an exact equation by multiplying it by an integrating factor $\mu(x, y)$, such that

$$\mu(x, y)\,[M(x, y)\,dx+N(x, y)\,dy]$$

is a complete differential. If so, $\mu(x, y)$ must satisfy the partial differential equation

$$\mu\left(\frac{\partial M}{\partial y}-\frac{\partial N}{\partial x}\right)=N\frac{\partial\mu}{\partial x}-M\frac{\partial\mu}{\partial y} \quad . \quad . \quad . \quad . \quad (4)$$

It is sufficient to find a particular solution of equation (4), and such a solution may sometimes be obtained by trial.

If a function z of x and y can be found such that

$$\left(\frac{\partial M}{\partial y}-\frac{\partial N}{\partial x}\right)\Big/\left(N\frac{\partial z}{\partial x}-M\frac{\partial z}{\partial y}\right)$$

is a function of z only, say $\psi(z)$, then $e^{\int\psi(z)\,dz}$ is an integrating factor.

If μ_1 and μ_2 are two integrating factors of equation (3) whose ratio is not a constant, the general solution of (3) is given by

$$\mu_2(x, y)=c\mu_1(x, y).$$

19.24. Transformation

Transform the equation to one in new variables u and v given by

$$x=X(u, v),\ y=Y(u, v).$$

Then
$$\frac{dy}{dx}=\left(\frac{\partial Y}{\partial u}+\frac{\partial Y}{\partial v}\frac{dv}{du}\right)\Bigg/\left(\frac{\partial X}{\partial u}+\frac{\partial X}{\partial v}\frac{dv}{du}\right).$$

The equation $F(x, y, y')=0$ is transformed into the equation

$$F\left(X(u, v),\ Y(u, v),\ \frac{\dfrac{\partial Y}{\partial u}+\dfrac{\partial Y}{\partial v}\dfrac{dv}{du}}{\dfrac{\partial X}{\partial u}+\dfrac{\partial X}{\partial v}\dfrac{dv}{du}}\right)=0,$$

which may be simpler than the given equation.

If $x\,dx+y\,dy$ is a component part of the equation, try the substitution $u=x^2+y^2$. If $x\,dy-y\,dx$ occurs, try $v=x/y$ or $v=y/x$. If both $x\,dx+y\,dy$ and $x\,dy-y\,dx$ occur, change to polar co-ordinates $x=r\cos\theta$, $y=r\sin\theta$.

19.25. Further differentiation

If the equation can be solved for y in the form

$$y=f(x, p), \qquad (5)$$

where $p=dy/dx$, differentiate with respect to x, obtaining

$$p=\frac{\partial f}{\partial x}+\frac{\partial f}{\partial p}\frac{dp}{dx}. \qquad (6)$$

If equation (6) can be solved for p as a function of x or for x as a function of p, then by substitution in (5) we obtain y as a function of x or both x and y as functions of a parameter p.

If the differential equation can be solved for x in the form

$$x=\psi(y, p), \qquad (7)$$

where $p=\dfrac{dy}{dx}$, differentiation with respect to y gives,

$$\frac{1}{p}=\frac{\partial\psi}{\partial y}+\frac{\partial\psi}{\partial p}\frac{dp}{dy}.$$

If this equation can be solved for p as a function of y or y as a function of p, substitution in (7) gives x as a function of y or both x and y as functions of the parameter p.

19.3. Particular equations

The *homogeneous* equation $\dfrac{dy}{dx}=f\left(\dfrac{y}{x}\right)$.

Put $y=vx$. General solution: $x=ce^{\int\frac{dv}{f(v)-v}}$.

19.31. The equation

$$\frac{dy}{dx}=f\left(\frac{ax+by+c}{a'x+b'y+c'}\right).$$

If $a/b=a'/b'$, put $ax+by=u$. Then the variables u and x are separable.

If $a/b\neq a'/b'$, the lines $ax+by+c=0$, $a'x+b'y+c'=0$ intersect in a finite point (α, β). Transfer the origin to (α, β) by the substitution $x=\alpha+X$, $y=\beta+Y$. The equation in X and Y is homogeneous.

19.32. Linear equation

$$\frac{dy}{dx}+P(x)\,.\,y=Q(x).$$

Integrating factor: $e^{\int P\,dx}$

Solution: $ye^{\int P\,dx}=c+\int Q\,.\,e^{\int P\,dx}\,dx.$

If one particular integral y_1 is known, the general integral is

$$y=ce^{-\int P\,dx}+y_1.$$

If two particular integrals y_1 and y_2 are known, the general solution is

$$y-y_1=c(y_2-y_1).$$

19.33. Bernoulli's equation

$$\frac{dy}{dx}+P(x)\,.\,y=Q(x)\,.\,y^n.$$

Transformation: $z=y^{1-n}$ reduces it to a linear equation in z.

The equation

$$\phi\left(\frac{y}{x}\right)\left(xy'-y\right)+\chi\left(\frac{y}{x}\right)y'+\psi\left(\frac{y}{x}\right)=0$$

is reduced by the transformation $y=vx$ to a Bernoulli equation in which v is the independent variable.

19.34. Riccati's equation

$$\frac{dy}{dx}=P(x)y^2+Q(x)y+R(x)$$

is integrable if one particular solution y_0 is known.

The transformation $y=y_0+1/v$ then yields

$$v'+[2P(x)y_0+Q(x)]v+P(x)=0,$$

which is linear in v.

If three solutions are known, the general integral is given by

$$\frac{y-y_1}{y-y_2}=c\frac{y_3-y_1}{y_3-y_2}.$$

The Riccati equation is transformed by the substitution

$$y=-\frac{1}{P\,.\,v}\frac{dv}{dx}$$

to a reduced linear equation of the second order, viz.

$$\frac{d^2v}{dx^2}-\left(Q+\frac{1}{P}\frac{dP}{dx}\right)\frac{dv}{dx}+PRv=0$$

Conversely, the reduced linear equation of the second order

$$y''+f_1(x)y'+f_2(x)y=0$$

can be reduced to a Riccati equation by the substitution $u=y'/y$, giving

$$u'+u^2+f_1(x)u+f_2(x)=0.$$

19.4. Equation of degree greater than one

$$F(x, y, p)=0, \qquad . \quad . \quad . \quad . \quad (8)$$

where $p=dy/dx$. If p can be expressed explicitly in terms of x and y, the equation can be reduced to the set of equations

$$p=f_1(x, y),\ p=f_2(x, y),\ \ldots, \qquad . \quad . \quad . \quad (9)$$

If the general solution of each of equations (9) can be found as

$$\phi_1(x, y, c)=0,\ \phi_2(x, y, c)=0,\ \ldots,$$

respectively, the general integral of (8) is given by any equation $\psi(x, y, c)=0$ which is satisfied when any one of equations (9) is satisfied. If equation (8) is of degree k, its general integral is

$$\phi_1(x, y, c)\ \phi_2(x, y, c)\ \ldots\ \phi_k(x, y, c)=0.$$

19.41. Clairant's equation

$$y=px+f(p), \text{ where } p=\frac{dy}{dx}.$$

Solve by differentiating with respect to x.

General solution: $y=cx+f(c)$.

Singular solution: $x=-f'(p), y=-pf'(p)+f(p)$,

where p is a parameter.

19.42. D'Alembert's or Lagrange's equation

$$y=x\,g(p)+f(p), \qquad (10)$$

where $g(p)\neq p$.

Solve by differentiating with respect to x and then treating p as the independent variable.
General solution: given parametrically in terms of p by

$$x\exp\int\frac{g'(p)}{g(p)-p}\,dp=c-\int\frac{f'(p)}{g(p)-p}\exp\left\{\int\frac{g'(p)}{g(p)-p}\,dp\right\}dp$$

and equation (10).

Singular solutions: The straight lines given by

$$y=x\,g(m)+f(m),$$

where m is a root of the equation $g(m)-m=0$.

19.43. p-discriminant and c-discriminant

The *p-discriminant* is the curve whose equation is obtained by eliminating p from the equations

$$F(x, y, p)=0, \; F_p=0.$$

A branch of this curve will be a singular solution of the equation $F\left(x, y, \frac{dy}{dx}\right)=0$ (and an envelope of the curves forming the general integral) if, and only if, it satisfies the further condition

$$F_x(x, y, p)+pF_y(x, y, p)=0$$

at every point, and satisfies neither

$$F_x=F_y=0, \text{ nor } F_{pp}=0.$$

The *c-discriminant* is the locus of points obtained by eliminating c between the equations

$$\phi(x, y, c)=0, \ \phi_c=0,$$

where $\phi(x, y, c)$ is the general integral of the equation.

The locus of such points for which neither

$$\phi_x=\phi_y=0 \text{ nor } \phi_{cc}=0$$

is a singular solution of the differential equation.

The *tac-locus* is the locus of the point of contact of curves of the family $\phi(x, y, c)=0$ which touch each other, the *node-locus* and *cusp-locus* are the loci of points which are nodes or cusps of individual curves of the family. Then in general the

p-discriminant		c-discriminant
	contains	
(i) the envelope,		(i) the envelope,
(ii) the tac-locus squared,		(ii) the node-locus squared,
(iii) the cusp-locus.		(iii) the cusp-locus cubed.

Of these, the envelope only is a solution of the differential equation.

19.44. Isogonal trajectories

The curves which cut every curve of a given one-parameter family $f(x, y, c)=0$ at the same angle α are called *isogonal trajectories* of the family $f(x, y, c)=0$. If ψ is the angle which the tangent to a curve of the given family makes with the x-axis, then for the trajectory

$$\frac{dy}{dx}=\tan(\alpha+\psi).$$

Hence the differential equation of the trajectories is obtained by eliminating c between

$$f(x, y, c)=0$$

and $$\left(\frac{\partial f}{\partial x}\cos\alpha-\frac{\partial f}{\partial y}\sin\alpha\right)+\left(\frac{\partial f}{\partial x}\sin\alpha+\frac{\partial f}{\partial y}\cos\alpha\right)\frac{dy}{dx}=0.$$

For orthogonal trajectories $\alpha=\frac{1}{2}\pi$, and the last equation reduces to

$$-\frac{\partial f}{\partial y}+\frac{\partial f}{\partial x}\frac{dy}{dx}=0.$$

If the differential equation of the given family is

$$F\left(x, y, \frac{dy}{dx}\right)=0,$$

that of the required family is

$$F\left(x, y, \frac{y'-\tan \alpha}{1+y' \tan \alpha}\right)=0.$$

If the differential equation of the given family in polar co-ordinates is $f\left(r, \theta, \dfrac{dr}{d\theta}\right)=0$, the angle ϕ between the tangent and radius vector is given by $\tan \phi=\dfrac{rd\theta}{dr}$. For the trajectory

$$\phi_1=\phi+\alpha,$$

$$\tan \phi=\frac{rd\theta-\tan \alpha\, dr}{dr+r \tan \alpha \,.\, d\theta}.$$

The differential equation of the trajectories is obtained from that of the given family by replacing $rd\theta/dr$ by $(rd\theta-\tan \alpha\, dr)/(dr+rd\theta \tan \alpha)$.

19.5. Equations of higher order

If one of the variables is absent, the equation is reduced to one of lower order by putting $\dfrac{dy}{dx}=p$ and treating y as the independent variable if x is absent and x as such if y is absent.

Second order equation

y absent. Put $\dfrac{dy}{dx}=p$.

Then $F(x, y', y'')=0$ becomes $F\left(x, p, \dfrac{dp}{dx}\right)=0$.

x absent. Put $\dfrac{dy}{dx}=p$, $\dfrac{d^2y}{dx^2}=p\dfrac{dp}{dy}$.

Then $F(y, y', y'')=0$ becomes $F\left(y, p, p\dfrac{dp}{dy}\right)=0$.

$F(y, y'')=0$. If a parametric representation of the curve $F(\xi, \eta)=0$ can be found so that $\xi=\phi(t)$, $\eta=\psi(t)$, the given equation can be solved. The solution is

$$x=\int \frac{\phi\,(t)}{\left\{2\int \phi'(t)\, \psi(t)\, dt+c_1\right\}^{\frac{1}{2}}}\, dt, \quad y=\phi(t).$$

The equation

$$F(x, y^{(k)}, y^{(k+1)}, \ldots, y^{(n)})=0$$

is reduced by the transformation $y^{(k)}=p$ to the equation

$$F(x, p, p', \ldots, p^{(n-k)})=0.$$

If the differential equation

$$F(x, y, y', \ldots, y^{(n)})=0$$

is homogeneous for a choice of k when y is reckoned of degree k, y' of degree $k-1, \ldots, y^{(n)}$ of degree $k-n$ and x of degree one, its order can be reduced by the substitution $x=e^t$, $y=ze^{kt}$.

19.6. Linear differential equations with constant coefficients

The linear differential equation of order n with constant coefficients is

$$a_0 y^{(n)}+a_1 y^{(n-1)}+\ldots+a_{n-1}y'+a_n y=f(x). \quad . \quad . \quad (11)$$

If one solution y_0 of this equation is known, then the general solution is

$$y_0+c_1u_1+c_2u_2+\ldots+c_nu_n,$$

where $u_1, u_2, \ldots, u_n$ are n linearly independent integrals (see § 12.91) of the reduced equation

$$a_0u^{(n)}+a_1u^{(n-1)}+\ldots+a_{n-1}u'+a_nu=0, \quad . \quad . \quad (12)$$

and the c_i are arbitrary constants.

The expression

$$c_1u_1+c_2u_2+\ldots+c_nu_n,$$

called the *complementary function*, is the general solution of equation (12). The equation

$$\phi(\alpha)\equiv a_0\alpha^n+a_1\alpha^{n-1}+\ldots+a_n=0$$

is called the *auxiliary equation* of the differential equation (12).

If $\phi(\alpha)=0$ has n distinct roots $\alpha_1, \alpha_2, \ldots, \alpha_n$, then the general solution of equation (12) is

$$u=c_1e^{\alpha_1x}+c_2e^{\alpha_2x}+\ldots+c_ne^{\alpha_nx},$$

where the c_i are arbitrary constants.

If $\alpha_1=\beta+i\gamma$, $\alpha_2=\beta-i\gamma$ are conjugate complex roots of $\phi(\alpha)=0$, we may write $c_1e^{\alpha_1x}+c_2e^{\alpha_2x}$ in the form $e^{\beta x}\{A\cos(\gamma x)+B\sin(\gamma x)\}$, where A and B are arbitrary constants.

If α_1 is an r_1-ple root, α_2 an r_2-ple root, $\ldots$, α_k an r_k-ple root of $\phi(\alpha)=0$, where $r_1+r_2+\ldots+r_k=n$, then the general integral of (12) is

$$\begin{aligned}u=&e^{\alpha_1x}(c_{11}+c_{12}x+\ldots+c_{1,r_1}x^{r_1-1})\\&+e^{\alpha_2x}(c_{21}+c_{22}x+\ldots+c_{2,r_2}x^{r_2-1})\\&+\ldots\ldots\\&+e^{\alpha_kx}(c_{k1}+c_{k2}x+\ldots+c_{k,r_k}x^{r_k-1}),\end{aligned}$$

where the c_{ij} are arbitrary constants.

If the a_i are real and $(\beta+i\gamma)^r$ is a complex root, so is $(\beta-i\gamma)^r$, and the corresponding terms can be paired and expressed as

$$e^{\beta x}\{(A_1+A_2x+\ldots+A_rx^{r-1})\cos(\gamma x)+(B_1+B_2x+\ldots+B_rx^{r-1})\sin(\gamma x)\},$$

where A_i and B_i are arbitrary constants.

To find a particular solution of equation (11) when $f(x)=He^{px}$, where H and p are real or complex constants, try, by substitution in (11), to find the value of the constant d such that de^{px} is a solution, unless p is a root of the auxiliary equation. If p is an r-ple root of the auxiliary equation, try dx^re^{px}.

If $y_1, y_2, \ldots, y_s$ are particular solutions of equation (11) when $f(x)=f_1(x), f_2(x), \ldots, f_s(x)$ respectively, then $y_1+y_2+\ldots+y_s$ is a solution when $f(x)=f_1(x)+f_2(x)+\ldots+f_s(x)$. This statement is true of equation (14) also (see § 19.62).

19.61. The *homogeneous linear* differential equation

$$a_0x^ny^{(n)}+a_1x^{n-1}y^{(n-1)}+\ldots+a_{n-1}xy'+a_ny=f(x), \qquad (13)$$

where the a_i are constants, is reduced by the transformation $x=e^t$ to a linear differential equation with constant coefficients.

19.62. The *general linear* differential equation of the nth order is

$$y^{(n)}+f_1(x)\,y^{(n-1)}+\ldots+f_{n-1}(x)\,y'+f_n(x)\,y=f(x). \qquad (14)$$

The equation of the same form, but with zero on the right-hand side, is called the reduced equation.

A practical method of solution of the reduced equation is to substitute

$$y=x^\rho(a_0+a_1x+\ldots+a_rx^r+\ldots)$$

and the values for $y^{(i)}$, obtained from it by term-by-term differentiation, in the reduced equation, after expanding the coefficients $f_i(x)$, if necessary, in powers of x. Equate coefficients of powers of x, so obtaining relations from which ρ and then a_r may be determined. Certain of the a_r may be taken arbitrarily.

If a linearly independent set (fundamental set) of n integrals, $y_1, y_2, \ldots, y_n$, of the reduced equation is known, the general integral of the equation (14) can be found by quadratures by the method of *Variation of Parameters:*

Let the general solution of (14) be written in the form

$$y=c_1y_1+c_2y_2+\ldots+c_ny_n,$$

where the c_i are functions of x. The first derivates of the c_i may be chosen to satisfy the following linear equations:

$$
\begin{aligned}
y_1c'_1+ \dots +y_nc'_n &\equiv 0,\\
y'_1c'_1+ \dots +y'_nc'_n &\equiv 0,\\
\cdot \quad \cdot \quad \cdot \quad & \cdot \quad \cdot \quad \cdot\\
\cdot \quad \cdot \quad \cdot \quad & \cdot \quad \cdot \quad \cdot\\
y_1{}^{(n-2)}c'_1+ \dots +y_n{}^{(n-2)}c'_n &\equiv 0,
\end{aligned}
$$

and will then also satisfy

$$y_1{}^{(n-1)}c'_1+ \dots +y_n{}^{(n-1)}c'_n=f(x).$$

The determinant of the left-hand side of these equations is the Wronskian (q.v.) of y_1, y_2, . . ., y_n, which does not vanish since $y_1, y_2, \dots, y_n$ are linearly independent solutions. Hence these equations give a unique solution for c'_1, c'_2, . . ., c'_n. The general integral is then

$$y=y_1\left\{\int c'_1(x)\,dx+k_1\right\}+ \dots +y_n\left\{\int c'_n(x)\,dx+k_n\right\},$$

where k_1, k_2, . . ., k_n are arbitrary constants.

19.7. System of simultaneous ordinary differential equations of the first order

Consider the n equations in $(n+1)$ variables x_1, . . ., x_n, t

$$
\left.
\begin{aligned}
\frac{dx_1}{dt}&=X_1(x_1, x_2, \dots, x_n),\\
\cdot \quad \cdot \quad & \cdot \quad \cdot \quad \cdot\\
\cdot \quad \cdot \quad & \cdot \quad \cdot \quad \cdot\\
\frac{dx_n}{dt}&=X_n(x_1, x_2, \dots, x_n),
\end{aligned}
\right\} \quad . \quad . \quad . \quad (15)
$$

where X_1, X_2, . . ., X_n are regular functions of x_1, x_2, . . ., x_n in a given domain and do not contain the independent variable t. (If they do, introduce another variable s and add the equation $dt/ds=1$.)

The curve $x_1=\phi_1(t)$, $x_2=\phi_2(t)$, . . ., $x_n=\phi_n(t)$ (of n-dimensional space) is a *particular solution* of the equations (15) if the equations are satisfied identically in t when $\phi_i(t)$ is substituted for x_i. If a function $F(x_1, x_2, \dots, x_n)$ remains constant in virtue of (15) or of the $n-1$ equivalent equations

$$\frac{dx_1}{X_1}=\frac{dx_2}{X_2}= \dots =\frac{dx_n}{X_n},$$

$F=$constant is called a *first integral* of the equations. If $n-1$ independent first integrals $F_1=a_1$, . . ., $F_{n-1}=a_{n-1}$, involving $n-1$ constants are known, the system (15) is solved. Any other first integral will be a function of F_1, . . ., F_{n-1}, say $\psi(F_1, F_2, \dots, F_{n-1})$.

The first integrals $F_1=a_1, \ldots, F_{n-1}=a_{n-1}$ intersect in a curve which is a particular solution.

To find a first integral look for functions $\lambda_1, \ldots, \lambda_n$ such that

$$\lambda_1 X_1+\lambda_2 X_2+\ldots+\lambda_n X_n=0$$

and $\lambda_1 dx_1+\lambda_2 dx_2+\ldots+\lambda_n dx_n$ is a perfect differential dF. Then $F=c$ is a first integral.

The integral curve through a point $(x_1^0, x_2^0, \ldots, x_n^0)$ lies entirely on the first integral $F(x_1, x_2, \ldots, x_n)=c$, where $c=F(x_1^0, x_2^0, \ldots, x_n^0)$. Hence the first integral $F(x_1, x_2, \ldots, x_n)=c$ satisfies the partial differential equation

$$\frac{\partial F}{\partial x_1}X_1+\frac{\partial F}{\partial x_2}X_2+\ldots+\frac{\partial F}{\partial x_n}X_n=0 \quad . \quad . \quad . \quad (16)$$

Conversely, all the integrals of (16) are included in

$$\psi(F_1, F_2, \ldots, F_{n-1})=0,$$

where ψ is an arbitrary function.

If $X_1, \ldots, X_n$ are functions of the independent variable t as well as of $x_1, x_2, \ldots, x_n$, it is possible that special integrals not included in $\psi(F_1, F_2, \ldots, F_{n-1})=0$ may exist, but for these some of $X_1, \ldots, X_n$ will cease to be regular.

19.8. The equation

$$P(x, y, z)\, dx+Q(x, y, z)\, dy+R(x, y, z)\, dz=0 \quad . \quad . \quad (17)$$

expresses that the direction $dx : dy : dz$ is perpendicular to the direction $P : Q : R$.

Case I

Condition of integrability satisfied. The equation is said to be *integrable* if a function $F(x, y, z)$ can be found such that the constancy of F involves the relation (17), i.e. if a family of surfaces $F(x, y, z)=c$ exist for which $F_x/P=F_y/Q=F_z/R$. Then the curves (see § 19.7), given by

$$\frac{dx}{P}=\frac{dy}{Q}=\frac{dz}{R}, \quad . \quad . \quad . \quad . \quad (18)$$

possess a system of orthogonal trajectory surfaces $F(x, y, z)=c$. The differential equation is then properly said to represent a family of surfaces. Such a family does not in general exist. The necessary and sufficient condition for integrability (in this sense) is

$$P(Q_z-R_y)+Q(R_x-P_z)+R(P_y-Q_x)=0 \quad . \quad . \quad (19)$$

or, if P, Q, R are the components of a vector $\mathbf{A}$.

$$\mathbf{A} \text{ curl } \mathbf{A}=0.$$

If this condition is not satisfied identically it will itself define a surface which may or may not be an integral, and in this case no other integral surface exists.

To solve the equation (17) when the condition (19) is satisfied:

(1) Find an integral $V=c$ of $P\,dx+Q\,dy=0$ treating z as a constant.

(2) Assume $V=f(z)$ as a solution. Differentiate this and by comparison with (17) find an equation for $f'(z)$.

(3) Integrate this equation, obtaining a solution involving one arbitrary constant.

Case II

Condition (19) *not satisfied.* In this case equation (17) represents a family of curves, the direction ratios of whose tangents are $dx : dy : dz$. These curves are perpendicular to the curves given by equations (18). The curves of the family (17) which lie on an arbitrary surface $\phi(x, y, z)=0$ satisfy (17) and

$$\phi_x\,dx+\phi_y\,dy+\phi_z\,dz=0,$$

and hence satisfy

$$(P\phi_z-R\phi_x)\,dx+(Q\phi_z-R\phi_y)\,dy=0. \quad . \quad . \quad . \quad (20)$$

Eliminate z between (20) and $\phi(x, y, z)=0$, obtaining an equation

$$M\,dx+N\,dy=0, \quad . \quad . \quad . \quad . \quad (21)$$

where M and N are functions of x and y only. The required curves are the curves of intersection of the integral surface of (21) with $\phi(x, y, z)=0$.

Thus on every arbitrary surface in space there is a one-parameter family of curves whose tangents $dx : dy : dz$ satisfy (17). Through any point in space passes a curve of (18) and infinities of curves of (17) perpendicular to it. In the special case when all the curves of (17) through the point lie on a surface the condition (19) is satisfied.

19.9. Partial differential equations

A partial differential equation of the first order with independent variables x and y is a relation

$$F(x, y, z, p, q)=0,$$

where $p=\dfrac{\partial z}{\partial x}$, $q=\dfrac{\partial z}{\partial y}$. The equation is solved when all functions $z=\phi(x, y)$ which satisfy the equation are determined.

19.91. The linear partial equation

$$P(x, y, z)p+Q(x, y, z)q=R(x, y, z). \quad . \quad . \quad . \tag{22}$$

If two independent first integrals $F_1(x, y, z)=c_1$, $F_2(x, y, z)=c_2$ of the equations

$$\frac{dx}{P}=\frac{dy}{Q}=\frac{dz}{R}$$

can be found, then the general solution of (22) is the function z defined by the equation

$$\phi(F_1, F_2)=0, \quad . \quad . \quad . \quad . \tag{23}$$

where ϕ is an arbitrary function.

Equation (22) expresses that the normal to the surface (23) is perpendicular to the curves (18). The curves of (18) given by the two equations $F_1(x, y, z)=c_1$, $F_2(x, y, z)=c_2$, for which $\phi(c_1, c_2)=0$, all lie on the surface (23). Thus every surface satisfying (22) contains a single infinity of curves, satisfying (18).

19.92. The condition that the two equations $F(x, y, z, p, q)=0$ and $G(x, y, z, p, q)=0$ are compatible is

$$F_p(G_x+pG_z)+F_q(G_y+qG_z)-G_p(F_x+pF_z)$$
$$-G_q(F_y+qF_z)=0.$$

19.93. The equation F(x, y, z, p, q,)=0 (24)

A *complete* integral of this equation is one of the form $V(x, y, z, a, b)=0$, which defines a function $z=f(x, y, a, b)$ which satisfies (24) for all values of the parameters a, b. If V is known, all solutions of (24) can be obtained from it by differentiation and elimination. The *general integral* is the equation representing the aggregate of the envelopes (see § 20.9) of every possible singly-infinite set of solutions contained in the complete integral. These sets are defined by putting $b=\phi(a)$, in the complete integral. The *singular integral* is the envelope of the two-parameter family of complete integrals. It is included among the surfaces found by eliminating a and b from the equations

$$V(x, y, z, a, b)=0, \frac{\partial V}{\partial a}=0, \frac{\partial V}{\partial b}=0,$$

and also among those found by eliminating p and q from the equations

$$F(x, y, z, p, q)=0, \frac{\partial F}{\partial p}=0, \frac{\partial F}{\partial q}=0.$$

In each individual case one should test whether what is apparently a singular integral actually satisfies the differential equation.

To find the complete integral of $F(x, y, z, p, q)$ find (by the method of § 19.7 or otherwise) a first integral $\phi(x, y, z, p, q)=a$ of *Charpit's equations* (the subsidiary equations), viz.:

$$\frac{dx}{\dfrac{\partial F}{\partial p}}=\frac{dy}{\dfrac{\partial F}{\partial q}}=\frac{dz}{p\dfrac{\partial F}{\partial p}+q\dfrac{\partial F}{\partial q}}=\frac{-dp}{\dfrac{\partial F}{\partial x}+p\dfrac{\partial F}{\partial z}}=\frac{-dq}{\dfrac{\partial F}{\partial y}+q\dfrac{\partial F}{\partial z}},$$

and such that $\dfrac{\partial(F, \phi)}{\partial(p, q)}\neq 0$.

Then solve the equations $F=0$, $\phi=a$ for p and q and so form the equation

$$dz=p\,dx+q\,dy,$$

which is integrable. From it obtain $z=f(x, y, a, b)$, where b is the arbitrary constant introduced by the last integration.

If two independent first integrals $\phi=a$, $\psi=b$ of Charpit's equations can be found, then the complete integral of (24) is obtained by eliminating p and q from $F=0$, $\phi=a$, $\psi=b$. The general integral is $\phi=f(\psi)$, where f is an arbitrary function.

19.94. Laplace's equation in two dimensions

$$\frac{\partial^2 V}{\partial x^2}+\frac{\partial^2 V}{\partial y^2}=0.$$

A function $V=V(x, y)$ which satisfies this equation is called a *harmonic function*. The general integral of the equation is

$$V=f(x+iy)+\phi(x-iy),$$

where f and ϕ are arbitrary functions. The real and imaginary parts u and v of an analytic function $f(z)=u(x, y)+i\,v(x, y)$ are harmonic functions.

19.95. Euler's equation

$$A\frac{\partial^2 z}{\partial x^2}+2B\frac{\partial^2 z}{\partial x\,\partial y}+C\frac{\partial^2 z}{\partial y^2}=0 \quad (A, B, C \text{ constants}, C\neq 0).$$

The general integral is

$$z=f(x+\lambda_1 y)+\phi(x+\lambda_2 y),$$

where λ_1 and λ_2 are the roots of the equation

$$C\lambda^2+2B\lambda+A=0,$$

and f and ϕ are arbitrary functions. If $\lambda_1=\lambda_2$, the general integral is

$$z=y\,f(x+\lambda_1 y)+\phi(x+\lambda_1 y).$$

CHAPTER 20

DIFFERENTIAL GEOMETRY

IN Differential Geometry the Calculus is used like a microscope to enable us to examine the behaviour of a curve or surface in the neighbourhood of a point.

All the functions mentioned in this chapter are differentiable a sufficient number of times unless the contrary is stated.

20.1. Plane differential geometry

Notation. (x, y) is a general point on the curve considered and (X, Y) a general point in the plane. The curve may be given in one of the forms (i) $y=f(x)$, (ii) $F(x, y)=0$, (iii) parametrically by $x=\phi(t)$, $y=\psi(t)$, (iv) $r=f(\theta)$ in polar co-ordinates, (v) $r=F(p)$ in tangential polar co-ordinates. The positive direction along the curves (i), (iii), (iv) is that in which x, t and θ respectively increase.

We write

$$y'=\frac{dy}{dx},\ y''=\frac{d^2y}{dx^2},\ r'=\frac{dr}{d\theta},\ r''=\frac{d^2r}{d\theta^2},\ \phi'=\frac{d\phi}{dt},\ \psi'=\frac{d\psi}{dt}.$$

Then

$$y'=-F_x/F_y=\psi'/\phi'.$$

$$y''=-(F_{xx}F_y^2-2F_{xy}F_xF_y+F_{yy}F_x^2)/F_y^3.$$

$$=(\phi'\psi''-\psi'\phi'')/\phi'^3.$$

If the curve is given by equation (ii) or (iii), make the appropriate substituting for y' and y'' in the following formulae.

The length of the arc measured from a fixed point A on the curve (see § 16.5) is given by

$$\frac{ds}{dx}=\sqrt{(1+y'^2)},\ \frac{ds}{d\theta}=\sqrt{(r'^2+r^2)},\ \frac{ds}{dt}=\sqrt{(\phi'^2+\psi'^2)},$$

where the positive roots are taken.

20.11. Tangent and normal

The equation of the tangent to the curves (i)-(iii): (i) $Y-y=y'(X-x)$, (ii) $F_x(X-x)+F_y(Y-y)=0$, (iii) $(Y-y)\phi'-(X-x)\psi'=0$.

The positive direction along the tangent corresponds to the positive direction along the curve.

The normal at P is the line through P perpendicular to the tangent at P. Its equation is

$$(Y-y)y'+X-x=0.$$

The positive direction along the normal is obtained by turning the positive tangent through a positive (anti-clockwise) angle $\frac{1}{2}\pi$. The slope, $\tan\psi$, of the tangent is given by $\tan\psi = y'$ (see Fig. 20.1).

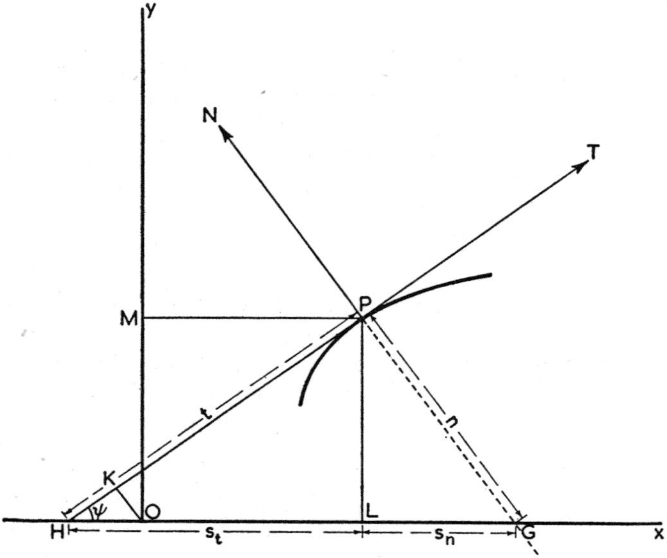

Fig. 20.1

The distances PH and PG from P to the points of intersection of the tangent and normal respectively with the x-axis are called the lengths t and n of the tangent and normal. t is positive if PH is the positive direction along the tangent, and similarly for n. The projections LH and LG of t and n on the x-axis are called the *sub-tangent* and *sub-normal*, respectively. Then

$$t = \frac{-y}{y'}\sqrt{(1+y'^2)},\ n = -y\sqrt{(1+y'^2)},\ s_n = yy',\ s_t = -y/y'.$$

The lengths p_t and p_n of the polar-tangent and polar-normal are the lengths of the intercepts on the tangent and normal between the point of contact P and their points of intersection with the perpendicular OB through the pole O to the radius vector OP (see Fig. 20.2). The polar sub-tangent s_t and polar sub-normal s_n are the projections of p_t and p_n on OB. The positive direction along the radius vector is $\overline{OP}$ and along OB is the direction obtained by turning $\overline{OP}$ through $+\frac{1}{2}\pi$. The angle between OP and the positive direction of the tangent at P is ϕ.

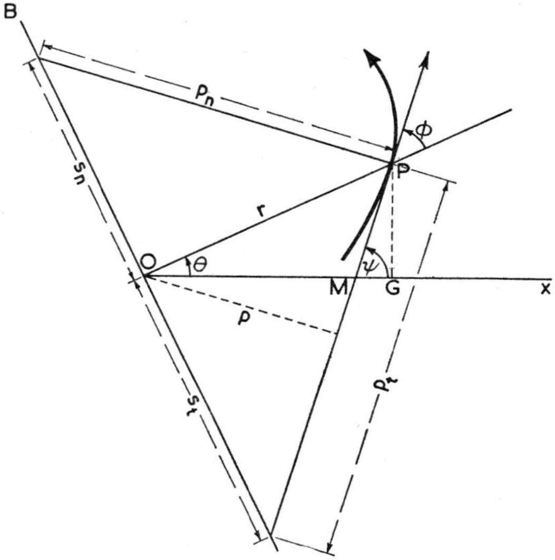

Fig. 20.2

Then $$\tan\phi=\frac{rd\theta}{dr},\ \cos\phi=\frac{dr}{ds},\ \sin\phi=\frac{rd\theta}{ds}, \quad . \quad . \quad . \quad (1)$$

$$p_t=\frac{-r}{r'}\sqrt{(r^2+r'^2)},\ p_n=\sqrt{(r^2+r'^2)},\ s_t=-r^2/r',\ s_n=r'. \quad . \quad . \quad (2)$$

$$\psi=\theta+\phi,\ p=r\sin\phi,$$

$$\frac{r}{\sin(\theta+\phi)}=\frac{OM}{\sin\phi}=\frac{PM}{\sin\theta}, \quad . \quad . \quad . \quad (3)$$

$$PG=PM\sin\psi=PM\sin(\theta+\phi), \quad . \quad . \quad . \quad (4)$$

$$MG=PM\cos\psi=PM\cos(\theta+\phi). \quad . \quad . \quad . \quad (5)$$

The *asymptotes* of a curve are the tangents at its points of intersection with the line at infinity. An algebraic curve of order n has n complex asymptotes, distinct or coincident. To find the equations of the asymptotes of the algebraic curve

$$u_n+u_{n-1}+\ldots+u_1+u_0=0, \quad . \quad . \quad . \quad (6)$$

where u_r is homogeneous of degree r in x and y, substitute $mx+c$ for y in (6), obtaining

$$x^n v_n+x^{n-1}v_{n-1}+\ldots+v_0=0,$$

where v_n is of degree $k\leqslant n$ in m and does not involve c, and v_{n-1} is linear in c. Let the roots of $v_n=0$ be $m_1, m_2, \ldots, m_k$. Corresponding to each root m_i find the value c_i from the relation $v_{n-1}=0$. Then asymptotes are given by

$$y=m_i x+c_i \quad (i=1, \ldots, k).$$

If v_n is of degree less than n in m, $v_n=0$ has $n-k$ infinite roots and the equations of $n-k$ corresponding asymptotes are of the form $x=d_i$. Find these values d_i by substituting d for x in (6) and equating to zero the coefficient of the highest power of y, i.e. of y^{n-k}.

If the curve is given in polars by $r=f(\theta)$, the gradients of the asymptotes are given by

$$1/f(\theta)=0.$$

The distance of an asymptote from the pole is

$$\lim_{r\to\infty} s_t=\lim_{r\to\infty}(-r^2/r')=-[f(\theta_i)]^2/f'(\theta_i),$$

where θ_i is the corresponding root of $1/f(\theta)=0$.

20.12. Contact of two curves

Two curves, $y=f(x)$ and $y=\phi(x)$, have *n-point contact* or *contact of order* $(n-1)$ at a point (x_0, y_0) if n of the points of intersection of the two curves coalesce at (x_0, y_0). This happens if and only if

$$f(x_0)=\phi(x_0), f'(x_0)=\phi'(x_0), \ldots, f^{(n-1)}(x_0)=\phi^{(n-1)}(x_0),$$

while $f^{(n)}(x_0)\neq\phi^{(n)}(x_0)$. If two curves have two-point contact they are said to touch.

The line $y=mx+c$ has n-point contact with the curve $y=f(x)$ at (x_0, y_0) if

$$f'(x_0)=m,\ c=f(x_0)-x_0 f'(x_0),$$
$$f''(x_0)=f'''(x_0)=\ldots=f^{(n-1)}(x_0)=0, f^{(n)}(x_0)\neq 0.$$

The point of contact is called an *inflexion* if n is odd (and >1) and a *point of undulation* if n is even (and >2). The curve crosses the tangent or not according as n is odd or even.

If the y-axis is vertical and $y'=0$, the curve is convex from below when $y''>0$ and concave from below when $y''<0$.

20.13. Curvature

The *curvature* κ at a point P on the curve is

$$\lim_{Q\to P}(\Delta\psi/\Delta s)$$

as $Q\to P$ along the curve, where $\Delta\psi$ is the angle between the tangents at P and Q, and Δs is the arc PQ.

The *radius of curvature* ρ at P is $1/\kappa$.

$$\rho=\left\{1+\left(\frac{dy}{dx}\right)^2\right\}^{3/2}\bigg/\frac{d^2y}{dx^2}=\left(\phi'^2+\psi'^2\right)^{3/2}\bigg/\left(\phi'\psi''-\psi'\phi''\right).$$

Take the positive root. Then d^2y/dx^2 gives the sign of ρ.
In polar co-ordinates

$$\rho=\left\{r^2+\left(\frac{dr}{d\theta}\right)^2\right\}^{3/2}\bigg/\left\{r^2+2\left(\frac{dr}{d\theta}\right)^2-r\frac{d^2r}{d\theta^2}\right\}, \quad . \quad . \quad . \quad (7)$$

In tangential-polar co-ordinates (p, r),

$$\rho=r\frac{dr}{dp}. \quad . \quad . \quad . \quad . \quad . \quad . \quad (8)$$

When a curve is given in polar co-ordinates by $f(r, \theta)=0$, it is often simpler to find the tangential polar equation by eliminating θ and ϕ from

$$f(r, \theta)=0, \ \tan\phi=\frac{rd\theta}{dr}, \quad p=r\sin\phi$$

and use (8), rather than to use (7) directly.

The *circle of curvature* at P is the limiting position, as $Q\to P$ along the curve, of the circle touching at P the tangent at P and passing through a point Q on the curve. Its radius is ρ and it has three-point contact (at least) with the curve at P. Its centre (α, β) is called the *centre of curvature* at P and is given by

$$\alpha=x-\rho\sin\psi, \ \beta=y+\rho\cos\psi, \quad . \quad . \quad . \quad (9)$$

where

$$\sin\psi=\frac{dy}{dx}\bigg/\sqrt{\left\{1+\left(\frac{dy}{dx}\right)^2\right\}}=\frac{dy}{ds}, \ \cos\psi=1\bigg/\sqrt{\left\{1+\left(\frac{dy}{dx}\right)^2\right\}}=\frac{dx}{ds}.$$

It is wise to draw a rough figure as a check on the signs of ρ, $\sin\psi$ and $\cos\psi$. If the tangent at (x_0, y_0) is parallel to Oy, either draw a figure, or turn the axes through a right angle by the substitution $x=-\eta$, $y=\xi$ and deal with the curve $\xi=f(-\eta)$ at $(y_0, -x_0)$.

Newton's formula for ρ. Let PT be the tangent at P and TQ be perpendicular to PT meeting the curve at Q. Then

$$2\rho=\lim_{T\to P}\frac{TP^2}{TQ}=\lim_{x\to 0}\frac{x^2}{y},$$

if the origin is taken at P and the axis of x along PT.

20.14. Envelope of a one-parameter family of curves, $F(x, y, \alpha)=0$.

Definition. The *envelope* of a one parameter family of curves is a curve which touches every member of the family.

The equation of the envelope is contained in the equation obtained by eliminating α between the equations

$$F(x, y, \alpha)=0, \quad \frac{\partial F}{\partial \alpha}(x, y, \alpha)=0.$$

The equation obtained is of the form $f_1 f_2^2 f_3^3=0$, where $f_1=0$ is the envelope, $f_2=0$ is the locus of the double-points and $f_3=0$ the locus of the cusps on curves of the family. In the case of a family of straight lines the envelope $f_1=0$ only is obtained.

20.15. Evolute and involutes of a curve

The *evolute* of a curve is the envelope of its normals.

This is identical with the locus of the centre of curvature of a curve and is given parametrically by equations (9).

A curve Γ is an *involute* of a curve C if C is the evolute of Γ.

Any given curve C has an infinite number of involutes. If s is the length of arc of the given curve C measured from a fixed point A on it and k is any constant, then the locus of $Q(\xi, \eta)$, where

$$\xi=x-(s+k)\cos\psi, \quad \eta=y-(s+k)\sin\psi$$

is an involute of C.

The involutes form a set of parallel curves.

20.2. Multiple points and tangents of an algebraic curve

The point	The tangential
equation of an algebraic curve of	
order n is	class m is
$f(x, y)\equiv \Sigma a_{pq}x^p y^q=0,\ p+q\leqslant n,$ in Cartesian co-ordinates and	
$f(x, y, z)\equiv \Sigma a_{pqr}x^p y^q z^r=0,$ $p+q+r=n,$ in homogeneous co-ordinates.	$F(l, m, n)\equiv \Sigma A_{pqr}l^p m^q n^r=0,$ $p+q+r=m,$ in homogeneous co-ordinates.
P is a *multiple point* of *multiplicity* r if a general line through P meets the curve at P in r coincident points.	p is a *multiple tangent* of *multiplicity* r if r of the tangents to the curve through a general point on p coincide with p.
A double point may be a node, at which the tangents are distinct, or a cusp at which they are coincident.	A double tangent may be a bitangent which has two distinct points of contact or an inflexional tangent at which the points of contact coincide.

The condition that (0, 0) is an r-ple point of

$$f(x, y) \equiv w_n + w_{n-1} + \dots + w_0 = 0,$$

or (0, 0, 1) of

$$f(x, y, z) \equiv w_n + w_{n-1}z + \dots + w_0 z^n = 0,$$

where w_r is homogeneous in x and y of degree r, is that the terms of lowest degree in x and y together are of degree r. The combined equation of the tangents at (0, 0) or (0, 0, 1) is then

$$w_r = 0.$$

The condition that the line (0, 0, 1) is an r-ple tangent of

$$F(l, m, n) \equiv \rho_m + \rho_{m-1}n + \dots + \rho_0 n^m = 0,$$

where ρ_r is homogeneous in l and m of degree r, is that the terms of lowest degree in l and m together are of degree r. The combined equation of the points of contact is then

$$\rho_r = 0.$$

The necessary and sufficient conditions that $f(x, y) = 0$ shall have an r-ple point at (x_0, y_0) are that all partial derivatives of total order less than r vanish at (x_0, y_0).

The tangents at an r-ple point $P(x, y)$ are

$$Y - y - m(X - x) = 0,$$

where m is a root of

$$\left(\frac{\partial}{\partial x} + m\frac{\partial}{\partial y}\right)^{(r)} f(x, y) = 0.$$

A double point (x, y) is a node with real distinct tangents, cusp, or isolated point with unreal tangents according as

$$f^2_{xy} \gtreqless f_{xx} f_{yy}$$

at the point.

The necessary and sufficient condition that (x, y, z) be an r-ple point of $f(x, y, z) = 0$ is

$$f_{x^i y^j z^k} = 0$$

for all $i + j + k = r - 1$, $i \geqslant 0$, $j \geqslant 0$, $k \geqslant 0$, i.e. all partial derivatives of total order less than r vanish at (x, y, z).

The necessary and sufficient condition that (l, m, n) be an r-ple tangent of $F(l, m, n) = 0$ is

$$F_{l^i m^j n^k} = 0$$

for all $i + j + k = r - 1$, $i \geqslant 0$, $j \geqslant 0$, $k \geqslant 0$, i.e. all partial derivatives of total order less than r vanish at (l, m, n).

20.21. The *polar curves* of a point $P_0(x_0, y_0, z_0)$ with respect to a curve $f(x, y, z)=0$ are the curves obtained by equating to zero the coefficients of $\lambda, \lambda^2, \ldots, \lambda^{n-1}$ in the expansion of

$$f(x+\lambda x_0, y+\lambda y_0, z+\lambda z_0)=0.$$

The rth polar curve Γ^r is

$$\left(x_0\frac{\partial}{\partial x}+y_0\frac{\partial}{\partial y}+z_0\frac{\partial}{\partial z}\right)^{(r)} f(x, y, z)=0$$

or

$$\left(x\frac{\partial}{\partial x_0}+y\frac{\partial}{\partial y_0}+z\frac{\partial}{\partial z_0}\right)^{(n-r)} f(x_0, y_0, z_0)=0.$$

It is of order $n-r$ and is also called the *polar* $(n-r)$-ic. The coordinates of the n points of intersection of the line joining P_0 to an arbitrary point P can be expressed in the form $P+\lambda_i P_0$ $(i=1, \ldots, n)$. The locus of the point P, for which the sum of the products of the λ_r taken r at a time vanishes, is Γ^r. This relation between P_0, P and the n points $P+\lambda_i P_0$ is invariant for linear transformations of coordinates and the curves Γ^r are covariants (q.v.) of P_0 and C.

The *first polar* of P_0 passes through the points of contact of the tangents from P_0, through the nodes and cusps and touches the cuspidal tangent at each cusp. It meets C only at multiple points of C and at points of contact of tangents from P_0.

The *polar conic* of P_0 is the curve

$$\left(x\frac{\partial}{\partial x_0}+y\frac{\partial}{\partial y_0}+z\frac{\partial}{\partial z_0}\right)^{(2)} f(x_0, y_0, z_0)=0.$$

The locus of a point P whose polar conic degenerates into a line-pair is the *Hessian* of $f(x, y, z)=0$.

Its equation is

$$H\equiv\begin{vmatrix} f_{xx} & f_{xy} & f_{xz} \\ f_{yx} & f_{yy} & f_{yz} \\ f_{zx} & f_{zy} & f_{zz} \end{vmatrix}=0.$$

H is a covariant of order $3(n-2)$ of $f(x, y, z)=0$. It passes through the points of inflexion of C, has a double point at each node A of C and its tangents at A coincide with the tangents of C at A. It has a triple point at each cusp of C and two of its tangents there coincide with the cuspidal tangent of C. It meets the curve only at multiple points and points of inflexion.

Let m be the class of $f(x, y, z)=0$, δ the number of its nodes and κ the number of cusps, τ of bitangents and i of inflexions, where both real and complex points are counted.

For curves whose only multiple points are double points with distinct tangents or simple cusps:

Plucker's equations

$$\left.\begin{aligned} n(n-1) &= m+2\delta+3\kappa \\ 3n(n-2) &= i+6\delta+8\kappa \\ m(m-1) &= n+2\tau+3i \\ 3m(m-2) &= \kappa+6\tau+8i \end{aligned}\right\} \quad . \quad . \quad . \quad . \quad (10)$$

The equations hold for a curve with an r-ple point with r distinct tangents if this is reckoned as equivalent to $r(r-1)/2$ nodes.

The maximum number of double points which a non-degenerate plane curve of order n can have is $\frac{1}{2}(n-1)(n-2)$. If the curve has an r-ple point, this may be reckoned as equivalent to $\frac{1}{2}r(r-1)+h$ double points, where $h \geqslant 0$. If the tangents are distinct, $h=0$. A curve which has this maximum number of double points can be expressed parametrically by

$$x:y:z=p(\theta):q(\theta):r(\theta),$$

where p, q, r are polynomials in θ of degree $\leqslant n$. (One at least is of degree n.) Such a curve is said to be *rational* or *unicursal.*

20.3. Skew curves

In this section x, y, z are rectangular Cartesian co-ordinates and dashes denote differentiation with respect to the arc s of the curve.

Representation of a curve

(1) Parametrically:

$$x=f_1(t),\ y=f_2(t),\ z=f_3(t),$$

where the f_i are functions of t with continuous second order derivates.

(2) A curve which is the complete intersection of two surfaces can be represented by $F_1(x, y, z)=0$, $F_2(x, y, z)=0$.

(3) By three surfaces $F_1(x, y, z)=0$, $F_2(x, y, z)=0$, $F_3(x, y, z)=0$ through the curve. These may intersect further in isolated points.

The positive direction along the curve is the direction in which t increases. This is also the positive direction along the tangent.

The *line element* of the curve is

$$ds=+\sqrt{\left\{\left(\frac{df_1}{dt}\right)^2+\left(\frac{df_2}{dt}\right)^2+\left(\frac{df_3}{dt}\right)^2\right\}}\,dt.$$

The length of the curve from t_0 to t_1 is

$$s=\int_{t_0}^{t_1}\sqrt{\left\{\left(\frac{df_1}{dt}\right)^2+\left(\frac{df_2}{dt}\right)^2+\left(\frac{df_3}{dt}\right)^2\right\}}\,dt.$$

Theoretically the curve can be represented by

$$x=\phi(s),\ y=\psi(s),\ z=\chi(s), \quad . \quad . \quad . \ (11)$$

where ϕ, ψ, χ are differentiable functions of s. Then

$$\Sigma x'^2=1,\ \Sigma x'x''=0,$$

where Σ indicates summation over x, y, z.

An *ordinary* point on the curve is one at which not all of x', y', z' or of $y'z''-y''z'$, $z'x''-z''x'$, $x'y''-x''y'$ vanish. Points which are not ordinary are *singular*.

The moving trihedral

Definition. The *osculating plane* at P is the limiting position of the plane through the tangent PT (see § 9.5) and through a close point Q on the curve as $Q \to P$ along the curve.

The *normal plane* at P is the plane through P perpendicular to the tangent at P. Every line through P in this plane is a normal to the curve at P. The *principal normal* is the normal which lies in the osculating plane. The *binormal* is the normal to the osculating plane at P. The positive direction along the principal normal is the direction from P towards the centre of the osculating circle at P (see § 20.13). That along the binormal is such that the tangent, principal normal and binormal are oriented in the same way as the x, y and z axes. The *rectifying plane* at P is the plane through the tangent and binormal. The trihedral consisting of the tangent, principal normal and binormal exists at every ordinary point of the curve.

Notation Direction cosines of the tangent: l_1, m_1, n_1; principal normal: l_2, m_2, n_2; binormal: l_3, m_3, n_3. Then

$$l_1=x',\ m_1=y',\ n_1=z';$$

$$l_2=x''/\surd(\Sigma x''^2)=\rho x'', \text{ etc.};$$

$$l_3=(y'z''-z'y'')/\surd(\Sigma x''^2), \text{ etc.}$$

Equations of tangent: $$\frac{X-x}{x'}=\frac{Y-y}{y'}=\frac{Z-z}{z'}(=r).$$

Princ. normal: $$\frac{X-x}{x''}=\frac{Y-y}{y''}=\frac{Z-z}{z''}\left[=\frac{r}{\surd(\Sigma x''^2)}\right].$$

Binormal: $$\frac{X-x}{y'z''-z'y''}=\frac{Y-y}{z'x''-x'z''}=\frac{Z-z}{x'y''-y'x''}\left[=\frac{r}{\surd(\Sigma x''^2)}\right],$$

where r is the distance from (x, y, z) to (X, Y, Z).

Normal plane: $\Sigma x'(X-x)=0,$

Rectifying plane: $\Sigma x''(X-x)=0,$

Osculating plane: $\begin{vmatrix} X-x & Y-y & Z-z \\ x' & y' & z' \\ x'' & y'' & z'' \end{vmatrix} = 0.$

20.4. The *curvature* κ at $P = \lim_{Q\to P} \dfrac{\epsilon}{\text{arc } PQ}$, where ϵ is the angle between the tangent at P and at a close point Q on the curve. The *radius of curvature* at P is $\rho = 1/\kappa$, where

$$\kappa = 1/\rho = +\sqrt{(\Sigma x''^2)} = +\sqrt{(\Sigma l_1'^2)}.$$

The circle of curvature (see § 20.13) lies in the osculating plane and its centre, called the centre of curvature, is the point

$$(x+\rho l_2,\ y+\rho m_2,\ z+\rho n_2),\ \text{i.e. } (x+\rho^2 x'',\ y+\rho^2 y'',\ z+\rho^2 z'').$$

The *torsion* $\tau = 1/\sigma$ at P is $\lim_{Q\to P} \dfrac{\theta}{\text{arc } PQ}$, where θ is the angle between the binormals at P and at a close point Q on the curve. σ is called the *radius of torsion*. The sign of τ is determined by equation (14) below.

Serret-Frenet equations:

$$\frac{dl_1}{ds} = \frac{l_2}{\rho}, \qquad \frac{dm_1}{ds} = \frac{m_2}{\rho}, \qquad \frac{dn_1}{ds} = \frac{n_2}{\rho}; \qquad (12)$$

$$\frac{dl_2}{ds} = -\left(\frac{l_1}{\rho} + \frac{l_3}{\sigma}\right), \quad \frac{dm_2}{ds} = -\left(\frac{m_1}{\rho} + \frac{m_3}{\sigma}\right), \quad \frac{dn_2}{ds} = -\left(\frac{n_1}{\rho} + \frac{n_3}{\sigma}\right); \qquad (13)$$

$$\frac{dl_3}{ds} = \frac{l_2}{\sigma}, \qquad \frac{dm_3}{ds} = \frac{m_2}{\sigma}, \qquad \frac{dn_3}{ds} = \frac{n_2}{\sigma}. \qquad (14)$$

A formula for σ:

$$\frac{1}{\rho^2 \sigma} = -\begin{vmatrix} x' & y' & z' \\ x'' & y'' & z'' \\ x''' & y''' & z''' \end{vmatrix}.$$

The curve is plane if, and only if, the above determinant is identically zero.

20.41. *Definition.* The *osculating sphere* at P is the sphere which has four-point contact with the curve at P. Its centre is the point

$$(x+\rho l_2 - \rho'\sigma l_3,\ y+\rho m_2 - \rho'\sigma m_3,\ z+\rho n_2 - \rho'\sigma n_3),$$

and its radius R is the *radius of spherical curvature* at P given by

$$R^2 = \rho^2 + \sigma^2 \rho'^2.$$

The osculating plane cuts the osculating sphere in the circle of curvature. The centre of the osculating sphere lies on the normal to the osculating plane through the centre of curvature at a distance $(-\sigma\rho')$ from the osculating plane in the direction of the positive binormal.

The equations $\rho=\rho(s)$, $\sigma=\sigma(s)$ are called the *intrinsic equations* of the curve. Two curves with the same intrinsic equations are congruent.

20.42. Canonical equations of the curve

Let the tangent, principal normal and binormal at a fixed point A on the curve be taken as axes of reference and the arc s be measured from A to P. Let ρ and σ be the radii of curvature and torsion at A. Then the co-ordinates of P are

$$x=s-\frac{1}{6\rho^2}s^3+\frac{1}{8}\frac{\rho'}{\rho^3}s^4+\ldots,$$

$$y=\frac{1}{2\rho}s^2-\frac{\rho'}{6\rho^2}s^3+\frac{1}{24}\left\{\left(\frac{1}{\rho}\right)''-\frac{1}{\rho^3}-\frac{1}{\rho\sigma^2}\right\}s^4+\ldots,$$

$$z=-\frac{1}{6\rho\sigma}s^3+\frac{1}{24}\left\{\frac{2\rho'}{\rho^2\sigma}+\frac{\sigma'}{\sigma^2\rho}\right\}s^4+\ldots.$$

20.43. Particular skew curves

A *helix* is a curve whose tangents make a constant angle with a fixed direction.

A curve is a helix if, and only if, ρ/σ is constant.

A curve which lies on a right circular cylinder and cuts the generators at a constant angle is a *right circular helix*. Its equations may be written

$$x=a\cos\theta,\ y=a\sin\theta,\ z=k\theta,$$

where a and k are constants. For this curve

$$\rho=(a^2+k^2)/a,\quad \sigma=-(a^2+k^2)/k.$$

A *spherical curve* is a curve which lies on a sphere. A curve is spherical if and only if $\rho/\sigma+(\sigma\rho')'=0$.

The necessary and sufficient condition that the radius R of spherical curvative is constant is that either the curvature is constant or the curve is spherical.

20.5. Surfaces

Representation of a surface:

(i) $x=f_1(u, v),\ y=f_2(u, v),\ z=f_3(u, v)$. . . . (15)

(ii) $F(x, y, z)=0$. . . . . (16)

(iii) $z=f(x, y)$. . . . . (17)

The domain of u and v considered contains no *singular* points of the surface, i.e. no points at which

$$\frac{\partial(y, z)}{\partial(u, v)}=\frac{\partial(z, x)}{\partial(u, v)}=\frac{\partial(x, y)}{\partial(u, v)}=0.$$

The equation (16) may be solved for z giving one or more equations of the form (17), and the equation (17) can be written in the form (15) by taking $u=x$, $v=y$. We give results for the form (15). If equations (16) or (17) are used, substitute the following in the expressions given for the fundamental quadratic forms of the surface (15).

Write $$p=f_x,\ q=f_y,\ r=f_{xx},\ s=f_{xy},\ t=f_{yy}.$$

Then $$p=-F_x/F_z,\ q=-F_y/F_z,$$

$$r=-\{F_x^2F_{zz}-2F_xF_zF_{xz}+F_z^2F_{xx}\}/F_z^3,$$

$$s=-\{F_z^2F_{xy}-F_xF_zF_{yz}-F_yF_zF_{xz}+F_xF_yF_{zz}\}/F_z^3,$$

$$t=-\{F_y^2F_{zz}-2F_yF_zF_{yz}+F_z^2F_{yy}\}/F_z^3.$$

Parametric curves. The curves $u=$constant, $v=$constant are called the *parametric curves.* One curve of each system passes through every point on the surface. The positive direction on the parametric curve $v=$constant is that in which the *curvilinear co-ordinate* u increases. The relation $\phi(u, v)=0$ defines a curve on the surface.

20.51. The *line element* or *First Quadratic Form* $ds^2=dx^2+dy^2+dz^2$ along a curve $\phi(u, v)=0$ on the surface is given by

$$ds^2=E\,du^2+2F\,du\,dv+G\,dv^2 \quad . \quad . \quad . \quad (18)$$

where $\phi_u\,du+\phi_v\,dv=0$, and

$$E=\sum_{x,y,z} x_u^2,\ F=\sum_{x,y,z} x_ux_v,\ G=\sum_{x,y,z} x_v^2.$$

For the surface (17), $E=1+p^2$, $F=pq$, $G=1+q^2$.

We write also

$$H^2=EG-F^2=\left[\frac{\partial(y, z)}{\partial(u, v)}\right]^2+\left[\frac{\partial(z, x)}{\partial(u, v)}\right]^2+\left[\frac{\partial(x, y)}{\partial(u, v)}\right]^2.$$

$$H=+\sqrt{(EG-F^2)}.$$

$$P=\frac{1}{H}\frac{\partial(y, z)}{\partial(u, v)},\ Q=\frac{1}{H}\frac{\partial(z, x)}{\partial(u, v)},\ R=\frac{1}{H}\frac{\partial(x, y)}{\partial(u, v)},$$

$$P^2+Q^2+R^2=1.$$

If the surface and the parameters are real, $\sqrt{E}$ and $\sqrt{G}$ are real.

For the surface $F(x, y, z)=0$

$$P=F_x/\sqrt{(F_x^2+F_y^2+F_z^2)},\ Q=F_y/\sqrt{(F_x^2+F_y^2+F_z^2)},$$
$$R=F_z/\sqrt{(F_x^2+F_y^2+F_z^2)},$$

and for $z=f(x, y)$

$$P=-p/\sqrt{(1+p^2+q^2)},\ Q=-q/\sqrt{(1+p^2+q^2)},\ R=1/\sqrt{(1+p^2+q^2)}.$$

20.52. Tangent plane and normal

Definition. A tangent at A to a curve on a surface is a *tangent* line to the surface at A. All the tangent lines at an ordinary point $A(x, y, z)$ of the surface lie in a plane called the *tangent plane* at A whose equation is

$$\begin{vmatrix} X-x & Y-y & Z-z \\ x_u & y_u & z_u \\ x_v & y_v & z_v \end{vmatrix}=0.$$

The *normal* at A is the line through A perpendicular to the tangent plane at A. Its equations are

$$\frac{X-x}{P}=\frac{Y-y}{Q}=\frac{Z-z}{R}.$$

The positive direction along the normal is that which has the direction cosines P, Q, R. The tangents to the curves $v=$constant, $u=$constant, at a point and the normal at the point have the same mutual orientation as the x, y and z axes.

A rotation from the positive direction along $v=$constant to the positive direction along $u=$constant is reckoned positive. The direction cosines of the curve $\phi(u, v)=0$ on the surface are

$$(x_u\,du+x_v\,dv)/(E\,du^2+2F\,du\,dv+G\,dv^2)^{\frac{1}{2}},\ \ldots,\ \ldots,$$

where
$$\frac{\partial\phi}{\partial u}du+\frac{\partial\phi}{\partial v}dv=0.$$

The angle θ between the curves $\phi_2(u, v)=0$ and $\phi_1(u, v)=0$ measured from ϕ_2 to ϕ_1 is given by

$$\cos\theta=\frac{E\,du\,\delta u+F(du\,\delta v+dv\,\delta u)+G\,dv\,\delta v}{\sqrt{\{(E\,du^2+2F\,du\,dv+G\,dv^2)\,(E\,\delta u^2+2F\,\delta u\,\delta v+G\,\delta v^2)\}}},$$

where

$$\frac{\partial\phi_1}{\partial u}du+\frac{\partial\phi_1}{\partial v}dv=0,\ \frac{\partial\phi_2}{\partial u}\delta u+\frac{\partial\phi_2}{\partial v}\delta v=0,$$

and by $\sin\theta = H\left(\frac{\delta u}{\delta s}\frac{dv}{ds} - \frac{\delta v}{\delta s}\frac{du}{ds}\right)$

or $\tan\theta = H\dfrac{(\delta u\, dv - \delta v\, du)}{\{E\, du\, \delta u + F(du\, \delta v + \delta u\, dv) + G\, dv\, \delta v\}}$.

20.53. The *second quadratic form* of a surface is

$$L\, du^2 + 2M\, du\, dv + N\, dv^2,$$

where L, M, N, the *fundamental coefficients of the second order*, are given by

$$L = \sum_{x,y,z} P \,.\, x_{uu} = -\sum P_u\, x_u$$

$$M = \sum P \,.\, x_{uv} = -\sum P_u x_v = -\sum P_v x_u$$

$$N = \sum P \,.\, x_{vv} = -\sum P_v x_v.$$

These coefficients are invariant for any displacement of the surface in space.

20.6. The following formulae take a simpler form given in § 20.71 when the lines of curvature are parametric. The general formulae are:

Weingarten's formulae

$$\left.\begin{aligned} P_u &= \frac{FM - GL}{H^2}\, x_u + \frac{FL - EM}{H^2}\, x_v \\ P_v &= \frac{FN - GM}{H^2}\, x_u + \frac{FM - EN}{H^2}\, x_v \end{aligned}\right\} \quad . \quad . \quad . \quad (19)$$

The expressions for $Q_u, \ldots, R_v$ are obtained by replacing x by y and z respectively.

Equations of Gauss, satisfied by the first and second fundamental coefficients E, F, G; L, M, N of a surface:

$$\left.\begin{aligned} x_{uu} &= \begin{Bmatrix} 1\ 1 \\ 1 \end{Bmatrix} x_u + \begin{Bmatrix} 1\ 1 \\ 2 \end{Bmatrix} x_v + LP \\ x_{uv} &= \begin{Bmatrix} 1\ 2 \\ 1 \end{Bmatrix} x_u + \begin{Bmatrix} 1\ 2 \\ 2 \end{Bmatrix} x_v + MP \\ x_{vv} &= \begin{Bmatrix} 2\ 2 \\ 1 \end{Bmatrix} x_u + \begin{Bmatrix} 2\ 2 \\ 2 \end{Bmatrix} x_v + NP \end{aligned}\right\} \quad . \quad . \quad . \quad (20)$$

with similar equations in y, Q; z, R respectively, where the *Christoffel symbols* $\left\{\begin{matrix} i\ j \\ k \end{matrix}\right\}$ denote

$$\left\{\begin{matrix} 1\ 1 \\ 1 \end{matrix}\right\} = \frac{GE_u - 2FF_u + FE_v}{2H^2}, \quad \left\{\begin{matrix} 1\ 1 \\ 2 \end{matrix}\right\} = \frac{-FE_u + 2EF_u - EE_v}{2H^2},$$

$$\left\{\begin{matrix} 1\ 2 \\ 1 \end{matrix}\right\} = \frac{GE_v - FG_u}{2H^2}, \quad \left\{\begin{matrix} 1\ 2 \\ 2 \end{matrix}\right\} = \frac{EG_u - FE_v}{2H^2},$$

$$\left\{\begin{matrix} 2\ 2 \\ 1 \end{matrix}\right\} = \frac{-FG_v + 2GF_v - GG_u}{2H^2}, \quad \left\{\begin{matrix} 2\ 2 \\ 2 \end{matrix}\right\} = \frac{EG_v - 2FF_v + FG_u}{2H^2}.$$

The conditions of integrability of the equations of Gauss (20) reduce to *the* Gauss equation (below) and the two Codazzi equations, which are therefore the necessary and sufficient conditions that a surface exists having six given functions E, F, G; L, M, N of u and v as its first and second fundamental coefficients.

The Gauss equation

$$\frac{LN - M^2}{H^2} = \frac{1}{2H}\left[\frac{\partial}{\partial u}\left\{\frac{F}{EH}\frac{\partial E}{\partial v} - \frac{1}{H}\frac{\partial G}{\partial u}\right\} + \frac{\partial}{\partial v}\left\{\frac{2}{H}\frac{\partial F}{\partial u} - \frac{1}{H}\frac{\partial E}{\partial v} - \frac{F}{EH}\frac{\partial E}{\partial u}\right\}\right] \tag{21}$$

Codazzi or Mainardi-Codazzi equations

$$\begin{aligned} L_v + \left\{\begin{matrix} 1\ 1 \\ 1 \end{matrix}\right\} M + \left\{\begin{matrix} 1\ 1 \\ 2 \end{matrix}\right\} N &= M_u + \left\{\begin{matrix} 1\ 2 \\ 1 \end{matrix}\right\} L + \left\{\begin{matrix} 1\ 2 \\ 2 \end{matrix}\right\} M, \\ M_v + \left\{\begin{matrix} 1\ 2 \\ 1 \end{matrix}\right\} M + \left\{\begin{matrix} 1\ 2 \\ 2 \end{matrix}\right\} N &= N_u + \left\{\begin{matrix} 2\ 2 \\ 1 \end{matrix}\right\} L + \left\{\begin{matrix} 2\ 2 \\ 2 \end{matrix}\right\} M. \end{aligned} \tag{22}$$

(See § 20.71 for a simpler form of these equations.)

20.7. Curvature of a surface

Curvature of a curve on a surface. A *normal section* of the surface at a point M is a plane section whose plane passes through the normal to the surface at M.

Let θ be the angle between the principal normal to the curve $\phi(u, v) = 0$ at A and the normal to the surface at A, ρ the radius of curvature of the curve and R that of the normal section through the tangent to the curve at M.

Then
$$\frac{\cos\theta}{\rho} = \frac{L\,du^2 + 2M\,du\,dv + N\,dv^2}{E\,du^2 + 2F\,du\,dv + G\,dv^2},$$

where
$$\phi_u du + \phi_v dv = 0.$$

All curves on the surface which have the same osculating plane at P have the same curvature at P, viz. the curvature of the plane section of the surface by the osculating plane at P.

Meusnier's theorem: $\rho = R \cos \theta$.

i.e. the radius of curvature of the curve is the projection on its osculating plane of the radius of curvature of the normal section through the tangent to the curve.

The radius of curvature of a normal section is given by

$$\frac{1}{R} = \frac{L\,du^2 + 2M\,du\,dv + N\,dv^2}{E\,du^2 + 2F\,du\,dv + G\,dv^2}.$$

R is positive or negative according as the positive direction of the principal normal of the normal section coincides with the positive direction of the normal to the surface or not.

At a general point of the surface there is a direction for which the radius of normal curvature is a maximum and a perpendicular direction for which it is a minimum. These are called the *principal directions* for the point and the corresponding values ρ_1 and ρ_2 of R are called the *principal radii of curvature.* ρ_1 and ρ_2 are the roots of the equation

$$(EG - F^2) - (EN - 2FM + GL)\rho + (LN - M^2)\rho^2 = 0.$$

$$K_m = 1/\rho_1 + 1/\rho_2$$

is called the *mean curvature* and

$$K = 1/(\rho_1 \rho_2)$$

the *total* or *Gaussian curvature* of the surface at A. K is a function of E, F, G and their partial derivates only {see (21)}.

The principal directions at the point are given by

$$\begin{vmatrix} dv^2 & -du\,dv & du^2 \\ E & F & G \\ L & M & N \end{vmatrix} = 0. \qquad (23)$$

A *line of curvature* is a curve on the surface whose tangent at every point coincides with one of the principal directions at the point. Equation (23) is the differential equation of the lines of curvature.

In the exceptional case in which the normal curvature has no maximum or minimum at every point on the surface then

$$L : M : N = E : F : G$$

and the surface is a plane or a sphere. A point is said to be elliptic, parabolic or hyperbolic according as $LN - M^2 \gtreqless 0$.

Euler's theorem: Let ψ be the angle between the principal direction of normal curvature ρ_1 at M and a direction through M whose normal curvature is R.

Then
$$\frac{1}{R}=\frac{\cos^2\psi}{\rho_1}+\frac{\sin^2\psi}{\rho_2}.$$

20.71. The lines of curvature are the parametric curves if, and only if, $F=M=0$. In this case Weingarten's equations reduce to

Rodriques' equations:
$$\frac{P_u}{x_u}=\frac{Q_u}{y_u}=\frac{R_u}{z_u}=-\frac{1}{\rho_1},$$
$$\frac{P_v}{x_v}=\frac{Q_v}{y_v}=\frac{R_v}{z_v}=-\frac{1}{\rho_2},$$
where ρ_1 and ρ_2 are the principal radii of curvature along $v=$constant and $u=$constant respectively.

The Gauss equation takes the form
$$KH^2=LN=\frac{1}{4}\left(\frac{G_u{}^2}{G}+\frac{G_uE_u}{E}+\frac{E_v{}^2}{E}+\frac{E_vG_v}{G}-2E_{vv}-2G_{uu}\right).$$

The Codazzi equations reduce to
$$\frac{L_v}{E_v}=\frac{N_u}{G_u}=\frac{1}{2}\left(\frac{L}{E}+\frac{N}{G}\right),$$
or if
$$a=\frac{1}{\rho_1},\quad b=\frac{1}{\rho_2},$$
$$\tfrac{1}{2}(a-b)E_v=-E\,a_v,$$
$$\tfrac{1}{2}(a-b)G_u=G\,b_u.$$

20.72. Curves on a surface

The *minimal* curves are given by
$$E\,du^2+2F\,du\,dv+G\,dv^2=0.$$

Conjugate systems

Definition. If C is a curve on a surface through a point A, the direction *conjugate* to the tangent at A is the limiting position, as $A'\to A$, of the line of intersection of the tangent planes at A and at a point A' on C.

The directions $\frac{dv}{du}$ and $\frac{\delta v}{\delta u}$ are conjugate if

$$L\,du\,\delta u+M(du\,\delta v+dv\,\delta u)+N\,dv\,\delta v=0.$$

If α and β are the angles these directions make with the direction of principal curvature ρ_1 at A, then $\tan\alpha\tan\beta=-\rho_2/\rho_1$.

The curves of two simply infinite systems are said to be conjugate if their tangents at every point are in conjugate directions.

The parametric curves form a conjugate system if, and only if, $M=0$.

The *asymptotic* directions at a point are the self-conjugate directions. A curve which touches an asymptotic direction at every point is called an *asymptotic* line. The equation of the asymptotic lines is

$$L\,du^2+2M\,du\,dv+N\,dv^2=0.$$

Two such curves (real or imaginary) pass through each point on the surface.

The parametric curves $u=$constant or $v=$constant are asymptotic lines if $N=0$ or $L=0$ respectively.

A *geodesic* is a curve on a surface whose principal normal at every point is the normal to the surface at that point. The differential equation of the geodesics $v=v(u)$ is

$$\begin{vmatrix} E+F\dfrac{dv}{du}, & \dfrac{1}{2}E_u+E_v\dfrac{dv}{du}+\left(F_v-\dfrac{1}{2}G_u\right)\left(\dfrac{dv}{du}\right)^2+F\dfrac{d^2v}{du^2} \\ F+G\dfrac{dv}{du}, & F_u-\dfrac{1}{2}E_v+G_u\dfrac{dv}{du}+\dfrac{1}{2}G_v\left(\dfrac{dv}{du}\right)^2+G\dfrac{d^2v}{du^2} \end{vmatrix}=0.$$

The geodesics are a doubly infinite system of curves on a surface; one curve passes through any point on the surface in any given direction along the surface. The shortest distance along the surface between two points on it is along a geodesic.

20.8. Particular surfaces

A *minimal* surface is a surface whose mean curvature at every point is zero. Its differential equation is

$$GL-2FM+EN=0.$$

The surface of least area with given edges is a minimal surface.

Surface generated by a moving curve. As the parameter a varies the curve of intersection of the two surface $F(x, y, z, a)=0$, $f(x, y, z, a)=0$ generates a surface whose equation is obtained by eliminating a between the given equations. If the equations $F(x, y, z, a, b, \ldots)=0$,

$f(x, y, z, a, b, \ldots)=0$ involve n parameters $a, b, \ldots$, which are connected by $n-1$ equations, then the equation of the locus of the curve of intersection of the two surfaces is obtained by eliminating the n parameters between the equations $F=0$, $f=0$ and the $n-1$ equations between the parameters.

A *ruled surface* is the locus of a line whose equations involve one parameter:

$$X=x+lr,\ Y=y+mr,\ Z=z+nr, \qquad (24)$$

where $x, y, z;\ l, m, n$ are functions of one variable t.

The number of degrees of freedom of a line in three-dimensional space is four, so that a line which obeys three independent conditions generates a ruled surface.

A *developable* is a surface whose total curvature is zero. The surface generated by the tangents of a curve is a developable. The equations of the developable which is the tangent surface of the curve $x=x(s)$, $y=y(s)$, $z=z(s)$ are

$$X=x+l_1r,\ Y=y+m_1r,\ Z=z+n_1r,$$

where l_1, m_1, n_1 are the direction cosines of the tangent to the curve at (x, y, z).

A ruled surface is either a developable surface or a *scroll*.

The necessary and sufficient condition that the surface given by equations (24) is developable is

$$\begin{vmatrix} x' & y' & z' \\ l & m & n \\ l' & m' & n' \end{vmatrix}=0,$$

where dashes denote differentiation with respect to t.

The envelope of a one parameter family of planes is a developable surface. The planes are the osculating planes of the curve of which the developable is the tangent surface. The generators of the developable, i.e. the tangents of the curve, are the characteristics and the edge of regression is the curve itself (see below).

A developable surface can be applied to a plane without stretching or tearing, but a scroll cannot.

The cone and cylinder are also developable and may be obtained as limiting cases of a tangent surface, but in practice it is usually easier to consider them on their own merits.

A *cylinder* is the locus of a line which moves parallel to itself and meets a given curve (called the base curve).

Base curve $$\phi(x, y, z)=\psi(x, y, z)=0. \qquad (25)$$

Generator $$\frac{x-x_0}{l}=\frac{y-y_0}{m}=\frac{z}{n}. \qquad (26)$$

If the result of eliminating x, y, z from the four equations (25) and (26) is

$$F(x_0, y_0)=0,$$

then the equation of the cylinder is

$$F[(x-lz/n), (y-mz/n)]=0.$$

The general equation of a cylinder is

$$F[(ax+by+cz+d), (a_1x+b_1y+c_1z+d_1)]=0.$$

A *cone* is the surface generated by a line which passes through a fixed point (x_1, y_1, z_1) and meets a given curve.

Base curve $$\phi(x, y, z)=\psi(x, y, z)=0. \qquad (27)$$

Generator $$\frac{x-x_1}{l}=\frac{y-y_1}{m}=\frac{z-z_1}{n}. \qquad (28)$$

Eliminate x, y, z from (27) and (28), obtaining

$$F\left(\frac{l}{n}, \frac{m}{n}\right)=0 \qquad (29)$$

The equation of the cone is obtained by eliminating $l : m : n$ between (28) and (29), and is

$$F\left(\frac{x-x_1}{z-z_1}, \frac{y-y_1}{z-z_1}\right)=0.$$

The necessary and sufficient condition that an equation represents a cone vertex (x_1, y_1, z_1) is that it is homogeneous in $x-x_1, y-y_1, z-z_1$.

The general equation of a cone is

$$F\left(\frac{a_1x+b_1y+c_1z+d_1}{ax+by+cz+d}, \frac{a_2x+b_2y+c_2z+d_2}{ax+by+cz+d}\right)=0$$

A *Surface of revolution* is a surface obtained by revolving a curve about an axis.

(1) Z-axis as axis of revolution.

Curve: $$\phi(x, y, z)=\psi(x, y, z)=0. \qquad (30)$$

The equation of the curve obtained by rotating the point (x_1, y_1, z_1) is

$$x^2+y^2=x_1^2+y_1^2, \quad z=z_1 \qquad (31)$$

If (x, y, z) is any point on the surface equations (31) hold, where

$$\phi(x_1, y_1, z_1)=\psi(x_1, y_1, z_1)=0. \qquad (32)$$

Eliminating (x_1, y_1, z_1) between (31) and (32), the equation of the surface is

$$F[(x^2+y^2), z]=0. \qquad (33)$$

(2) Let the axis be $\frac{x-\alpha}{l}=\frac{y-\beta}{m}=\frac{z-\gamma}{n}$, ... (34)

and the circle be
$$\left.\begin{aligned}(x-\alpha)^2+(y-\beta)^2+(z-\gamma)^2&=r^2\\ xl+ym+zn&=d\end{aligned}\right\} \qquad (35)$$

Eliminating x, y, z from (30) and (35), we have

$$F(r^2, d)=0. \qquad (36)$$

Eliminating r and d from (35) and (36), the equation is

$$F[\{(x-\alpha)^2+(y-\beta)^2+(z-\gamma)^2\}, \{xl+ym+zn\}]=0,$$

where (α, β, γ) is any point on the axis of revolution.

A *conoid* is the locus of a line which meets a given straight line and a given curve and is parallel to a given plane. If the given line and plane are perpendicular, the conoid is right.

If the given line is the axis of z, plane $ax+by+cz=0$, and curve (30), eliminate x, y, z between (30) and

$$y/x=m \qquad (37)$$

$$ax+by+cz=d \qquad (38)$$

obtaining

$$F(m, d)=0 \qquad (39)$$

The equation of the conoid is obtained by eliminating m and d between (37), (38) and (39), viz.:

$$F\left(\frac{y}{x}, ax+by+cz\right)=0.$$

The equation of the right conoid, locus of a line parallel to $z=0$ and meeting the z axis and a curve is

$$F\left(\frac{y}{x}, z\right)=0.$$

If the base is a helix whose tangents make a constant angle with the given line, the corresponding right conoid is a helicoid. If the line is the axis of z and the helix is

$$x=a \cos \theta, y=a \sin \theta, z=k\theta,$$

the helicoid is $y=x \tan (z/k)$.

20.9. Envelope of a one-parameter family of surfaces

$$F(x, y, z, \alpha)=0.$$

If a surface exists which touches every member of the family along a curve it is called the *envelope* and the curve is called the *characteristic* curve.

The equation obtained by eliminating α from

$$F(x, y, z, \alpha)=0, \frac{\partial F}{\partial \alpha}(x, y, z, \alpha)=0 . \quad . \quad . \quad (40)$$

represents one or more surfaces each of which is an envelope or is the locus of the singular points of the surfaces. The characteristic curve, given by (40) for any fixed α, is the limiting curve of intersection of $F(x, y, z, \alpha)=0$ with a neighbouring surface of the family.

As $\alpha_1 \to \alpha$, the characteristic of the surface $F(x, y, z, \alpha_1)=0$ tends to a limiting position in which it intersects the characteristic (40) in a point or points satisfying

$$F(x, y, z, \alpha)=0, \frac{\partial F}{\partial \alpha}=0, \frac{\partial^2 F}{\partial \alpha^2}=0. \quad . \quad . \quad . \quad (41)$$

The locus of this point as α varies is called the *edge of regression* of the family of surfaces. The characteristic (40) touches the edge of regression at the point satisfying (41), unless this point is a singular point of the surface.

Two-parameter family $F(x, y, z, \alpha, \beta)=0$. The envelope is a surface which touches each member of the family at one or more points. The equation, obtained by eliminating α and β from

$$F(x, y, z, \alpha, \beta)=0, \frac{\partial F}{\partial \alpha}(x, y, z, \alpha, \beta)=0, \frac{\partial F}{\partial \beta}(x, y, z, \alpha, \beta)=0,$$

represents one or more surfaces, each of which is either an envelope or the locus of the singular points of the surfaces of the family.

CHAPTER 21

VECTORS

Table of alternative notations

Vector	Scalar product	Vector product	Gradient	Divergence	Curl
$\mathbf{a}$	$\mathbf{a} \cdot \mathbf{b}$	$\mathbf{a} \times \mathbf{b}$	grad	div	curl
$\underset{\sim}{A}$	$(\mathbf{a}\ \mathbf{b})$	$\mathbf{a}_\wedge \mathbf{b}$	∇	$\nabla .$	$\nabla \times$
	$(\mathbf{A} \cdot \mathbf{B})$	$[\mathbf{A} \cdot \mathbf{B}]$			rot.

21.1. Scalars and vectors

A *scalar* is a physical quantity which is completely specified by its sign and magnitude. It is not related to any definite direction in space. It may therefore be represented completely by a real number.

A *vector* quantity is one which has a magnitude and is related to a definite direction in space, and is such that two or more vectors compound according to the parallelogram law of addition (see below). It may be represented by a directed straight line whose direction is that of the vector and whose length represents the magnitude of the vector on some convenient scale.

A vector is usually denoted by bold-face type $\mathbf{r}$ or by $\overline{AB}$, where A and B are the terminal points of its representative line taken in the correct order. The magnitude of the vector is called its length. We denote the length of $\mathbf{r}$ by r.

A vector may be free or localized. A free vector is related only to a direction, not to a particular line or point, and may be equally well represented by any equal and parallel straight line, e.g. a displacement of a rigid body through an assigned length in an assigned direction and sense. A vector may be localized either at a point, e.g. the velocity of a particle, or along a line, e.g. a force acting on a rigid body.

The parallelogram law of addition. If $\mathbf{r}$, $\mathbf{s}$ are represented by the lines OA, OB respectively, then $\mathbf{r}+\mathbf{s}$ is represented by the diagonal OC of the parallelogram OACB. $\overline{OC}$ is the sum or resultant of $\overline{OA}$ and $\overline{OB}$.

A vector of zero magnitude can have no direction. Such a vector is denoted by $\mathbf{0}$ and called a zero vector. If $\mathbf{r}+\mathbf{s}=\mathbf{0}$, O and C coincide and $\mathbf{s}=-\mathbf{r}$, so $-\mathbf{r}$ is a vector of the same length as $\mathbf{r}$ but in the opposite direction. The difference $\mathbf{r}-\mathbf{s}$ is defined as $\mathbf{r}+(-\mathbf{s})$.

Laws of vector addition

The commutative law

$$\mathbf{a}+\mathbf{b}=\mathbf{b}+\mathbf{a},$$

and the associative law

$$\mathbf{a}+(\mathbf{b}+\mathbf{c})=(\mathbf{a}+\mathbf{b})+\mathbf{c}$$

hold for vector addition.

If n is a scalar, $n\mathbf{a}$ is defined to be the vector with the same direction as $\mathbf{a}$ and of length na. Then

$$(m+n)\mathbf{a}=m\mathbf{a}+n\mathbf{a},$$

$$m(n\mathbf{a})=n(m\mathbf{a})=mn\mathbf{a},$$

$$m(\mathbf{a}+\mathbf{b})=m\mathbf{a}+m\mathbf{b}.$$

Resolution of vectors

If $\mathbf{r}$ can be represented as the sum of a finite number of vectors, $\mathbf{r}=\mathbf{a}+\mathbf{b}+\ldots+\mathbf{h}$, we say that $\mathbf{r}$ can be resolved into *components* $\mathbf{a}$, $\mathbf{b}$, . . ., $\mathbf{h}$. Any vector $\mathbf{r}$ can be resolved into components in any three given non-coplanar directions and this resolution is unique. Any vector $\mathbf{r}$ can be uniquely resolved into components in any two directions in a plane through itself or, in the case of a free vector, in any two directions which are parallel to any given plane through $\mathbf{r}$.

Take rectangular co-ordinate axes Ox, Oy, Oz. Let $\mathbf{i}$, $\mathbf{j}$, $\mathbf{k}$ be vectors of unit length in the directions Ox, Oy, Oz respectively. If $\mathbf{r}$ is the vector represented by $\overline{OP}$, where P is the point (x, y, z), then

$$\mathbf{r}=x\mathbf{i}+y\mathbf{j}+z\mathbf{k}$$

and $x=r\cos\alpha$, $y=r\cos\beta$, $z=r\cos\gamma$, where $\cos\alpha$, $\cos\beta$, $\cos\gamma$ are the direction cosines of the line OP. The notation $\mathbf{r}=(x, y, z)$ is also used,* and x, y, z, are called the Cartesian components of $\mathbf{r}$.

The components of the resultant of a finite number of concurrent vectors may be obtained by adding their like components,

i.e. if
$$\mathbf{a}=a_1\mathbf{i}+a_2\mathbf{j}+a_3\mathbf{k},$$

then
$$\Sigma\mathbf{a}=(\Sigma a_1)\mathbf{i}+(\Sigma a_2)\mathbf{j}+(\Sigma a_3)\mathbf{k}.$$

* In Chapter 3 an $n\times 1$ matrix has been called a vector. In space of three dimensions a vector $\mathbf{r}$ as defined in this chapter may be written in the form of such a matrix

$$\mathbf{r}=\begin{bmatrix} a_1 \\ a_2 \\ a_3 \end{bmatrix},$$

where the components of r in the directions of three given non-coplanar vectors $\mathbf{a}$, $\mathbf{b}$, $\mathbf{c}$ are $a_1\mathbf{a}$, $a_2\mathbf{b}$, $a_3\mathbf{c}$.

21.2. Products of vectors

The *scalar* or *dot product* $\mathbf{a} \cdot \mathbf{b}$ of two vectors $\mathbf{a}$ and $\mathbf{b}$ is $ab \cos \theta$, where θ is the angle between the directions of the two vectors.

If $\mathbf{a}$ is perpendicular to $\mathbf{b}$, $\mathbf{a} \cdot \mathbf{b}=0$. If $\mathbf{a}$ and $\mathbf{b}$ are parallel, $\mathbf{a} \cdot \mathbf{b}=ab$. The square of the vector $\mathbf{a}$ is $\mathbf{a}^2=\mathbf{a} \cdot \mathbf{a}=a^2$. In particular

$$\mathbf{i} \cdot \mathbf{j}=\mathbf{j} \cdot \mathbf{k}=\mathbf{k} \cdot \mathbf{i}=\mathbf{j} \cdot \mathbf{i}=\mathbf{k} \cdot \mathbf{j}=\mathbf{i} \cdot \mathbf{k}=0,$$

$$\mathbf{i} \cdot \mathbf{i}=\mathbf{j} \cdot \mathbf{j}=\mathbf{k} \cdot \mathbf{k}=1.$$

Laws of algebra for scalar products

The commutative and distributive laws hold,

i.e. $$\mathbf{a} \cdot \mathbf{b}=\mathbf{b} \cdot \mathbf{a},$$

$$\mathbf{a} \cdot (\mathbf{b}+\mathbf{c})=\mathbf{a} \cdot \mathbf{b}+\mathbf{a} \cdot \mathbf{c}.$$

If m is a scalar,

$$m(\mathbf{a} \cdot \mathbf{b})=(m\mathbf{a}) \cdot \mathbf{b}=\mathbf{a} \cdot (m\mathbf{b}).$$

$\mathbf{a} \cdot \mathbf{b}$ is equal to the length of $\mathbf{a}$ multiplied by the length of the projection of $\mathbf{b}$ on $\mathbf{a}$. If

$$\mathbf{a}=a_1\mathbf{i}+a_2\mathbf{j}+a_3\mathbf{k}, \quad \mathbf{b}=b_1\mathbf{i}+b_2\mathbf{j}+b_3\mathbf{k},$$

$$\mathbf{a} \cdot \mathbf{b}=a_1b_1+a_2b_2+a_3b_3.$$

Rotations

A rotation may be represented in magnitude and direction by an interval on the axis of rotation of a length which is proportional to the angle of rotation on some known scale. To distinguish between rotations in opposite directions about the same axis we define a *positive* rotation about an axis OA to be that of a right-handed screw with respect to the same axis. Rotations can thus be represented by a directed line segment, but finite rotations are not vectors since they do not obey the parallelogram law of addition. Infinitesimal rotations obey this law and hence angular velocities are vectors.

The *vector* or *cross product* $\mathbf{a}\times\mathbf{b}$ of two vectors $\mathbf{a}$ and $\mathbf{b}$ is the vector $ab \sin \theta\, \hat{\mathbf{c}}$, where θ is the angle between the directions of $\mathbf{a}$ and $\mathbf{b}$, and $\hat{\mathbf{c}}$ is a vector of unit length perpendicular to both $\mathbf{a}$ and $\mathbf{b}$ and in the direction of a line which would represent a positive rotation from $\mathbf{a}$ to $\mathbf{b}$.

If $\mathbf{a}$ and $\mathbf{b}$ are parallel $\mathbf{a}\times\mathbf{b}=\mathbf{0}$. In particular

$$\mathbf{i}\times\mathbf{i}=\mathbf{j}\times\mathbf{j}=\mathbf{k}\times\mathbf{k}=\mathbf{0}.$$

Also $$\mathbf{i}\times\mathbf{j}=\mathbf{k}=-\mathbf{j}\times\mathbf{i}, \quad \mathbf{j}\times\mathbf{k}=\mathbf{i}=-\mathbf{k}\times\mathbf{j}, \quad \mathbf{k}\times\mathbf{i}=\mathbf{j}=-\mathbf{i}\times\mathbf{k}.$$

Laws of Algebra for vector products

The commutative law does *not* hold, since

$$\mathbf{a}\times\mathbf{b}=-\mathbf{b}\times\mathbf{a}.$$

The distributive law holds,

i.e.
$$\mathbf{a}\times(\mathbf{b}+\mathbf{c})=\mathbf{a}\times\mathbf{b} \;+\; \mathbf{a}\times\mathbf{c},$$
$$(\mathbf{b}+\mathbf{c})\times\mathbf{a}=\mathbf{b}\times\mathbf{a} \;+\; \mathbf{c}\times\mathbf{a},$$

but the order in which the vectors occur in each term must be maintained.

In Cartesian components $\mathbf{a}\times\mathbf{b}=(a_1\mathbf{i}+a_2\mathbf{j}+a_3\mathbf{k})\times(b_1\mathbf{i}+b_2\mathbf{j}+b_3\mathbf{k})$
$$=(a_2b_3-a_3b_2)\mathbf{i}+(a_3b_1-a_1b_3)\mathbf{j}+(a_1b_2-a_2b_1)\mathbf{k}$$
$$=\begin{vmatrix} \mathbf{i} & \mathbf{j} & \mathbf{k} \\ a_1 & a_2 & a_3 \\ b_1 & b_2 & b_3 \end{vmatrix}.$$

The *triple scalar product* $[\mathbf{a}, \mathbf{b}, \mathbf{c}]$ of the vectors $\mathbf{a}$, $\mathbf{b}$, $\mathbf{c}$ is the scalar product of $\mathbf{a}$ and $\mathbf{b}\times\mathbf{c}$, i.e. $\mathbf{a}\,.\,(\mathbf{b}\times\mathbf{c})$. In terms of Cartesian components of $\mathbf{a}$, $\mathbf{b}$, $\mathbf{c}$,
$$[\mathbf{a}, \mathbf{b}, \mathbf{c}]=a_1(b_2c_3-b_3c_2)+a_2(b_3c_1-b_1c_3)+a_3(b_1c_2-b_2c_1)$$
$$=\begin{vmatrix} a_1 & a_2 & a_3 \\ b_1 & b_2 & b_3 \\ c_1 & c_2 & c_3 \end{vmatrix}.$$

The value of the product is unaltered by interchanging the dot and the cross or by interchanging the order of the factors provided the cyclic order is unaltered,

i.e.
$$\mathbf{a}\,.\,(\mathbf{b}\times\mathbf{c})=(\mathbf{b}\times\mathbf{c})\,.\,\mathbf{a}=\mathbf{b}\,.\,(\mathbf{c}\times\mathbf{a})=(\mathbf{c}\times\mathbf{a})\,.\,\mathbf{b}$$
$$=\mathbf{c}\,.\,(\mathbf{a}\times\mathbf{b})=(\mathbf{a}\times\mathbf{b})\,.\,\mathbf{c}.$$

If the cyclic order is changed, the sign of the product is changed,
$$[\mathbf{a}, \mathbf{b}, \mathbf{c}]=[\mathbf{b}, \mathbf{c}, \mathbf{a}]=[\mathbf{c}, \mathbf{a}, \mathbf{b}]=-[\mathbf{a}, \mathbf{c}, \mathbf{b}]$$
$$=-[\mathbf{b}, \mathbf{a}, \mathbf{c}]=-[\mathbf{c}, \mathbf{b}, \mathbf{a}].$$

$[\mathbf{a}, \mathbf{b}, \mathbf{c}]=0$ is the necessary and sufficient condition that the free vectors $\mathbf{a}$, $\mathbf{b}$, $\mathbf{c}$ be co-planar, or that the three vectors $\mathbf{a}$, $\mathbf{b}$, $\mathbf{c}$ be parallel to a plane.

The product $\mathbf{a}\times(\mathbf{b}\times\mathbf{c})$ is called a *triple vector product.* It lies in a plane parallel to $\mathbf{b}$ and $\mathbf{c}$ and can therefore be expressed in terms of $\mathbf{b}$ and $\mathbf{c}$:
$$\mathbf{a}\times(\mathbf{b}\times\mathbf{c})=(\mathbf{a}\,.\,\mathbf{c})\mathbf{b}-(\mathbf{a}\,.\,\mathbf{b})\mathbf{c}.$$
$$\mathbf{a}\times(\mathbf{b}\times\mathbf{c})+\mathbf{b}\times(\mathbf{c}\times\mathbf{a})+\mathbf{c}\times(\mathbf{a}\times\mathbf{b})\equiv\mathbf{0}.$$
$$(\mathbf{b}\times\mathbf{c})\times\mathbf{a}=-\mathbf{a}\times(\mathbf{b}\times\mathbf{c})=(\mathbf{a}\,.\,\mathbf{b})\mathbf{c}-(\mathbf{a}\,.\,\mathbf{c})\mathbf{b}.$$

Note that $\mathbf{a}\times(\mathbf{b}\times\mathbf{c})\neq(\mathbf{a}\times\mathbf{b})\times\mathbf{c}$.

The *scalar quadruple product* $(\mathbf{a}\times\mathbf{b})\cdot(\mathbf{c}\times\mathbf{d})$ is the scalar product of $\mathbf{a}\times\mathbf{b}$ and $\mathbf{c}\times\mathbf{d}$.

$$\begin{aligned}(\mathbf{a}\times\mathbf{b})\cdot(\mathbf{c}\times\mathbf{d}) &= [\mathbf{a},\ \mathbf{b},\ \mathbf{c}\times\mathbf{d}] = [\mathbf{b},\ \mathbf{c}\times\mathbf{d},\ \mathbf{a}]\\ &= \mathbf{b}\times(\mathbf{c}\times\mathbf{d})\cdot\mathbf{a} = \{(\mathbf{b}\cdot\mathbf{d})\mathbf{c}-(\mathbf{b}\cdot\mathbf{c})\mathbf{d}\}\cdot\mathbf{a}\\ &= (\mathbf{b}\cdot\mathbf{d})(\mathbf{c}\cdot\mathbf{a})-(\mathbf{b}\cdot\mathbf{c})(\mathbf{d}\cdot\mathbf{a})\\ &= \begin{vmatrix}\mathbf{a}\cdot\mathbf{c}, & \mathbf{a}\cdot\mathbf{d}\\ \mathbf{b}\cdot\mathbf{c}, & \mathbf{b}\cdot\mathbf{d}\end{vmatrix}.\end{aligned}$$

In particular

$$(\mathbf{a}\times\mathbf{b})^2 = b^2a^2-(\mathbf{b}\cdot\mathbf{a})^2.$$

The *quadruple vector product* $(\mathbf{a}\times\mathbf{b})\times(\mathbf{c}\times\mathbf{d})$ is perpendicular to $\mathbf{a}\times\mathbf{b}$ and therefore lies in a plane which is parallel to $\mathbf{a}$ and $\mathbf{b}$. Hence it is parallel to the line of intersection of a plane parallel to $\mathbf{a}$ and $\mathbf{b}$ with a plane parallel to $\mathbf{c}$ and $\mathbf{d}$, and so can be expressed in terms of $\mathbf{a}$ and $\mathbf{b}$ or of $\mathbf{c}$ and $\mathbf{d}$:

$$\begin{aligned}(\mathbf{a}\times\mathbf{b})\times(\mathbf{c}\times\mathbf{d}) &= (\mathbf{a}\times\mathbf{b}\cdot\mathbf{d})\mathbf{c}-(\mathbf{a}\times\mathbf{b}\cdot\mathbf{c})\mathbf{d}\\ &= [\mathbf{a},\ \mathbf{b},\ \mathbf{d}]\mathbf{c}-[\mathbf{a},\ \mathbf{b},\ \mathbf{c}]\mathbf{d}\\ &= (\mathbf{c}\times\mathbf{d})\times(\mathbf{b}\times\mathbf{a})\\ &= [\mathbf{c},\ \mathbf{d},\ \mathbf{a}]\mathbf{b}-[\mathbf{c},\ \mathbf{d},\ \mathbf{b}]\mathbf{a}.\end{aligned}$$

Equating these, the identity

$$[\mathbf{a},\ \mathbf{b},\ \mathbf{c}]\mathbf{d} \equiv [\mathbf{d},\ \mathbf{b},\ \mathbf{c}]\mathbf{a}+[\mathbf{a},\ \mathbf{d},\ \mathbf{c}]\mathbf{b}+[\mathbf{a},\ \mathbf{b},\ \mathbf{d}]\mathbf{c}$$

holds. This identity expresses any free vector $\mathbf{d}$ as a linear combination of any three given non-coplanar vectors $\mathbf{a}$, $\mathbf{b}$, $\mathbf{c}$ and gives the components of $\mathbf{d}$ when $\mathbf{d}$ is resolved in any three non-coplanar directions.

21.3. Differentiation and integration of vectors

If $\mathbf{a}$ is a single-valued continuous vector function of a scalar variable t and $\delta\mathbf{a}$ is the increment in $\mathbf{a}$ corresponding to the increment δt of t, and if $\delta\mathbf{a}/\delta t$ tends to a limit as $\delta t\to 0$, $\mathbf{a}$ is *differentiable* and its *derivate* is

$$\frac{d\mathbf{a}}{dt} = \lim_{\delta t\to 0}\frac{\delta\mathbf{a}}{\delta t}.$$

If $\overline{OP}$ represents $\mathbf{a}$, where O is fixed, $d\mathbf{a}/dt$ is in the direction of the tangent at P to the curve which is the locus of P.

The derivate of $d\mathbf{a}/dt$ is called the *second derivate* $d^2\mathbf{a}/dt^2$ of $\mathbf{a}$, and so on.

Rules for differentiation of sums and products of vectors are similar to those for algebraic sums and products, but it is important that the order of the vectors in all vector products be maintained as shown:

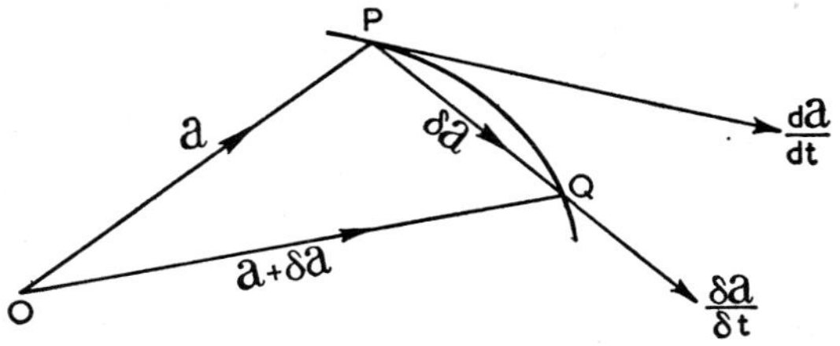

Fig. 21.1

$$\frac{d}{dt}(\mathbf{a}+\mathbf{b}+\ldots)=\frac{d\mathbf{a}}{dt}+\frac{d\mathbf{b}}{dt}+\ldots,$$

$$\frac{d}{dt}(\mathbf{a}\,.\,\mathbf{b})=\frac{d\mathbf{a}}{dt}\,.\,\mathbf{b}+\mathbf{a}\,.\,\frac{d\mathbf{b}}{dt},$$

$$\frac{d}{dt}(\mathbf{a}\times\mathbf{b})=\frac{d\mathbf{a}}{dt}\times\mathbf{b}+\mathbf{a}\times\frac{d\mathbf{b}}{dt},$$

$$\frac{d}{dt}\left[\mathbf{a},\,\mathbf{b},\,\mathbf{c}\right]=\left[\frac{d\mathbf{a}}{dt},\,\mathbf{b},\,\mathbf{c}\right]+\left[\mathbf{a},\,\frac{d\mathbf{b}}{dt},\,\mathbf{c}\right]+\left[\mathbf{a},\,\mathbf{b},\,\frac{d\mathbf{c}}{dt}\right].$$

$$\mathbf{a}\,.\,\frac{d\mathbf{a}}{dt}=a\frac{da}{dt},$$

$$\frac{d}{dt}\left[\mathbf{a}\times\frac{d\mathbf{a}}{dt}\right]=\mathbf{a}\times\frac{d^2\mathbf{a}}{dt^2}.$$

If $\quad \mathbf{a}=(a_1,\,a_2,\,a_3),\ \dfrac{d\mathbf{a}}{dt}=\dfrac{da_1}{dt}\mathbf{i}+\dfrac{da_2}{dt}\mathbf{j}+\dfrac{da_3}{dt}\mathbf{k}.$

Indefinite integration of a vector is the process reverse to differention. The *indefinite integral* with respect to t of a vector **a**, which is a function of t, is a vector **F** such that $d\mathbf{F}/dt=\mathbf{a}$. The vector **F** is called the *integral* of **a** with respect to t and is written

$$\mathbf{F}=\int\mathbf{a}\,dt.$$

F is indefinite to the extent of an additive constant of the same nature as itself. Thus the constant in

$$\int\mathbf{a}\times\frac{d^2\mathbf{a}}{dt^2}\,dt=\mathbf{a}\times\frac{d\mathbf{a}}{dt}+\mathbf{c}$$

is a vector **c**.

Where the integrand is a scalar product as in

$$\int\mathbf{a}\,.\,\frac{d\mathbf{a}}{dt}\,dt=\frac{1}{2}\mathbf{a}\,.\,\mathbf{a}+c=\frac{a^2}{2}+c,$$

the constant c is of course a scalar.

21.4. Scalar and vector point function

A function which is defined at each point of a region is said to be a point function in that region. Such a function may be a scalar, e.g. temperature, or a vector, e.g. the function which defines the velocity of the points of a fluid at any instant.

Scalar line integral. If $\mathbf{r}$ is the position vector $\overline{OP}$ of a point $P(x, y, z)$ on a curve C, $x=x(t)$, $y=y(t)$, $z=z(t)$, then the vector $\boldsymbol{\lambda}\equiv\dfrac{d\mathbf{r}}{dt}$ is a vector in the direction of the tangent to the curve at P. Moreover

$$\frac{d\mathbf{r}}{dt}=\frac{dx}{dt}\mathbf{i}+\frac{dy}{dt}\mathbf{j}+\frac{dz}{dt}\mathbf{k}$$

and the magnitude of $\boldsymbol{\lambda}$ is $\dfrac{ds}{dt}$, where s is the arc of the curve measured from a fixed point on it. If $\hat{\boldsymbol{\lambda}}$ be a unit vector in the direction of the tangent and $\mathbf{a}$ is a vector point function, then

$$\int_{t_0}^{t_1}(\mathbf{a}\,.\,\boldsymbol{\lambda})\,dt\equiv\int_{t_0}^{t_1}(\mathbf{a}\,.\,\hat{\boldsymbol{\lambda}})\,\frac{ds}{dt}\,dt$$

is the *scalar* or *tangential line integral* of $\mathbf{a}$ along the curve C from t_0 to t_1. This may by convention be written as

$$\int_{t_0}^{t_1}(\mathbf{a}\,.\,d\mathbf{r}),$$

where t_0 and t_1 are the parameters which correspond to the end points of the arc. If the curve C is simple and closed, the scalar line integral of $\mathbf{a}$ round the curve is written

$$\int_C(\mathbf{a}\,.\,\hat{\boldsymbol{\lambda}})\,ds \quad\text{or}\quad \oint(\mathbf{a}\,.\,\hat{\boldsymbol{\lambda}})\,ds \quad\text{or}\quad \int_C(\mathbf{a}\,.\,\boldsymbol{\lambda})\,dt.$$

The *vector line integral* of the vector $\mathbf{a}$ along the curve C from t_0 to t_1,

$$\int_{t_0}^{t_1}(\mathbf{a}\times\boldsymbol{\lambda})\,dt\equiv\int_{t_0}^{t_1}(\mathbf{a}\times\hat{\boldsymbol{\lambda}})\,\frac{ds}{dt}\,dt,$$

is the vector whose components parallel to the axes are the three scalar integrals

$$\int_{t_0}^{t_1}(a_2\dot{z}-a_3\dot{y})\,dt,\ \int_{t_0}^{t_1}(a_3\dot{x}-a_1\dot{z})\,dt,\ \int_{t_0}^{t_1}(a_1\dot{y}-a_2\dot{x})\,dt,$$

where $\dot{x}\equiv\dfrac{dx}{dt}$, etc.

Area as a vector

A plane area is represented by a vector $\mathbf{b}=b\hat{\mathbf{n}}$, where $\hat{\mathbf{n}}$ is a unit vector along a normal $\overline{MP}$ to the plane and b is the magnitude of the area. When the boundary of the area $RSTR$ is described so that the area is on the left, the convention is that the positive direction $\overline{MP}$ is that of translation of a right-handed screw.

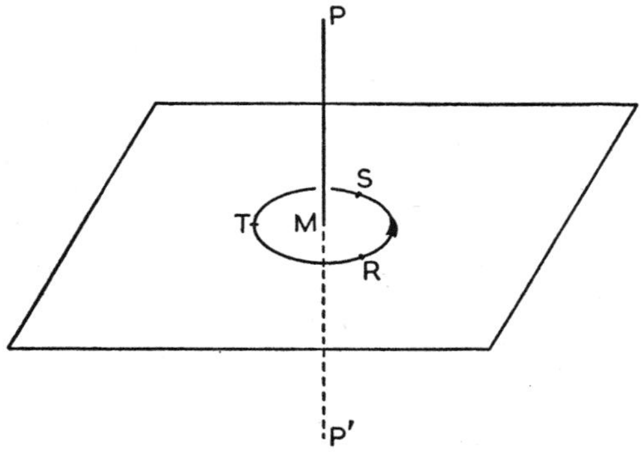

Fig. 21.2

Let Σ be the surface

$$x=x(u,\ v),\ y=y(u,\ v),\ z=z(u,\ v);$$

$$\mathbf{l}=\left(\frac{\partial x}{\partial u},\frac{\partial y}{\partial u},\frac{\partial z}{\partial u}\right),\ \mathbf{m}=\left(\frac{\partial x}{\partial v},\frac{\partial y}{\partial v},\frac{\partial z}{\partial v}\right),\ \mathbf{n}=\mathbf{l}\times\mathbf{m}.$$

If $\mathbf{a}$ is a one-valued continuous point-vector, $\mathbf{a}\,.\,\mathbf{n}\equiv[\mathbf{a},\mathbf{l},\mathbf{m}]$ is a continuous function of u and v at all points on the surface Σ.

The *scalar* or *normal surface integral* of $\mathbf{a}$ over Σ is the integral

$$\iint(\mathbf{a}\,.\,\mathbf{n})\,du\,dv=\iint\mathbf{a}\,.\,d\mathbf{S} \qquad . \quad . \quad . \quad (1)$$

over the required domain of u and v.

If S is the area of the surface Σ,

$$S=\iint\left(\frac{\mathbf{n}\,.\,\mathbf{n}}{n}\right)du\,dv=\iint n\,du\,dv=\iint lm\sin(\mathbf{l},\mathbf{m})\,du\,dv,$$

where $(\mathbf{l},\mathbf{m})$ denotes the angle that $\mathbf{l}$ makes with $\mathbf{m}$. If the surface Σ is closed, the positive direction along the normal is that of the outward drawn normal.

Gradient of a scalar point function

The rate of change at P of a scalar point function $V(x, y, z)$ in a given direction PQ is

$$\lim_{P' \to P} \frac{V(P') - V(P)}{PP'},$$

where $P' \to P$ along the line QP. This limit has a maximum value at P for the direction of the normal at P to the surface $V(x, y, z) = \text{constant}$. The *gradient* of V at P is *defined* as the vector through P in this direction and whose magnitude is this maximum value.

The gradient of V is invariant for change of co-ordinate system. It is a field vector and is written grad V.

In Cartesian co-ordinates

$$\text{grad } V \equiv \frac{\partial V}{\partial x}\mathbf{i} + \frac{\partial V}{\partial y}\mathbf{j} + \frac{\partial V}{\partial z}\mathbf{k},$$

and is written ∇V where ∇ (pronounced "nabla" or "del") is *defined* as the vector operator

$$\nabla \equiv \mathbf{i}\frac{\partial}{\partial x} + \mathbf{j}\frac{\partial}{\partial y} + \mathbf{k}\frac{\partial}{\partial z}.$$

If $\overline{OP} = \mathbf{r}$, $\overline{OQ} = \mathbf{r} + \delta\mathbf{r}$, where P and Q are the points $P(x, y, z)$, $Q(x+\delta x, y+\delta y, z+\delta z)$,

then

$$\begin{aligned} \delta V &= V(x+\delta x, y+\delta y, z+\delta z) - V(x, y, z) \\ &\simeq \frac{\partial V}{\partial x}\delta x + \frac{\partial V}{\partial y}\delta y + \frac{\partial V}{\partial z}\delta z \\ &= \delta\mathbf{r} \cdot \nabla V. \end{aligned}$$

The rate of change or directional derivate of V in the direction of a unit vector $\hat{\mathbf{b}} = (l, m, n)$ is

$$l\frac{\partial V}{\partial x} + m\frac{\partial V}{\partial y} + n\frac{\partial V}{\partial z} = \hat{\mathbf{b}} \cdot \nabla V$$

and this is a maximum in the direction of ∇V.

If $\mathbf{r} = \overline{OP}$, the scalar line integral of ∇V along a definite curve, locus of P, from A to B is

$$\int_A^B \nabla V \cdot d\mathbf{r} = \int_A^B dV = V_B - V_A.$$

If the curve is closed

$$\oint_C \nabla V \,.\, d\mathbf{r}=0.$$

Conversely, if $\oint_C \mathbf{F} \,.\, d\mathbf{r}=0$ round every closed path in a region, then $\mathbf{F}$ is the gradient of a scalar point function.

A vector point function $\mathbf{a}$ may be written

$$\mathbf{a}\equiv a_1\mathbf{i}+a_2\mathbf{j}+a_3\mathbf{k},$$

where $a_1(x, y, z)$, $a_2(x, y, z)$, $a_3(x, y, z)$ are scalar point functions. If $\delta\mathbf{a}$ is the increment of $\mathbf{a}$ corresponding to a displacement $\delta\mathbf{r}$ from $P(x, y, z)$ to $Q(x+\delta x, y+\delta y, z+\delta z)$, then

$$\begin{aligned}\delta\mathbf{a}&=\delta a_1\ \mathbf{i}+\delta a_2\ \mathbf{j}+\delta a_3\ \mathbf{k}\\ &\simeq\left(\frac{\partial a_1}{\partial x}\,\delta x+\frac{\partial a_1}{\partial y}\,\delta y+\frac{\partial a_1}{\partial z}\,\delta z\right)\mathbf{i}+\left(\frac{\partial a_2}{\partial x}\,\delta x+\frac{\partial a_2}{\partial y}\,\delta y+\frac{\partial a_2}{\partial z}\,\delta z\right)\mathbf{j}\\ &\qquad+\left(\frac{\partial a_3}{\partial x}\,\delta x+\frac{\partial a_3}{\partial y}\,\delta y+\frac{\partial a_3}{\partial z}\,\delta z\right)\mathbf{k}.\end{aligned}$$

Hence if δs is the length of PQ,

$$\lim\frac{\delta\mathbf{a}}{\delta s}=\frac{dx}{ds}\frac{\partial\mathbf{a}}{\partial x}+\frac{dy}{ds}\frac{\partial\mathbf{a}}{\partial y}+\frac{dz}{ds}\frac{\partial\mathbf{a}}{\partial z}.$$

Thus the rate of increase of $\mathbf{a}(x, y, z)$ in the direction of the unit vector $\hat{\mathbf{b}}=(l, m, n)$ is

$$\begin{aligned}&l\frac{\partial\mathbf{a}}{\partial x}+m\frac{\partial\mathbf{a}}{\partial y}+n\frac{\partial\mathbf{a}}{\partial z}\\ &=\left(l\frac{\partial}{\partial x}+m\frac{\partial}{\partial y}+n\frac{\partial}{\partial z}\right)\left(a_1\mathbf{i}+a_2\mathbf{j}+a_3\mathbf{k}\right)\\ &=(\hat{\mathbf{b}}\,.\,\nabla)\mathbf{a}.\end{aligned}$$

Thus $\hat{\mathbf{b}}\,.\,\nabla$ operating on either a scalar or a vector point function gives the directional derivate of the function parallel to $\hat{\mathbf{b}}$.

The *divergence* of a field vector $\mathbf{a}$ (written div $\mathbf{a}$) at a point P is defined as

$$\operatorname{div}\mathbf{a}\equiv\lim\frac{\displaystyle\iint_S \mathbf{a}\,.\,d\mathbf{S}}{V}=\lim\frac{\displaystyle\iint_S \mathbf{a}\,.\,\hat{\mathbf{n}}\,ds}{V},$$

where S is a simple closed surface surrounding P, V the volume enclosed by S, and $\hat{\mathbf{n}}$ the unit outward normal at a point of S, and the limits are taken as all the dimensions of S tend to zero.

The limit is independent of the shape of V. Div $\mathbf{a}$ is a scalar and is invariant under change of co-ordinate system. Its value in Cartesians is obtained by taking S as a rectangular box with sides parallel to the co-ordinate planes and is

$$\operatorname{div} \mathbf{a}=\frac{\partial}{\partial x} a_1+\frac{\partial}{\partial y} a_2+\frac{\partial}{\partial z} a_3=\boldsymbol{\nabla} \cdot \mathbf{a},$$

where $\mathbf{a}=(a_1, a_2, a_3)$.

The *curl* of field vector $\mathbf{a}$ (written curl $\mathbf{a}$) is the field vector whose component in a direction $\hat{\mathbf{n}}$ at a point P is defined as

$$\lim \frac{\int_L \mathbf{a} \cdot d\mathbf{r}}{S},$$

where L is a simple closed curve surrounding P in the plane through P which is perpendicular to $\hat{\mathbf{n}}$, and S is the area enclosed by L, the integration round L being in the sense of a rotation represented by $\hat{\mathbf{n}}$, and the limit is taken as all the dimensions of L tend to zero.

This does actually define a vector. The limit is independent of the shape of S. Curl $\mathbf{a}$ is invariant under change of co-ordinate system. The values of its components in Cartesians are found by considering a rectangle L with sides parallel to two of the axes and

$$\begin{aligned}\operatorname{curl} \mathbf{a} &= \left(\frac{\partial a_3}{\partial y}-\frac{\partial a_2}{\partial z}\right) \mathbf{i}+\left(\frac{\partial a_1}{\partial z}-\frac{\partial a_3}{\partial x}\right) \mathbf{j}+\left(\frac{\partial a_2}{\partial x}-\frac{\partial a_1}{\partial y}\right) \mathbf{k} \\ &= \boldsymbol{\nabla} \times \mathbf{a} \\ &= \begin{vmatrix} \mathbf{i} & \mathbf{j} & \mathbf{k} \\ \dfrac{\partial}{\partial x} & \dfrac{\partial}{\partial y} & \dfrac{\partial}{\partial z} \\ a_1 & a_2 & a_3 \end{vmatrix}.\end{aligned}$$

21.5. Identities and expansions in which the operator $\boldsymbol{\nabla}$ obeys the ordinary laws of vector algebra:

(i) Curl grad $V \equiv 0$, i.e. $\boldsymbol{\nabla} \times \boldsymbol{\nabla} V=0$.

Conversely, if curl $\mathbf{a} \equiv 0$, $\mathbf{a}$ is the gradient of a scalar point function, i.e. $\mathbf{a}=\boldsymbol{\nabla} V$. Then $\mathbf{a}$ is said to be *irrotational.*

(ii) Div curl $\mathbf{a} \equiv 0$, i.e. $\boldsymbol{\nabla} \cdot \boldsymbol{\nabla} \times \mathbf{a} \equiv 0$.

Conversely, if div $\mathbf{b} \equiv 0$, $\mathbf{b}$ is the curl of a field vector $\mathbf{a}$. Then $\mathbf{b}$ is said to be *solenoidal.*

(iii) Div grad $V \equiv \boldsymbol{\nabla} \cdot (\boldsymbol{\nabla} V)=\dfrac{\partial^2 V}{\partial x^2}+\dfrac{\partial^2 V}{\partial y^2}+\dfrac{\partial^2 V}{\partial z^2}$.

This is written $\nabla^2 V$, where ∇^2 denotes Laplace's operator:

$$\nabla^2 \equiv \frac{\partial^2}{\partial x^2} + \frac{\partial^2}{\partial y^2} + \frac{\partial^2}{\partial z^2}.$$

Thus

$$\boldsymbol{\nabla} . (\boldsymbol{\nabla} V) = (\boldsymbol{\nabla} . \boldsymbol{\nabla}) V = \nabla^2 V.$$

$\mathbf{a} . \boldsymbol{\nabla}$ is the operator $a_1 \frac{\partial}{\partial x} + a_2 \frac{\partial}{\partial y} + a_3 \frac{\partial}{\partial z}$.

(iv) $$\text{Curl curl } \mathbf{a} \equiv \text{grad div } \mathbf{a} - \nabla^2 \mathbf{a},$$

i.e. $$\boldsymbol{\nabla} \times (\boldsymbol{\nabla} \times \mathbf{a}) \equiv \boldsymbol{\nabla}(\boldsymbol{\nabla} . \mathbf{a}) - \nabla^2 \mathbf{a}.$$

For co-ordinates other than Cartesians $\nabla^2 \mathbf{a}$ may be computed from the expressions for grad, div and curl using (iv).

(v) $$\boldsymbol{\nabla}(U + V) = \boldsymbol{\nabla} U + \boldsymbol{\nabla} V.$$

(vi) $$\boldsymbol{\nabla}(UV) = U(\boldsymbol{\nabla} V) + V(\boldsymbol{\nabla} U).$$

(vii) $$\boldsymbol{\nabla} . (\mathbf{a} + \mathbf{b}) = \boldsymbol{\nabla} . \mathbf{a} + \boldsymbol{\nabla} . \mathbf{b}.$$

(viii) $$\boldsymbol{\nabla} \times (\mathbf{a} + \mathbf{b}) = \boldsymbol{\nabla} \times \mathbf{a} + \boldsymbol{\nabla} \times \mathbf{b}.$$

21.6. The following expansions differ from the formal expansions for products:

$$\boldsymbol{\nabla} . (U\mathbf{a}) = \boldsymbol{\nabla} U . \mathbf{a} + U \boldsymbol{\nabla} . \mathbf{a},$$

i.e. $$\text{div } (U\mathbf{a}) = \text{grad } U . \mathbf{a} + U \text{ div } \mathbf{a}.$$

$$\boldsymbol{\nabla} \times (U\mathbf{a}) = \boldsymbol{\nabla} U \times \mathbf{a} + U \boldsymbol{\nabla} \times \mathbf{a},$$

i.e. $$\text{curl } (U\mathbf{a}) = \text{grad } U \times \mathbf{a} + U \text{ curl } \mathbf{a}.$$

$$\boldsymbol{\nabla} . (\mathbf{a} \times \mathbf{b}) = (\boldsymbol{\nabla} \times \mathbf{a}) . \mathbf{b} - \mathbf{a} . (\boldsymbol{\nabla} \times \mathbf{b}),$$

i.e. $$\text{div } (\mathbf{a} \times \mathbf{b}) = \mathbf{b} . \text{curl } \mathbf{a} - \mathbf{a} . \text{curl } \mathbf{b}.$$

$$\boldsymbol{\nabla} \times (\mathbf{a} \times \mathbf{b}) = \mathbf{a}(\boldsymbol{\nabla} . \mathbf{b}) - (\boldsymbol{\nabla} . \mathbf{a})\mathbf{b} + (\mathbf{b} . \boldsymbol{\nabla})\mathbf{a} - (\mathbf{a} . \boldsymbol{\nabla})\mathbf{b},$$

i.e. $$\text{curl } (\mathbf{a} \times \mathbf{b}) = \mathbf{a} \text{ div } \mathbf{b} - \mathbf{b} \text{ div } \mathbf{a} + (\mathbf{b} . \boldsymbol{\nabla})\mathbf{a} - (\mathbf{a} . \boldsymbol{\nabla})\mathbf{b},$$

where $\mathbf{a} . \boldsymbol{\nabla}$ is the operator $a_1 \frac{\partial}{\partial x} + a_2 \frac{\partial}{\partial y} + a_3 \frac{\partial}{\partial z}$.

$$\boldsymbol{\nabla}(\mathbf{a} . \mathbf{b}) = (\mathbf{a} . \boldsymbol{\nabla})\mathbf{b} + (\mathbf{b} . \boldsymbol{\nabla})\mathbf{a} + \mathbf{a} \times (\boldsymbol{\nabla} \times \mathbf{b}) + \mathbf{b} \times (\boldsymbol{\nabla} \times \mathbf{a})$$

i.e. $$\text{grad } (\mathbf{a} . \mathbf{b}) = (\mathbf{a} . \boldsymbol{\nabla})\mathbf{b} + (\mathbf{b} . \boldsymbol{\nabla})\mathbf{a} + \mathbf{a} \times \text{curl } \mathbf{b} + \mathbf{b} \times \text{curl } \mathbf{a}$$

Curvilinear co-ordinates

If u, v, w form an *orthogonal* system of curvilinear co-ordinates in space with line element

$$ds^2 = h_1^2\, du^2 + h_2^2\, dv^2 + h_3^2\, dw^2,$$

where $$h_1^2 = \sum_{x,y,z} x_u^2,\ h_2^2 = \sum_{x,y,z} x_v^2,\ h_3^2 = \sum_{x,y,z} x_w^2,$$

the following relations hold.

The components of all vectors are in the directions du, dv, dw.

Let $$\mathbf{a} = (a_u, a_v, a_w).$$

$$\operatorname{div} \mathbf{a} = \frac{1}{h_1h_2h_3}\left\{\frac{\partial}{\partial u}(h_2h_3a_u) + \frac{\partial}{\partial v}(h_3h_1a_v) + \frac{\partial}{\partial w}(h_1h_2a_w)\right\}.$$

$$\operatorname{curl} \mathbf{a} = \left[\frac{1}{h_2h_3}\left\{\frac{\partial}{\partial v}(a_wh_3) - \frac{\partial}{\partial w}(a_vh_2)\right\},\right.$$

$$\left.\frac{1}{h_3h_1}\left\{\frac{\partial}{\partial w}(a_uh_1) - \frac{\partial}{\partial u}(a_wh_3)\right\},\ \frac{1}{h_1h_2}\left\{\frac{\partial}{\partial u}(a_vh_2) - \frac{\partial}{\partial v}(a_uh_1)\right\}\right].$$

$$\operatorname{grad} V = \left(\frac{1}{h_1}\frac{\partial V}{\partial u}, \frac{1}{h_2}\frac{\partial V}{\partial v}, \frac{1}{h_3}\frac{\partial V}{\partial w}\right).$$

$$\operatorname{div}\operatorname{grad} V = \nabla^2 V = \frac{1}{h_1h_2h_3}\left\{\frac{\partial}{\partial u}\left(\frac{h_2h_3}{h_1}\frac{\partial V}{\partial u}\right)\right.$$

$$\left. + \frac{\partial}{\partial v}\left(\frac{h_3h_1}{h_2}\frac{\partial V}{\partial v}\right) + \frac{\partial}{\partial w}\left(\frac{h_1h_2}{h_3}\frac{\partial V}{\partial w}\right)\right\}.$$

Some writers use $\nabla \cdot \nabla V$ for div grad V in curvilinear co-ordinates, but if such a notation is used the ∇ is purely symbolic and is not strictly an operator.

In *spherical polar co-ordinates* r, θ, ϕ

$$ds^2 = dr^2 + r^2\, d\theta^2 + r^2 \sin^2\theta\, d\phi^2.$$

$$\operatorname{div} \mathbf{a} = \frac{1}{r^2\sin\theta}\left\{\frac{\partial}{\partial r}(a_r r^2 \sin\theta) + \frac{\partial}{\partial \theta}(a_\theta r\sin\theta) + \frac{\partial}{\partial\phi}(a_\phi r)\right\}.$$

$$\operatorname{curl} \mathbf{a} = \left[\frac{1}{r^2\sin\theta}\left\{\frac{\partial}{\partial\theta}(a_\phi r\sin\theta) - \frac{\partial}{\partial\phi}(a_\theta r)\right\},\right.$$

$$\left.\frac{1}{r\sin\theta}\left\{\frac{\partial}{\partial\phi}(a_r) - \frac{\partial}{\partial r}(a_\phi r\sin\theta)\right\},\ \frac{1}{r}\left\{\frac{\partial}{\partial r}(a_\theta r) - \frac{\partial}{\partial\theta}(a_r)\right\}\right].$$

$$\operatorname{grad} V = \left(\frac{\partial V}{\partial r}, \frac{1}{r}\frac{\partial V}{\partial\theta}, \frac{1}{r\sin\theta}\frac{\partial V}{\partial\phi}\right).$$

$$\operatorname{div}\operatorname{grad} V = \nabla^2 V = \frac{\partial^2 V}{\partial r^2} + \frac{2}{r}\frac{\partial V}{\partial r} + \frac{1}{r^2}\frac{\partial^2 V}{\partial\theta^2} + \frac{\cot\theta}{r^2}\frac{\partial V}{\partial\theta} + \frac{1}{r^2\sin^2\theta}\frac{\partial^2 V}{\partial\phi^2}.$$

Cylindrical polar co-ordinates r, ϕ, z

$$ds^2 = dr^2 + r^2\, d\phi^2 + dz^2.$$

$$\operatorname{div} \mathbf{a} = \frac{1}{r}\left\{\frac{\partial}{\partial r}(a_r r) + \frac{\partial}{\partial \phi}(a_\phi) + \frac{\partial}{\partial z}(a_z r)\right\}.$$

$$\operatorname{curl} \mathbf{a} = \left[\frac{1}{r}\left\{\frac{\partial}{\partial \phi}(a_z) - \frac{\partial}{\partial z}(a_\phi r)\right\},\ \left\{\frac{\partial}{\partial z}(a_r) - \frac{\partial}{\partial r}(a_z)\right\},\ \frac{1}{r}\left\{\frac{\partial}{\partial r}(a_\phi r) - \frac{\partial}{\partial \phi}(a_r)\right\}\right].$$

$$\operatorname{grad} V = \left(\frac{\partial V}{\partial r}, \frac{1}{r}\frac{\partial V}{\partial \phi}, \frac{\partial V}{\partial z}\right).$$

$$\operatorname{div}\operatorname{grad} V = \nabla^2 V = \frac{\partial^2 V}{\partial r^2} + \frac{1}{r}\frac{\partial V}{\partial r} + \frac{1}{r^2}\frac{\partial^2 V}{\partial \phi^2} + \frac{\partial^2 V}{\partial z^2}.$$

21.7. Gauss' and Stokes' theorems

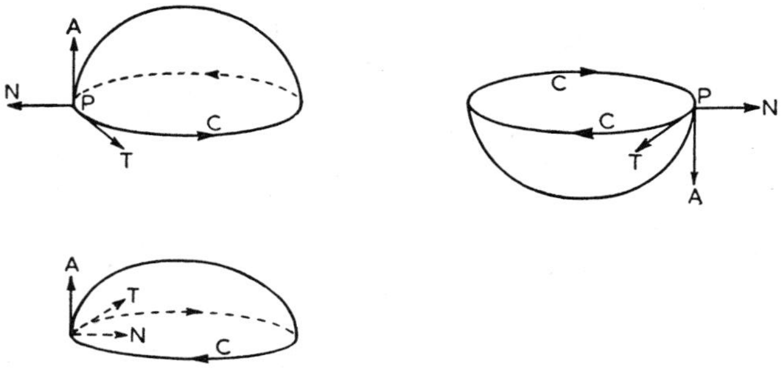

Fig. 21.3

One-sided and two-sided surfaces. Consider a two-sided surface S bounded by a continuous closed curve C. A convention links the positive side of the surface with the direction in which the boundary curve C is described. Let PT be the tangent at a point P of C in the direction in which C is described. Draw PA perpendicular to PT in the tangent plane to S at P and towards the surface. Then the positive direction to the normal at P is PN, where PN, PT, PA form a right-handed system. The side of the surface facing N is the positive side.

One-sided surfaces exist, e.g. the Mobius band which is formed by rotating one end of a strip of paper through 180° and then fastening the ends together. One can pass from any point on this surface to any other without crossing the boundary.

If a two-sided surface is closed, the outward direction along the normal is the positive direction.

The following theorems apply to two-sided surfaces. All integrations are over the positive side of the surface and along the bounding curve in the positive direction.

Gauss' (*or Green's*) *theorem.* If V is a region of space bounded by a simple closed surface S, which can be divided into a finite number of portions with continuously turning tangent planes, and **a** is a field vector such that **a** and div **a** are continuous, then

$$\iiint_V \operatorname{div} \mathbf{a}\, dV = \iiint_V (\boldsymbol{\nabla} . \mathbf{a})\, dV = \iint_S \mathbf{a} . d\mathbf{S},$$

or in Cartesian components

$$\iiint_V \left(\frac{\partial a_1}{\partial x}+\frac{\partial a_2}{\partial y}+\frac{\partial a_3}{\partial z}\right) dx\, dy\, dz = \iint_S (la_1+ma_2+na_3)\, dS,$$

where (l, m, n) are the direction cosines of the outward drawn normal to dS, and $\mathbf{a}=(a_1, a_2, a_3)$.

Green's second theorem is obtained by putting $\mathbf{a}=U \operatorname{grad} W$, and states that if U and W are scalars with continuous partial derivates

$$\iiint_V U\nabla^2 W\, dV + \iiint_V (\boldsymbol{\nabla} U . \boldsymbol{\nabla} W) dV = \iint_S U \frac{\partial W}{\partial n}\, dS,$$

and

$$\iiint_V (U\nabla^2 W - W\nabla^2 U)\, dV = \iint_S \left(U\frac{\partial W}{\partial n} - W\frac{\partial U}{\partial n}\right) dS,$$

where $\dfrac{\partial}{\partial n}$ denotes differentiation along the outward drawn normal.

Stokes' theorem. Let S be a continuous open surface consisting of a finite number of portions with continuously turning tangent planes, and bounded by a simple continuous (skew or plane) curve C such that the direction cosines l, m, n of the tangent at P to C are continuous or sectionally continuous. Let **a** be a field vector with continuous partial derivates. Then

$$\int_C \mathbf{a} . d\mathbf{r} = \iint_S (\operatorname{curl} \mathbf{a}) . d\mathbf{S} \equiv \iint_S (\boldsymbol{\nabla} \times \mathbf{a}) . d\mathbf{S},$$

where **dr** is the arc of C.

In Cartesian components

$$\int_C (a_1 dx + a_2 dy + a_3 dz)$$
$$= \iint_S \left\{\left(\frac{\partial a_3}{\partial y}-\frac{\partial a_2}{\partial z}\right)l + \left(\frac{\partial a_1}{\partial z}-\frac{\partial a_3}{\partial x}\right)m + \left(\frac{\partial a_2}{\partial x}-\frac{\partial a_1}{\partial y}\right)n\right\} dS$$
$$\equiv \iint_S \left(\frac{\partial a_3}{\partial y}-\frac{\partial a_2}{\partial z}\right) dy\, dz + \iint_S \left(\frac{\partial a_1}{\partial z}-\frac{\partial a_3}{\partial x}\right) dz\, dx$$
$$+ \iint_S \left(\frac{\partial a_2}{\partial x}-\frac{\partial a_1}{\partial y}\right) dx\, dy.$$

(See §16·8).

CHAPTER 22

STATISTICS

Frequency distributions

A frequency distribution is a set of observations arranged to show the number of times, or frequency, with which an event happens in a particular way (e.g. f_x is the number of men, in a certain group, or population, of height x).

The *mean* $\bar{x}$ of the distribution is defined by

$$\bar{x}=\frac{1}{N}\sum_{i=1}^{n} f_i\, x_i,$$

where f_i is the frequency corresponding to x_i, N is the total frequency $\sum_{i=1}^{n} f_i$ and n is the number of observations available.

The kth *moment* of the distribution about a value a of x is

$$\mu_k(a)=\frac{1}{N}\sum_{i=1}^{n} f_i(x_i-a)^k.$$

The *variance* σ^2 is the second moment about the mean, i.e.

$$\sigma^2=\frac{1}{N}\sum_{i=1}^{n} f_i(x_i-\bar{x})^2.$$

The *standard deviation* of the distribution is σ. The *mean deviation* η is defined by

$$\eta=\frac{1}{N}\sum_{i=1}^{n} f_i|x_i-\bar{x}|.$$

If the distribution is specified by a continuous function $f(x)$, instead of discrete values f_i, the corresponding definitions are

mean: $$\bar{x}=\int_a^b x\, f(x)\, dx \div \int_a^b f(x)\, dx,$$

kth moment about $x=a$: $$\mu_k(a)=\int_a^b (x-a)^k f(x)\, dx \div \int_a^b f(x)\, dx,$$

variance: $$\sigma^2=\int_a^b (x-\bar{x})^2 f(x)\, dx \div \int_a^b f(x)\, dx.$$

The *mode* is the position of the maximum ordinate of the distribution. The mode and mean coincide in a symmetrical distribution. Otherwise, the distribution is *skew*.

Binomial distribution

If p is the chance of an event happening, and q the chance of it not happening, in a single trial, the chances of 0, 1, 2, . . ., n events happening in n independent trials are given by the individual terms of the binomial expansion $(p+q)^n$. The mean of the distribution is np and the variance is npq.

Poisson distribution

When the chance of an event is small and the number of trials is large, the chances of 0, 1, 2, . . . events happening are $e^{-\mu}$, $\mu e^{-\mu}$, $(\mu^2/2!)e^{-\mu}$, . . ., where μ is the mean number of events happening. The variance is equal to the mean.

Normal distribution

When n is large, the binomial distribution merges into the normal distribution

$$y=\frac{1}{\sigma\sqrt{(2\pi)}}\exp\left\{-\frac{(x-\bar{x})^2}{2\sigma^2}\right\}.$$

Usually, $\bar{x}=0$, i.e. the mean is at the origin of co-ordinates.

Zones. The fractions of the area included between lines parallel to the y-axis are as follows:

Zone	*Range*
50 per cent.	$\pm 0.6745\sigma$
90 ,,	$\pm 1.645\sigma$
95 ,,	$\pm 1.96\sigma$
99.7 ,,	$\pm 3\sigma$

Linear correlation

The product moment p of a bivariate distribution (x, y) is called the *covariance* and is given by

$$p=\frac{1}{N}\sum_{i=1}^{n} f_i(x_i-\bar{x})(y_i-\bar{y}),$$

where f_i is the frequency with which the values (x_i, y_i) occur and $N=\sum_{i=1}^{n} f_i$.

The *lines of regression* of the distribution are:

y on x: $\quad y-\bar{y}=(p/\sigma_x^2)\,(x-\bar{x})$.

x on y: $\quad x-\bar{x}=(p/\sigma_y^2)\,(y-\bar{y})$.

The quantity $r=p/\sigma_x\sigma_y$ is the *coefficient of correlation* between x and y. If $r=\pm 1$, the lines of regression coincide and the correlation is perfect; if $r=0$, the lines of regression are at maximum divergence, being parallel to the axis of co-ordinates, respectively, and there is no relation between x and y. If $r<0$, on the average y decreases as x increases and if $r>0$, y increases with x.

Analysis of observations

The means of a number of samples, each of n members of a large population, form the sampling distribution of the mean. This distribution has the same mean as the whole population with the standard deviation $\sigma/\sqrt{n}$, where σ is the standard deviation of the whole population.

If $x_1, x_2, \ldots, x_n$ are n equally reliable observed values of a quantity, the result of the experiment is usually given as $\bar{x}\pm\epsilon$, where $\bar{x}$ is the arithmetic mean of the observations and $\epsilon^2=\dfrac{\sum^n (x_i-\bar{x})^2}{n(n-1)}$.

Fitting a straight line by "least squares". The constants a and b in the "best" straight line $y=ax+b$ through n points (x_1, y_1), (x_2, y_2), $\ldots$, (x_n, y_n) are found by solving the simultaneous equations

$$\sum_{i=1}^{n} y_i=na+b\sum_{i=1}^{n} x_i$$

$$\sum_{=1}^{n} x_i y_i=a\sum_{i=1}^{n} x_i+b\sum_{i=1}^{n} x_i^2.$$

Table I

USEFUL LIMITS

a is a real constant

Variable	*Function*	*Limit*
$x \to 0$	$\sin x/x$	1
$x \to 0$	$\tan x/x$	1
$x \to +\infty$	$\log x$	$\to +\infty$
$x \to +\infty$	$\ln x$	$\to +\infty$
$x \to +0$	$\log x$	$\to -\infty$
$x \to +0$	$\ln x$	$\to -\infty$
$x \to +\infty$	$(\ln x)/x^a$ for all $a > 0$	0
$x \to +0$	$x^a \ln x$ for all $a > 0$	0
$x \to +\infty$	$\exp x$	$\to +\infty$
$x \to -\infty$	$\exp x$	0
$x \to +\infty$	$(\exp x)/x^a$ for all real a	$\to +\infty$
$x \to -\infty$	$x^a \exp x$ for all real a	0
$x \to +\infty$	a^x if $a > 1$	$\to +\infty$
	if $0 < a < 1$	0
$x \to 0$	$(1+x)^{1/x}$	e
$x \to 0$	$(1+x)^{a/x}$	$\exp a$
$n \to \infty$	$\left(1+\frac{1}{n}\right)^n$	e
$n \to \infty$	$\left(1-\frac{1}{n}\right)^n$	$1/e$
$n \to \infty$	$\left(1+\frac{x}{n}\right)^n$	$\exp x$
$x \to 0$	$(a^x - 1)/x$	$\ln a$
$x \to \infty$	$x^{1/x}$	1
$n \to \infty$	$(n!)^{1/n}/n$	$1/e$
$n \to \infty$	$n!e^n/\{n^n\sqrt{(2\pi n)}\}$	1 (Stirling's formula)
$n \to \infty$	$\dfrac{2.2.4.4.6.6.\ldots(2n-2)2n}{1.3.3.5.5.7.\ldots(2n-1)(2n-1)}$	$\frac{\pi}{2}$ (Wallis' product)

Cauchy's arithmetic mean. If $a_n \to a$ as $n \to \infty$, then

$$(a_1 + a_2 + \ldots + a_n)/n \to a.$$

Cauchy's geometric mean. If $a_n \to a > 0$ as $n \to \infty$ and $a_n > 0$, then

$$(a_1 \, a_2 \ldots a_n)^{1/n} \to a.$$

Table II

DERIVATES

a and k are constants

Function	*First derivate*	n*th derivate*
x^k	kx^{k-1} if $k \neq 0$	$k(k-1)\ldots(k-n+1)x^{k-n}$, 0 if $n=k+1, k+2\ldots.$
$\sin x$	$\cos x \equiv \sin(x+\frac{1}{2}\pi)$	$\sin(x+\frac{1}{2}n\pi)$
$\cos x$	$-\sin x \equiv \cos(x+\frac{1}{2}\pi)$	$\cos(x+\frac{1}{2}n\pi)$
$\tan x$	$\sec^2 x$	
$\cot x$	$-\operatorname{cosec}^2 x$	
$\sec x$	$\sec x \tan x$	
$\operatorname{cosec} x$	$-\operatorname{cosec} x \cot x$	
$\sin^{-1}\dfrac{x}{a}$	$(a^2-x^2)^{-\frac{1}{2}}$ if $\lvert x\rvert < a$	
$\cos^{-1}\dfrac{x}{a}$	$-(a^2-x^2)^{-\frac{1}{2}}$ if $\lvert x\rvert < a.$	

The sign of the above roots is positive if the principal value of the inverse function is indicated.

$\tan^{-1} x$	$1/(1+x^2)$	$\dfrac{(-1)^{n-1}}{2i}(n-1)!\{(x-i)^{-n} - (x+i)^{-n}\}$
$\cot^{-1} x$	$-1/(1+x^2)$	$\dfrac{(-1)^{n}}{2i}(n-1)!\{(x-i)^{-n} - (x+i)^{-n}\}$
$\ln x$	$1/x$	$(-1)^{n-1}(n-1)!/x^n$
$\exp x \equiv e^x$	$\exp x$	$\exp x$
a^x	$a^x \ln a$	$a^x(\ln a)^n$
$\log_a x$	$(\log_a e)/x \equiv 1/(x \ln a)$	$(-1)^{n-1}(n-1)!\,(\log_a e)/x^n \equiv (-1)^{n-1}(n-1)!/(x^n \ln a).$
$\sinh x$	$\cosh x$	$\sinh x$ (n even); $\cosh x$ (n odd)

$\cosh x$	$\sinh x$	$\cosh x$ (n even); $\sinh x$ (n odd).
$\tanh x$	$\operatorname{sech}^2 x$	
$\coth x$	$-\operatorname{cosech}^2 x$	
$\operatorname{sech} x$	$-\operatorname{sech} x \tanh x$	
$\operatorname{cosech} x$	$-\coth x \operatorname{cosech} x$	
$\sinh^{-1} \frac{x}{a}$	$(x^2+a^2)^{-\frac{1}{2}}$	
$\ln \{x+\sqrt{(x^2+a^2)}\}$	$(x^2+a^2)^{-\frac{1}{2}}$	
$\cosh^{-1} \frac{x}{a}$	$\pm (x^2-a^2)^{-\frac{1}{2}}$	
$\ln \{x \pm \sqrt{(x^2-a^2)}\}$	$(x^2-a^2)^{-\frac{1}{2}}$	
$\tanh^{-1} (x/a)$	$a/(a^2-x^2)$, $\|x\| < \|a\|$	$(n-1)!(\frac{1}{2})\{(a-x)^{-n} + (-1)^{n-1}(a+x)^{-n}\}$
$\coth^{-1} (x/a)$	$-a/(x^2-a^2)$, $\|x\| > \|a\|$	$(n-1)!(\frac{1}{2})\{(-1)^n(x-a)^{-n} + (-1)^{n-1}(x+a)^{-n}\}$

Table III

INDEFINITE INTEGRALS—STANDARD FORMS

An arbitrary constant should be added

Function	*Integral with respect to x*	
$(x-a)^n$	$\dfrac{(x-a)^{n+1}}{n+1}$	$n \neq -1$
$1/(x-a)$	$\ln \lvert x-a\rvert$.	
$\dfrac{1}{x^2+a^2}$	$\dfrac{1}{a}\tan^{-1}\dfrac{x}{a}$	
$\dfrac{1}{a^2-x^2}$	$\dfrac{1}{2\lvert a\rvert}\ln\left\lvert\dfrac{a+x}{a-x}\right\rvert$	
$\dfrac{2x+p}{x^2+px+q}$	$\ln \lvert x^2+px+q\rvert$	
$\dfrac{2x+p}{(x^2+px+q)^n}$	$\dfrac{(x^2+px+q)^{1-n}}{1-n}$	$n \neq -1$
$\dfrac{1}{\sqrt{(a^2-x^2)}}$	$\sin^{-1}\dfrac{x}{\lvert a\rvert}$	
$\dfrac{1}{\sqrt{(a^2+x^2)}}$	$\ln\lvert x+\sqrt{(x^2+a^2)}\rvert$ or $\sinh^{-1}\dfrac{x}{\lvert a\rvert}$	
$\dfrac{1}{\sqrt{(x^2-a^2)}}$	$\ln\lvert x+\sqrt{(x^2-a^2)}\rvert$ or $\pm\cosh^{-1}\dfrac{\lvert x\rvert}{\lvert a\rvert}$ sign that of x	
$\dfrac{b+2ax}{\sqrt{(c+bx+ax^2)}}$	$2\sqrt{(c+bx+ax^2)}$	
$\sin x$	$-\cos x$	
$\cos x$	$\sin x$	
$\tan x$	$\ln\lvert\sec x\rvert$	
$\cot x$	$\ln\lvert\sin x\rvert$.	
$\sec x$	$\ln\lvert\sec x+\tan x\rvert=\ln\lvert\tan(\tfrac{1}{2}x+\tfrac{1}{4}\pi)\rvert$ $=\tfrac{1}{2}\ln\dfrac{1+\sin x}{1-\sin x}$	

$\operatorname{cosec} x$	$\ln \lvert\tan \tfrac{1}{2}x\rvert = \ln \lvert\operatorname{cosec} x - \cot x\rvert$ $= \tfrac{1}{2}\ln \dfrac{1-\cos x}{1+\cos x}$	
$\sec^2 x$	$\tan x$	
$\operatorname{cosec}^2 x$	$-\cot x$	
e^{ax}	e^{ax}/a	$a \neq 0$
a^x	$a^x/\ln a$	$a \neq 1$
$\sinh x$	$\cosh x$	
$\cosh x$	$\sinh x$	
$\tanh x$	$\ln \cosh x$	
$\coth x$	$\ln \lvert\sinh x\rvert$	
$\operatorname{sech} x$	$2 \tan^{-1} e^x$	
$\operatorname{cosech} x$	$\ln \lvert\tanh \tfrac{1}{2}x\rvert$	
$\operatorname{sech}^2 x$	$\tanh x$	
$\operatorname{cosech}^2 x$	$-\coth x$	

Table IV

INDEFINITE INTEGRALS

An arbitrary constant should be added

Let $X \equiv ax^2+bx+c$. $D \equiv b^2-4ac$

Function	*Integral with respect to x*	
$\dfrac{1}{\sqrt{X}}$	$\dfrac{1}{\sqrt{a}} \ln \left\lvert \sqrt{X}+x\sqrt{a}+\dfrac{b}{2\sqrt{a}} \right\rvert$	$a>0$
	$\dfrac{1}{\sqrt{a}} \sinh^{-1} \dfrac{2ax+b}{\sqrt{(-D)}}$	$a>0,\ D<0$
	$\dfrac{-1}{\sqrt{(-a)}} \sin^{-1} \dfrac{2ax+b}{\sqrt{D}}$	$a<0,\ D>0$ $\lvert 2ax+b \rvert < \sqrt{D}$
	$\dfrac{1}{\sqrt{a}} \ln \lvert 2ax+b \rvert$	$a>0,\ D=0$
$\sqrt{(a^2-x^2)}$	$\dfrac{1}{2} x\sqrt{(a^2-x^2)}+\dfrac{1}{2} a^2 \sin^{-1} \dfrac{x}{a}$	
$\sqrt{(x^2+a^2)}$	$\dfrac{1}{2} x\sqrt{(x^2+a^2)}+\dfrac{1}{2} a^2 \ln \lvert x+\sqrt{(x^2+a^2)} \rvert$	
	or $\dfrac{1}{2} x\sqrt{(x^2+a^2)}+\dfrac{1}{2} a^2 \sinh^{-1} \dfrac{x}{a}$	
$\sqrt{(x^2-a^2)}$	$\dfrac{1}{2} x\sqrt{(x^2-a^2)}-\dfrac{1}{2} a^2 \ln \lvert x+\sqrt{(x^2-a^2)} \rvert$	
	or $\dfrac{1}{2} x\sqrt{(x^2-a^2)}-\dfrac{1}{2} a^2 \cosh^{-1} \dfrac{x}{a}$	
$\sqrt{X}$	$\dfrac{(2ax+b)\sqrt{X}}{4a}-\dfrac{D}{8a}\displaystyle\int \dfrac{dx}{\sqrt{X}}$	
$\dfrac{x}{\sqrt{X}}$	$\dfrac{\sqrt{X}}{a}-\dfrac{b}{2a}\displaystyle\int \dfrac{dx}{\sqrt{X}}$	
$u_n = \displaystyle\int \cos^n x\, dx$	$\dfrac{1}{n} \sin x \cos^{n-1} x + \dfrac{(n-1)}{n} u_{n-2}$	$n \neq 1$

$v_k=\int \sin^k x\,dx$	$-\frac{1}{k}\cos x \sin^{k-1} x \quad + \quad \frac{k-1}{k} v_{k-2}$	$k\neq 1$
$I_{n,k}=\int \cos^n x \sin^k x\,dx$	$\frac{\sin^{k+1} x \cos^{n-1} x}{n+k}+\frac{n-1}{n+k} I_{n-2,k}$	$n\neq 1$ $n\neq -k$
	$=-\frac{\sin^{k-1} x \cos^{n+1} x}{n+k}+\frac{k-1}{n+k} I_{n,k-2},$	$k\neq 1$ $n\neq k$
$u_n=\int \tan^n x\,dx$	$\frac{\tan^{n-1} x}{n-1}-u_{n-2}$	$n\neq 1$
$v_n=\int \cot^n x\,dx$	$-\frac{\cot^{n-1} x}{n-1}-v_{n-2}$	$n\neq 1$
$\sin kx \cos nx$	$-\frac{\cos (k-n)x}{2(k-n)}-\frac{\cos (k+n)x}{2(k+n)}$	$k^2\neq n^2$
$\sin kx \sin nx$	$\frac{\sin (k-n)x}{2(k-n)}-\frac{\sin (k+n)x}{2(k+n)}$	$k^2\neq n^2$
$\cos kx \cos nx$	$\frac{\sin (k-n)x}{2(k-n)}+\frac{\sin (k+n)x}{2(k+n)}$	$k^2\neq n^2$
$\frac{1}{a+b\cos x}$	$\frac{1}{\sqrt{(b^2-a^2)}}\left\{\ln \left\|(b^2-a^2)^{\frac{1}{2}}+(b-a)\tan \frac{1}{2}x\right\| -\ln \left\|(b^2-a^2)^{\frac{1}{2}}-(b-a)\tan \frac{1}{2}x\right\|\right\}$	$b^2>a^2$
	$\frac{2}{\sqrt{(a^2-b^2)}}\tan^{-1}\left\{\frac{a-b}{\sqrt{(a^2-b^2)}}\tan \frac{1}{2}x\right\}$	$a^2>b^2$

The integrand becomes infinite when $x=\cos^{-1}(-a/b)$ if $|a|\leqslant|b|$. The range should not include this point.

$u_n=\int x^n e^{ax}\,dx$	$\frac{x^n e^{ax}}{a}-\frac{n}{a}u_{n-1}$	$n\neq 0$
$u_n=\int \sinh^n x\,dx$	$\frac{1}{n}\sinh^{n-1} x \cosh x-\frac{n-1}{n}u_{n-2}$	$n\neq 1$
$u_n=\int \cosh^n x\,dx$	$\frac{1}{n}\sinh x \cosh^{n-1} x+\frac{n-1}{n}u_{n-2}$	$n\neq 1$
$u_n=\int \tanh^n x\,dx$	$-\frac{\tanh^{n-1} x}{n-1}+u_{n-2}$	$n\neq 1$

$u_n = \int \coth^n x \, dx$	$-\dfrac{\coth^{n-1} x}{n-1} + u_{n-2}$	$n \neq 1$
$I_n = \int x^n \sinh x \, dx$	$x^n \cosh x \ - \ nx^{n-1} \sinh x \ + \ n(n-1) I_{n-2}$	
$J_n = \int x^n \cosh x \, dx$	$x^n \sinh x \ - \ nx^{n-1} \cosh x \ + \ n(n-1) J_{n-2}$	
$\sinh kx \sinh nx$	$\dfrac{\sinh (k+n)x}{2(k+n)} - \dfrac{\sinh (k-n)x}{2(k-n)}$	$k^2 \neq n^2$
$\cosh kx \cosh nx$	$\dfrac{\sinh (k+n)x}{2(k+n)} + \dfrac{\sinh (k-n)x}{2(k-n)}$	$k^2 \neq n^2$
$\sinh kx \cosh nx$	$\dfrac{\cosh (k+n)x}{2(k+n)} + \dfrac{\cosh (k-n)x}{2(k-n)}$	$k^2 \neq n^2$
$e^{ax} \cos (bx+c) \equiv P$	$\dfrac{e^{ax}}{a^2+b^2}[a \cos (bx+c) + b \sin (bx+c)]$	
$e^{ax} \sin (bx+c) \equiv Q$	$\dfrac{e^{ax}}{a^2+b^2}[a \sin (bx+c) - b \cos (bx+c)]$	

TABLE V

DEFINITE INTEGRALS

$\int_0^{\frac{1}{2}\pi} \sin^n x\,dx = \int_0^{\frac{1}{2}\pi} \cos^n x\,dx$	$= \frac{n-1}{n} \cdot \frac{n-3}{n-2} \cdots \frac{4}{5} \cdot \frac{2}{3}$	n odd integer > 1
	$= \frac{n-1}{n} \frac{n-3}{n-2} \cdots \frac{3}{4} \cdot \frac{1}{2} \cdot \frac{\pi}{2}$	n even positive integer
	$= \frac{1}{2}\sqrt{\pi}\,\Gamma(\frac{1}{2}n+\frac{1}{2})/\Gamma(1+\frac{1}{2}n)$ (See § 15.5.)	$n > -1$
$\int_0^{\frac{1}{2}\pi} \sin^m \theta \cos^n \theta\,d\theta$	$= \frac{1}{2}B(\frac{1}{2}m+\frac{1}{2}, \frac{1}{2}n+\frac{1}{2})$ (See § 15.5.)	$m > -1$, $n > -1$
$\int_0^{\infty} \frac{x^{m-1}}{(ax+b)^{m+n}}\,dx$	$= B(m, n) a^{-m} b^{-n}$	$m > 0$, $n > 0$
$\int_0^{a} x^{m-1} (a-x)^{n-1}\,dx$	$= a^{m+n-1} B(m, n)$	$m > 0$, $n > 0$
$\int_0^{1} \frac{x^{m-1}+x^{n-1}}{(1+x)^{m+n}}\,dx$	$= B(m, n)$	$m > 0$, $n > 0$
$\int_0^{\infty} \frac{x^{a-1}}{1+x}\,dx$	$= \pi \operatorname{cosec} a\pi$	$0 < a < 1$
$\int_0^{\infty} \frac{x^{m-1}}{1+x^n}\,dx$	$= \pi \operatorname{cosec} (m\pi/n)/n$	$0 < m < n$
$\int_0^{1} \frac{x^{2n+1}}{\sqrt{(1-x^2)}}\,dx$	$= \frac{2n}{2n+1} \cdot \frac{(2n-2)}{2n-1} \cdots \frac{4}{5} \cdot \frac{2}{3}$,	n positive integer
$\int_0^{1} \frac{x^{2n}}{\sqrt{(1-x^2)}}\,dx$	$= \frac{2n-1}{2n} \cdot \frac{2n-3}{2n-2} \cdots \frac{3}{4} \cdot \frac{1}{2} \cdot \frac{\pi}{2}$,	n positive integer
$\int_0^{1} \frac{x^{n}}{\sqrt{(1-x^2)}}\,dx$	$= \frac{1}{2}\sqrt{\pi}\Gamma\left(\frac{1}{2}n+\frac{1}{2}\right) \Big/ \Gamma\left(1+\frac{1}{2}n\right)$	$n > -1$
$\int_0^{\pi} \sin nx \sin kx\,dx$	$= 0$	$k \neq n$, n, k integers or zero
$\int_0^{\pi} \sin^2 nx\,dx$	$= \frac{\pi}{2}$	n non-zero integer

$\int_0^{\pi} \cos nx \cos kx \, dx$	$=0$	$k \neq n, k, n$ integers
	$=\pi$	$k=n=0$
$\int_0^{\pi} \cos^2 nx \, dx$	$=\frac{1}{2}\pi$	n non-zero integer
$\int_0^{\infty} \frac{\sin ax}{x} \, dx$	$=\frac{1}{2}\pi$	$a>0$
	$=0$	$a=0$
	$=-\frac{1}{2}\pi$	$a<0$
$\int_0^{\infty} \frac{\cos ax - \cos bx}{x} \, dx$	$=\ln (b/a)$	
$\int_0^{\infty} \frac{\sin x}{\sqrt{x}} \, dx = \int_0^{\infty} \frac{\cos x}{\sqrt{x}} \, dx$	$=\sqrt{\left(\frac{1}{2}\pi\right)}$	
$\int_0^{\infty} \frac{\sin x \cos mx}{x} \, dx$	$=0$	$m^2>1$
	$=\frac{1}{4}\pi$	$m^2=1$
	$=\frac{1}{2}\pi$	$m^2<1$
$\int_0^{\infty} \frac{\cos mx}{1+x^2} \, dx$	$=\frac{1}{2}\pi e^{-m}$	$m \geqslant 0$
	$=\frac{1}{2}\pi e^{m}$	$m \leqslant 0$
$\int_0^{\infty} \frac{\sin^2 x}{x^2} \, dx$	$=\frac{1}{2}\pi$	
$\int_0^{\infty} \sin (x^2) \, dx$	$=\int_0^{\infty} \cos (x^2) \, dx = \frac{1}{2}\sqrt{\left(\frac{1}{2}\pi\right)}$	
$\int_0^{\frac{1}{2}\pi} \frac{\sin x}{\sqrt{(1-k^2 \sin^2 x)}} \, dx$	$=\frac{1}{2k} \ln \frac{1+k}{1-k}$	$k^2<1$
$\int_0^{\frac{1}{2}\pi} \frac{\cos x}{\sqrt{(1-k^2 \sin^2 x)}} \, dx$	$=\frac{1}{k} \sin^{-1} k$	$k^2<1$

$$\int_0^{\frac{1}{2}\pi} \frac{dx}{1+a\cos x} = \frac{\cos^{-1} a}{\sqrt{(1-a^2)}} \qquad a^2<1$$

$$\int_0^{\pi} \frac{dx}{1+a\cos x} = \frac{\pi}{\sqrt{(1-a^2)}} \qquad a^2<1$$

$$\int_0^{\frac{1}{2}\pi} \frac{dx}{1+a\cos x} = \frac{1}{\sqrt{(a^2-1)}} \ln\{a+\sqrt{(a^2-1)}\} \qquad a>1$$

$$\int_{-\pi}^{\pi} \cos kx \cos nx\, dx = 0 \qquad k\neq n,\ k,\ n \text{ integers}$$

$$= \pi \qquad k=n, \text{ an integer}$$

$$\int_{-\pi}^{\pi} \sin kx \sin nx\, dx = 0 \qquad k\neq n,\ k,\ n \text{ integers}$$

$$= \pi \qquad k=n \text{ an integer}$$

$$\int_{-\pi}^{\pi} \sin kx \cos nx\, dx = 0$$

$$\int_{-\pi}^{\pi} \cos nx\, dx = 0 \qquad n \text{ a positive integer}$$

$$= 2\pi \qquad n=0$$

$$\int_{-\pi}^{\pi} \sin nx\, dx = 0$$

Table VI

SUMS OF FINITE SERIES

1. *Arithmetical progression*

$$a+(a+d)+(a+2d)+\dots+\{a+(n-1)d\}=\tfrac{1}{2}n\{2a+(n-1)d\}$$
$$=\tfrac{1}{2}n(a+l),\text{ where } l=\text{last term}$$

2. *Geometric progression*

$$a+ar+ar^2+\dots+ar^{n-1}=a(r^n-1)/(r-1) \qquad r\neq 1$$

3. *Powers of integers*

$$\sum_1^n r=\tfrac{1}{2}n(n+1)$$

$$\sum_1^n r^2=\tfrac{1}{6}n(n+1)\,(2n+1)$$

$$\sum_1^n r^3=\{\tfrac{1}{2}n(n+1)\}^2$$

$$\sum_1^n r^4=n(n+1)\,(2n+1)\,(3n^2+3n-1)/30$$

$$\sum_1^n r^p=\frac{n^{p+1}}{p+1}+\frac{1}{2}n^p+\frac{B_1}{2!}pn^{p-1}-\frac{B_2}{4!}p(p-1)(p-2)\,n^{p-3}+\dots$$

the last term being in n or n^2 and B_1, B_2 being Bernoulli's numbers (q.v.).

$$\sum_1^n (2r-1)=n^2$$

$$\sum_1^n (2r-1)^2=\tfrac{1}{3}n(4n^2-1)$$

$$\sum_1^n (2r-1)^3=n^2(2n^2-1)$$

$$\sum_1^n 1/r \simeq \gamma+\ln n+\frac{1}{2}n-\frac{a_2}{n(n+1)}-\frac{a_3}{n(n+1)(n+2)}-\dots$$

where $a_2=\dfrac{1}{12}$, $a_3=\dfrac{1}{12}$, $a_4=\dfrac{19}{80}$, $a_k=\dfrac{1}{k}\displaystyle\int_0^1\{x(1-x)(2-x)\dots(k-1-x)\}dx$

$$\sum_1^n 1/r^2 \simeq \frac{1}{6}\pi^2-\frac{d_1}{n+1}-\frac{d_2}{(n+1)(n+2)}-\frac{d_3}{(n+1)(n+2)(n+3)}-\dots$$

where $d_k=(k-1)!/k$.

4. *Inverse products*

$$\sum_{r=0}^{n-1}[\{(p+rd\}\{p+(r+1)d\}\ldots\{p+(r+k)d\}]^{-1}$$

$$=\frac{1}{kd}\left[\frac{1}{p\{p+d\}\ldots\{p+(k-1)d\}}\right.$$

$$\left.-\frac{1}{\{p+nd\}\{p+(n+1)d\}\ldots\{p+(k+n-1)d\}}\right].$$

5. *Trigonometrical sums*

$$\sum_{r=0}^{n-1}\sin(\theta+r\alpha)=\sin\{\theta+\tfrac{1}{2}(n-1)\alpha\}\sin\tfrac{1}{2}n\alpha\operatorname{cosec}\tfrac{1}{2}\alpha \qquad \alpha\neq 2k\pi$$

$$\sum_{r=0}^{n-1}\cos(\theta+r\alpha)=\cos\{\theta+\tfrac{1}{2}(n-1)\alpha\}\sin\tfrac{1}{2}n\alpha\operatorname{cosec}\tfrac{1}{2}\alpha \qquad \alpha\neq 2k\pi$$

In the following, if $a=1$, then $\theta\neq 2k\pi$.

$$\sum_{0}^{n-1}a^r\cos r\theta=\frac{\{1-a\cos\theta-a^n\cos n\theta+a^{n+1}\cos(n-1)\theta\}}{\{1-2a\cos\theta+a^2\}}$$

$$\sum_{0}^{n-1}a^r\sin r\theta=\frac{\{a\sin\theta-a^n\sin n\theta+a^{n+1}\sin(n-1)\theta\}}{\{1-2a\cos\theta+a^2\}}$$

$$\sum_{0}^{n-1}a^r\cosh r\theta=\frac{\{1-a\cosh\theta-a^n\cosh n\theta+a^{n+1}\cosh(n-1)\theta\}}{(1-2a\cosh\theta+a^2)}$$

$$\sum_{0}^{n-1}a^r\sinh r\theta=\frac{\{a\sinh\theta-a^n\sinh n\theta+a^{n+1}\sinh(n-1)\theta\}}{(1-2a\cosh\theta+a^2)}$$

Sums of the odd and even terms in these series can be found by writing ib for a, equating real and imaginary parts and writing $\theta+\pi$ for θ.

Table VII

BERNOULLI'S NUMBERS B_n AND EULER'S NUMBERS E_n

Some authors use a different notation. When quoting results involving these numbers the definitions should also be quoted. The notation given is used in *Traité Elementairè des Nombres de Bernoulli*, by N. Neilsen, Gauthier-Villars et Cie, Paris, 1923; *Introduction to the Theory of Infinite Series*, by T. J. I'a. Bromwich, Macmillan and Co., London, 1928; *American Standard Mathematical Symbols*, 1928, Report Z10 of American Engineering Standards Committee.

$(-1)^{n-1}B_n/(2n)!$ is the coefficient of x^{2n} in the expansion of $x/(e^x-1)$ in powers of x, $x^2<4\pi^2$,

i.e. $$\frac{x}{e^x-1}=1-\frac{x}{2}+\frac{B_1x^2}{2!}-\frac{B_2x^4}{4!}+\ldots+\frac{(-1)^{n-1}B_nx^{2n}}{(2n)!}+\ldots$$

$$B_n=\frac{(2n)!}{\pi^{2n}2^{2n-1}}\left[1+\frac{1}{2^{2n}}+\frac{1}{3^{2n}}+\frac{1}{4^{2n}}+\ldots\right]$$

$$B_n=\frac{(2n)!}{\pi^{2n}(2^{2n-1}-1)}\left[1-\frac{1}{2^{2n}}+\frac{1}{3^{2n}}-\frac{1}{4^{2n}}+\ldots\right]$$

$$B_n=\frac{2(2n)!}{\pi^{2n}(2^{2n}-1)}\left[1+\frac{1}{3^{2n}}+\frac{1}{5^{2n}}+\frac{1}{7^{2n}}+\ldots\right]$$

$$E_n=\frac{(2n)!}{(2n-2)!2!}E_{n-1}-\frac{(2n)!}{(2n-4)!4!}E_{n-2}+\ldots+(-1)^{n-1},$$

where $E_0=1$, $0!=1$.

$$E_n=\frac{2^{2n+2}(2n)!}{\pi^{2n+1}}\left[1-\frac{1}{3^{2n+1}}+\frac{1}{5^{2n+1}}-\frac{1}{7^{2n+1}}+\ldots\right].$$

$$B_n=\frac{2n}{2^{2n}(2^{2n}-1)}\cdot\left[\frac{(2n-1)!}{(2n-2)!\,1!}E_{n-1}-\frac{(2n-1)!}{(2n-4)!\,3!}E_{n-2}+\ldots+(-1)^{n-1}\right].$$

B_n	$\log B_n$	E_n	$\log E_n$
$B_1=\frac{1}{6}$	$\bar{1}\cdot 221\ 8487$	$E_1=1$	0
$B_2=\frac{1}{30}$	$\bar{2}\cdot 522\ 8787$	$E_2=5$	0·698 9700

$B_3 = \frac{1}{42}$	$\bar{2}\cdot376\ 7507$	$E_3 = 61$	1·785 3298
$B_4 = \frac{1}{30}$	$\bar{2}\cdot522\ 8787$	$E_4 = 1{,}385$	3·141 4498
$B_5 = \frac{5}{66}$	$\bar{2}\cdot879\ 4261$	$E_5 = 50{,}521$	4·703 4719
$B_6 = \frac{691}{2{,}730}$	$\bar{1}\cdot403\ 3154$	$E_6 = 2{,}702{,}765$	6·431 8083
$B_7 = \frac{7}{6}$	0·066 9468		
$B_8 = \frac{3{,}617}{510}$	0·850 7783		
$B_9 = \frac{43{,}867}{798}$	1·740 1350		
$B_{10} = \frac{174{,}611}{330}$	2·723 5577		

$$\text{Euler's constant } \gamma = \lim_{n\to\infty}\left(1+\frac{1}{2}+\frac{1}{3}+\ \dots\ +\frac{1}{n}-\ln n\right)$$
$$=0\cdot5772157\ \dots$$

Table VIII

SUMS OF INFINITE SERIES

Binomial series

$$\sum_{u=0}^{\infty} \binom{k}{n} x^n \qquad = (1+x)^k$$

for all $|x|<1$ and all real k. The series is absolutely convergent if $|x|<1$ for all real k and if $|x|=1$ and $k>0$.

$$\sum_{n=0}^{\infty} x^n \qquad = 1/(1-x) \qquad |x|<1$$

$$\sum_{n=0}^{\infty} (-1)^n \binom{k}{n} \frac{1}{x+n} \qquad = \frac{k!}{x(x+1)\ldots(x+k)}$$

$$\sum_{n=0}^{\infty} \frac{1.3\ldots(2n-1)}{2.4\ldots(2n)} x^{2n} \qquad \equiv \sum_{n=0}^{\infty} \frac{(2n)!}{2^{2n}(n!)^2} x^{2n} = (1-x^2)^{-\frac{1}{2}}, \quad |x|<1$$

$$\sum_{n=0}^{\infty} \frac{(2n)!}{2^{2n}(n!)^2} \frac{1}{x+n} \qquad = \frac{\Gamma(x)\Gamma(\frac{1}{2})}{\Gamma(\frac{1}{2}+x)} \qquad x>0$$

$$\sum_{1}^{\infty} n x^n \qquad = x/(1-x)^2 \qquad |x|<1$$

$$\sum_{0}^{\infty} a^n x^n/n! \qquad = \exp(ax)$$

$$\sum_{0}^{\infty} 1/n! \qquad = e = 2{\cdot}71828\ldots = \lim_{n\to\infty} \left(1+\frac{1}{n}\right)^n$$

$$\sum_{0}^{\infty} (x \ln a)^n/n! \qquad = a^x$$

$$\sum_{1}^{\infty} (-1)^{n-1} x^n/n \qquad = \ln(1+x)$$

for $|x|<1$ and for $|x|=1$ if $x \neq -1$

$$\sum_{0}^{\infty} x^{2n+1}/(2n+1) \qquad = \frac{1}{2} \ln \frac{1+x}{1-x} = \tanh^{-1} x$$

for $|x|<1$ and $|x|=1$ if $x \neq \pm 1$

$$\sum_{0}^{\infty} (-1)^n \frac{1.3.5\ldots(2n-1)}{2.4.6\ldots(2n)} \frac{x^{2n+1}}{2n+1} = \sum_{0}^{\infty} \frac{(-1)^n (2n)!\, x^{2n+1}}{2^{2n}(n!)^2(2n+1)}$$

$$= \ln(x+\sqrt{1+x^2}) = \sinh^{-1} x \qquad |x| \leqslant 1$$

$\sum_{0}^{\infty} (-1)^n x^{2n}/(2n)!$	$=\cos x$	
$\sum_{0}^{\infty} (-1)^n x^{2n+1}/(2n+1)!$	$=\sin x$	
$\sum_{1}^{\infty} \dfrac{2^{2n}(2^{2n}-1)}{(2n)!} B_n x^{2n-1}$	$=\tan x$	$-\frac{1}{2}\pi < x < \frac{1}{2}\pi$
$\dfrac{1}{x} - \sum_{1}^{\infty} \dfrac{2^{2n} B_n}{(2n)!} x^{2n-1}$	$=\cot x$	$0 < x^2 < \pi^2$
$\sum_{0}^{\infty} E_n x^{2n}/(2n)!$	$=\sec x$	$x^4 < \pi^2/4$
$\dfrac{1}{x} + \sum_{1}^{\infty} 2(2^{2n-1}-1) B_n x^{2n-1}/(2n)!$	$=\operatorname{cosec} x$	$0 < x^2 < \pi^2$
$\sum_{0}^{\infty} (-1)^n x^{2n+1}/(2n+1)$	$=\tan^{-1} x$	$\lvert x\rvert < 1$ and $\lvert x\rvert = 1$ if $x \neq \pm i$
$\sum_{0}^{\infty} \dfrac{(2n)!}{2^{2n}(n!)^2} \dfrac{x^{2n+1}}{2n+1}$	$=\sin^{-1} x$	$\lvert x\rvert \leqslant 1$
$\sum_{1}^{\infty} \dfrac{2^{2n-1}(2^{2n}-1) B_n}{n(2n)!} x^{2n}$	$=-\ln\cos x$	$x^2 < \frac{1}{4}\pi^2$
$\sum_{1}^{\infty} \dfrac{2^{2n-1} B_n x^{2n}}{n(2n)!}$	$=\ln\left\lvert \dfrac{x}{\sin x} \right\rvert$	$0 < x^2 < \pi^2$
$\sum \dfrac{2^{2n}(2^{2n-1}-1)}{n(2n)!} B_n x^{2n}$	$=\ln\left\lvert \dfrac{\tan x}{x} \right\rvert$	$x^2 < \frac{1}{4}\pi^2$
$\sum_{0}^{\infty} x^{2n}/(2n)!$	$=\cosh x$	
$\sum_{0}^{\infty} x^{2n+1}/(2n+1)!$	$=\sinh x$	
$\sum_{1}^{\infty} (-1)^{n-1} 2^{2n}(2^{2n}-1) B_n x^{2n-1}/(2n)!$	$=\tanh x$	$x^2 < \frac{1}{4}\pi^2$
$\dfrac{1}{x} + \sum_{1}^{\infty} (-1)^{n-1} 2^{2n} B_n x^{2n-1}/(2n)!$	$=\coth x$	$x^2 < \pi^2$
$1 + \sum_{1}^{\infty} (-1)^n E_n x^{2n}/(2n)!$	$=\operatorname{sech} x$	$x^2 < \frac{1}{4}\pi^2$
$\dfrac{1}{x} + 2\sum_{1}^{\infty} (-1)^n (2^{2n-1}-1) B_n x^{2n-1}/(2n)!$	$=\operatorname{cosech} x$	$x^2 < \pi^2$

By putting $x = e^{i\theta}$, e^{θ}, $ie^{i\theta}$, ie^{θ}, etc., in $\Sigma a^n x^n/n!$ and equating real and imaginary parts, the sums of such series as

$$\Sigma \frac{a^n \cos n\theta}{n!}, \ \Sigma \frac{a^n \cos (2n+1)\theta}{(2n)!}, \ \Sigma \frac{(-1)^n a^n \sin n\theta}{n!}, \ \Sigma \frac{\cosh n\theta}{n!}$$

may be written down. Similarly, if $|a| < 1$, the sums of $\Sigma a^n \cos n\theta$,

$$\Sigma \frac{a^{2n+1} \sin (2n+1)\theta}{2n+1}, \ \Sigma \frac{(-1)^n a^{2n+1} \sin (2n+1)\theta}{2n+1}$$

can be written down from Σx^n, $\Sigma x^n/n$ by writing $x = ae^{i\theta}$ and then $a = ib$.

PART II

PHYSICS

CHAPTER 1

MECHANICS OF PARTICLES AND RIGID BODIES

1.1. Units

The units of mechanics are based upon Newton's second law of motion, which relates force and rate of change of momentum.

Absolute units. In the c.g.s. system the unit of mass is the *gram* and the unit of force is the *dyne*, defined as the force required to give a mass of 1 g. an acceleration of 1 cm. sec.$^{-2}$. In the British system the unit of mass is the *pound* and the unit of force is the *poundal*, defined as the force required to give a mass of 1 lb. an acceleration of 1 ft. sec.$^{-2}$. In the m.k.s. (metre-kilogram-second) system the unit of mass is the *kilogram* (10^3 g.) and the unit of force is the *newton*, defined as the force required to give a mass of 1 kg. an acceleration of 1 m.sec.$^{-2}$.

Gravitational units. In the c.g.s. system the gravitational unit of force is the *gram-weight* $= g$ dynes $\simeq 981$ dynes; in the British system the corresponding unit is the *pound-weight* $= g$ poundals $\simeq 32$ poundals and in the m.k.s. system the gravitational unit is the *kilogram-weight* $= g$ newtons $\simeq 9{\cdot}81$ newtons.

Conversion factors are given on p. 372.

In engineering practice a larger unit of mass, called the *slug*, equal to g pounds, is sometimes used. A force of 1 lb.-wt. acting on a mass of 1 slug imparts an acceleration of 1 ft.sec.$^{-2}$.

The absolute units of work are: the *erg* = work done by 1 dyne acting through 1 cm., in the c.g.s. system; the *foot-poundal* = work done by 1 poundal acting through 1 ft., in the British system, and the *joule* $= 10^7$ ergs, or 1 newton-metre, in the m.k.s. system.

Power, or rate of doing work, is measured by the *watt* = 1 joule sec.$^{-1}$, the *horse-power* (h.p.) = 550 ft.-lb. sec.$^{-1}$ or the *force-de-cheval* = 75 m.-kg. sec.$^{-1}$.

The scientific unit of pressure is the *bar* $= 10^6$ dynes cm.$^{-2}$, which may be thought of as roughly one atmosphere (= 15 lb. in.$^{-2}$). Pressure is also measured in terms of the length of the column of mercury in a barometer. 1 bar = 1000 millibars (mb.) = 750·076 mm. Hg = 29·53 in. Hg at 273° K. in latitude 45°.

1.2. Statics

1.21. Forces, being vector quantities, may be added, subtracted or resolved into components by the usual vector laws.

The magnitude of the resultant R of two forces P and Q inclined at the angle α to each other is given by

$$R^2 = P^2 + Q^2 + 2PQ \cos \alpha.$$

Lami's theorem. If three forces act on a particle in equilibrium, each is proportional to the sine of the angle between the other two.

The *moment* of a force about a given point is defined to be the product of the magnitude of the force and the perpendicular distance from the point to the line of action of the force. The algebraic sum of the moments of any finite number of coplanar forces acting on a rigid body equals the moment of their resultant.

A *couple* is used to denote two equal unlike parallel forces with different lines of action. The moment of a couple about any point in the plane of the forces equals the product of the magnitude of one force and the perpendicular distance between their lines of action.

Any finite number of coplanar couples acting on a rigid body may be replaced by a single couple whose moment is the algebraic sum of their moments.

Any system of coplanar forces acting on a rigid body can be replaced by a force acting at a given point of the body, and a couple.

Conditions for equilibrium of a system of coplanar forces. These conditions may be expressed in a number of ways, e.g. (1) the sum of the projection of the forces on each of two perpendicular directions and the sum of the moments about any one point, vanish, or (ii) the sum of the moments of the given forces about each of three non-collinear points is zero.

1.22. Centroids

The general formulae for the co-ordinates of the centroid of a body of density ρ are

$$\bar{x} = \frac{\iiint \rho x \, dx \, dy \, dz}{\iiint \rho \, dx \, dy \, dz}, \quad \bar{y} = \frac{\iiint \rho y \, dx \, dy \, dz}{\iiint \rho \, dx \, dy \, dz}, \quad \bar{z} = \frac{\iiint \rho z \, dx \, dy \, dz}{\iiint \rho \, dx \, dy \, dz}.$$

For a plane area of uniform density enclosed by a curve and the x-axis the co-ordinates are given by

$$\bar{x} = \frac{\int xy \, dx}{\int y \, dx}, \quad \bar{y} = \frac{\int \frac{1}{2} y^2 \, dx}{\int y \, dx},$$

the integrals being evaluated between the appropriate limits.

Simple examples

Body	*Position of centroid*
Triangular lamina	At intersection of medians
Tetrahedron	At intersection of lines joining vertices to centroids of opposite faces
Pyramid, height h	On line joining vertex to centroid of base, $h/4$ above base
Solid cone	do.
Surface of cone, height h	At $\frac{1}{3}h$ above base
Circular arc, radius r, subtending angle 2α at centre	On line of symmetry, distance $(r/\alpha)\sin\alpha$ from centre of arc
Sector of a circle	On line of symmetry, distance $(2r/3\alpha)\sin\alpha$ from centre
Semicircle	On central radius, distance $4r/3\pi$ from centre
Uniform solid hemisphere	On axis of symmetry, distance $3r/8$ from centre
Uniform hemispherical shell	On axis of symmetry, distance $\frac{1}{2}r$ from centre
Segment of parabola $y^2=Cx$ bounded by double ordinate $x=h$	On line of symmetry, $\bar{x}=3h/5$
Paraboloid generated by $y^2=Cx$, section by $x=h$	$\bar{x}=2h/3$, $\bar{y}=0$

1.23. Theorems of Pappus

(i) If an arc of a plane curve rotates about an axis in its plane, not intersecting it, the product of the length of the arc and the length of the path of the centroid equals the surface generated.

(ii) The volume generated by a plane area rotating about a non-intersecting axis in its plane equals the area multiplied by the length of the path of the centroid.

1.24. Beams

At any section of a loaded beam, the vertical force is equal and opposite to the algebraic sum of the external forces (called the *shearing stress*) on one side of the section.

At any section, the couple is equal and opposite to the sum of the moments of the external forces (called the *bending moment*) on one side of the section about the section.

Simple cases of shearing stress (S) and bending moment (M):

(i) Light cantilever of length l, load W at free end, at position x from fixed end,

$$S=-W, \qquad M=W(l-x).$$

(ii) Cantilever with uniformly distributed load w per unit length,

$$S=-w(l-x), \qquad M=\tfrac{1}{2}w(l-x)^2.$$

(iii) End-supported beam of length $a+b$, load W distant a from one end,

$S=-Wb/(a+b)$, $M=-Wbx/(a+b)$ in one section,

$S=Wa/(a+b)$, $M=-Wax/(a+b)$ in the other section.

(iv) End-supported beam of length l, load w per unit length,

$$S=wx-\tfrac{1}{2}wl, \qquad M=\tfrac{1}{2}wx(x-l).$$

In general, if $w(x)$ is the load intensity along a beam,

$$\frac{dS}{dx}=w(x), \quad \frac{dM}{dx}=S, \text{ and so } \frac{d^2M}{dx^2}=w(x).$$

(For further information see Chapter 2).

1.25. Simple machines

P=effort applied, W=resistance overcome.

mechanical advantage$=W/P$.

$$\text{velocity ratio}=\frac{\text{distance moved by } P}{\text{distance moved by } W}$$

$$\text{efficiency}=\frac{\text{mechanical advantage}}{\text{velocity ratio}}=\frac{\text{work done by machine}}{\text{work supplied to machine}}.$$

(*Examples:* differential pulley, a and b the diameters of the larger and smaller wheels respectively, velocity ratio$=2a(a-b)$; wheel (diameter a) and axle (diameter b), mechanical advantage$=b/a$; screw, a=radius of arm, p=pitch of screw, velocity ratio$=2\pi a/p$.)

1.26. Friction is the force which opposes relative motion between surfaces in contact. A smooth surface can exert a pressure on a body in contact with it only along the normal to the surface. If the pressure is oblique, it is resolved into two components, the normal pressure R

and the tangential force, or friction, F. The friction F is further classified as F_s, the value for which relative motion begins and F_k, the value to be overcome to maintain sliding. The *static coefficient of friction* ("stiction") is defined to be the ratio $\mu = F_s/R$.

If the resultant pressure is inclined at θ to the normal, for equilibrium $\tan\theta \leqslant \mu$. The *angle of friction* λ is defined by $\lambda = \text{arc}\tan\mu$, and the plane of greatest slope on which a heavy particle can rest is inclined to the horizontal at the angle λ.

A force P making an angle θ with the line of greatest slope on a rough inclined plane will prevent sliding of a body of weight W when

$$P = \frac{W\sin(\alpha - \lambda)}{\cos(\theta - \lambda)},$$

where α is the inclination of the plane to the horizontal. For the body to move up the plane, P must not be less than $W\sin(\alpha+\lambda)/\cos(\theta+\lambda)$. For rolling friction (e.g. at a pivot) it is assumed that at the plane of contact the forces are (i) the tangential friction and (ii) a resisting couple whose maximum moment is proportional to the normal pressure.

Fluid friction. See Chapter 5.

1.27. Flexible strings

(i) String stretched over a smooth plane curve. The tension T is given by

$$T = R\rho,$$

where R is the normal pressure and ρ is the radius of curvature.

(ii) String stretched over a rough plane curve. Let ψ be the angle which the tangent makes with some fixed direction and let μ be the coefficient of friction. The tension is given by

$$T = T_0 e^{\mu\psi},$$

where T_0 is the value of T for $\psi = 0$.

(*Example:* for a rope wrapped n times around a post, unit tension at one end can balance a tension $e^{2\pi n\mu}$ at the other. This is the principle of the capstan.)

(iii) Constrained string of weight w per unit length.

$$T = R\rho + w\cos\psi.$$

If y be the height above some fixed level and w is constant,

$$T = wy + \text{constant}.$$

(iv) String hanging freely. The curve is the catenary

$$y = c \cosh (x/c),$$

where c is the height of the lowest point of the string above the origin, and

$$T = wc \sec \psi = wy.$$

(v) String nearly horizontal. Let l be the length between the points of suspension, W the total weight and δ the sag. The horizontal tension is given by

$$T \simeq (l/8\delta) W.$$

1.28. Attraction

Newton's law of gravitation. The attraction R between two particles, of masses m_1 and m_2 respectively, distance d apart, is Gm_1m_2/d^2, where G is the universal constant of gravitation $\simeq 6{\cdot}67 \times 10^{-8}$ dyne cm.^{2} g^{-2}.

Special cases

(i) Thin rod AB on an external point P: $R = (2Gk\rho/p) \sin \frac{1}{2} APB$, where k is the cross-section of the rod, ρ its density and p the perpendicular distance of P from AB.

(ii) Uniform circular plate: $R = 2\pi Gk\rho(1 - \cos \alpha)$, where α is angle subtended by the radius of the plate at P.

(iii) Uniform thin spherical shell: the attraction on an external point is the same as if the whole mass were collected at the centre and there is no attraction on an internal point.

(iv) Uniform solid sphere: on an external point, as if the whole mass were collected at the centre; on an internal point distance r from the centre, attraction $= \frac{4}{3}\pi G\rho r$.

Potential. The potential V of a mass M at a point P is defined to be the work done on unit mass as it moves from an infinite distance by any path to P; $V = G \int_M \frac{dm}{r}$, where dm is an element of mass distance r from P.

If V be the potential of any attracting mass at $P(x, y, z)$, the components of the attraction along the axes Ox, Oy, Oz are $\frac{dV}{dx}, \frac{dV}{dy}, \frac{dV}{dz}$ respectively.

For a thin uniform rod AB the potential at P is

$$V = Gk\rho \log \left(\cot \frac{ABP}{2} \, . \cot \frac{BAP}{2} \right),$$

which becomes: constant—$2Gk\rho \log p$ for an infinite rod.

The potential of a thin uniform circular plate at its centre is $2\pi G k\rho a$, where a is the radius of the plate.

Spherical shell, bounded by spheres of radii a and b. Let the reference point be distant r from the centre.

	$r<b$	$b<r<a$	$r>a$
V	$2\pi G\rho(a^2-b^2)$	$2\pi G\rho\left(a^2-\frac{1}{3}r^2-\frac{2}{3}\frac{b^3}{r}\right)$	$\frac{4}{3}\pi G\rho\left(\frac{a^3-b^3}{r}\right)$
$\frac{dV}{dr}$	0	$-\frac{4}{3}\pi G\rho\left(r-\frac{b^3}{r^2}\right)$	$-\frac{4}{3}\pi G\rho\left(\frac{a^3-b^3}{r^2}\right)$

1.3. Dynamics

1.31. Kinematics of a particle

Rectilinear motion. A particle moving with a constant acceleration f, initial velocity u, velocity v at time t, distance covered x, satisfies the following relations:

$$v=u+ft.$$
$$x=ut+\tfrac{1}{2}ft^2$$
$$v^2=u^2+2fx.$$

The acceleration is $du/dt=d^2x/dt^2$.

(*a*) If $\frac{d^2x}{dt^2}=f(t)$ the distance x is obtained immediately by integrating twice

$$x=\iint f(t)dtdt+At+B,$$

where A and B are the constants of integration.

(*b*) If $\frac{d^2x}{dt^2}=f(x)$, then

$$\frac{1}{2}\left(\frac{dx}{dt}\right)^2-\frac{1}{2}u^2=\int f(x)\,dx+A,$$

whence x or t by a further integration.

Trajectory of a projectile fired *in vacuo* with initial velocity V_0 at angle ϕ to the horizontal. If the axis of x is horizontal and that of y vertical, the equation of the parabolic trajectory is

$$y=x\tan\phi-\frac{gx^2}{2V_0^2\cos^2\phi}$$

and the *range* on the horizontal plane is given by

$$x=\frac{V_0^2}{g}\sin 2\phi$$
$$=\frac{V_0^2}{g}\text{ when }\phi=45°\text{ (maximum range).}$$

The *vertex* is at the height $V_0^2 \sin^2 \phi/2g$ and is reached in time $(V/g) \sin \phi$. The "time of flight" (i.e. time to cover range) is twice the time to the vertex.

Simple harmonic motion. The equation of motion is

$$\frac{d^2x}{dt^2} = -\mu x$$

and the solution is

$$x = a \cos (t\sqrt{\mu} + \epsilon),$$

where a and ϵ are arbitrary constants. The time of a complete oscillation is $2\pi/\sqrt{\mu}$.

Lissajous' figures. If a particle possesses simple harmonic motions in two directions,

$$x = a \cos nt, \; y = b \cos (n't + \epsilon),$$

the path is known as a Lissajous' figure.

If $n = n'$ (equal periods), the path is an ellipse

$$\frac{x^2}{a^2} - \frac{2xy}{ab} \cos \epsilon + \frac{y^2}{b^2} = \sin^2 \epsilon,$$

which reduces to an ellipse with principal axes in the directions Ox, Oy if $\epsilon = \frac{1}{2}\pi$, i.e. when the phase of the y-oscillation at $t=0$ is one-quarter of the periodic time.

If $n' = 2n$, the path is given by

$$\frac{y}{b} = \cos \epsilon \left(\frac{2x^2}{a^2} - 1 \right) - \sin \epsilon \, . \, \frac{2x}{a} \left(\frac{a^2 - x^2}{a^2} \right)^{\frac{1}{2}}.$$

If $\epsilon = \pi$ (phase of y-oscillation at $t=0$ equals half the y-period), the path is parabolic.

Curvilinear uniplanar motion of a particle

Let u, v be the velocities of the particle along and perpendicular to the radius vector OP defined by r, θ,

$$u = \text{radial velocity} = \frac{dr}{dt}; \quad v = \text{tangential velocity} = r\frac{d\theta}{dt}.$$

$$\text{Acceleration along } OP = \frac{d^2r}{dt^2} - r\left(\frac{d\theta}{dt}\right)^2.$$

$$\text{Acceleration normal to } OP = \frac{1}{r}\frac{d}{dt}\left(r^2\frac{d\theta}{dt}\right) = 2\frac{dr}{dt}\frac{d\theta}{dt} + r\frac{d^2\theta}{dt^2}.$$

Rotating axes. Suppose Ox, Oy rotate about O and let OA be a line fixed in space making at any instant an angle θ with Ox.

Velocity of $P(x, y)$ parallel to $Ox = \frac{dx}{dt} - y\frac{d\theta}{dt}$.

Velocity of $P(x, y)$ parallel to $Oy = \frac{dy}{dt} + x\frac{d\theta}{dt}$.

The accelerations are

parallel to Ox: $\frac{d^2x}{dt^2} - \frac{1}{y}\frac{d}{dt}\left(y^2\frac{d\theta}{dt}\right) - x\left(\frac{d\theta}{dt}\right)^2$,

parallel to Oy: $\frac{d^2y}{dt^2} + \frac{1}{x}\frac{d}{dt}\left(x^2\frac{d\theta}{dt}\right) - y\left(\frac{d\theta}{dt}\right)^2$.

Central forces. If a particle moves in a plane with an acceleration A which is always directed towards a fixed point O, the differential equation of its path is

$$\frac{d^2u}{d\theta^2} + u = \frac{A}{h^2u^2},$$

where r, θ are the polar co-ordinates of the particle, $u = 1/r$ and $h = r^2\frac{d\theta}{dt} =$ constant. If the acceleration varies inversely as the square of the distance from the fixed point the path is a conic section.

Kepler's laws

I. Each planet moves in an ellipse with the sun at one of the foci.

II. The areas swept out by the radii from the planet to the sun are, in the same orbit, proportional to the times of describing them.

III. The squares of the periodic times of the planets are proportional to the cubes of the major axes of their orbits.

1.32. Dynamics of a particle

Definitions

Momentum is the product of the mass of a particle and its velocity.

The *impulse of a force* in a small interval of time is the product of the force and the time interval.

The *work done by a force* when a particle receives a small displacement is the product of the force and the displacement.

The *kinetic energy* of a particle of mass m moving with velocity v is $\frac{1}{2}mv^2$.

Newton's laws of motion

I. A body persists in a state of rest or in uniform motion unless it is compelled by applied external forces to change its state ("law of inertia").

II. The change of momentum is equal to the impulse which produces it, and is in the same direction.

III. Action and reaction are equal and opposite.

The mathematical formulations of Law II are:

$$\frac{d}{dt}(m\mathbf{V}) = \mathbf{P} = \text{force},$$

or

$$m\mathbf{V}_2 - m\mathbf{V}_1 = \int_{t_1}^{t_2} \mathbf{P}\, dt = \text{total impulse},$$

where **V** is the velocity. If the mass is invariable, these may be written in cartesian co-ordinate as follows:

$$m\frac{du}{dt} = X, \quad m\frac{dv}{dt} = Y, \quad m\frac{dw}{dt} = Z,$$

or

$$m\frac{d^2x}{dt^2} = X, \quad m\frac{d^2y}{dt^2} = Y, \quad m\frac{d^2z}{dt^2} = Z,$$

where u, v, w, X, Y, Z, are the components of velocity and force, respectively, along rectangular axes Ox, Oy, Oz.

Relation between energy and work ("equation of energy"). The work done by the force P in changing the motion of a particle is equal to the increase of kinetic energy during the time that the force acts. If V is the resultant velocity and the suffixes denote the initial and final values,

$$\frac{1}{2}mV_2^2 - \frac{1}{2}mV_1^2 = \int_{t_1}^{t_2}\left(X\frac{dx}{dt} + Y\frac{dy}{dt} + Z\frac{dz}{dt}\right)dt = \text{work done on particle},$$

or

$$\text{rate of change of k.e.} = \frac{d}{dt}\left(\frac{1}{2}mV^2\right) = X\frac{dx}{dt} + Y\frac{dy}{dt} + Z\frac{dz}{dt}$$

$$= \text{rate at which work is being done.}$$

Rotating axes. The above equations apply to axes fixed in space. If axes Ox, Oy rotate about their origin O with a constant angular velocity ω, the equations of motion in two dimensions become, relative to the rotating axes,

$$m\left(\frac{d^2x}{dt^2}-2\omega\frac{dy}{dt}-\omega^2x\right)=X$$

$$m\left(\frac{d^2y}{dt^2}+2\omega\frac{dx}{dt}-\omega^2y\right)=Y,$$

where X, Y are the components of force parallel to the instantaneous directions of the axes.

Coriolis forces. When the axes rotate, the particle is acted upon by an apparent centrifugal force $m\omega^2r$, where r is distance from the origin, and by an apparent force with components $-2m\omega\frac{dx}{dt}$ and $2m\omega\frac{dy}{dt}$.

Systems of particles. Linear momentum is defined as the vector sum of the momenta of the particles. Angular momentum is defined as the sum of the moments of the momenta of the particles with respect to a fixed axis.

Principle of linear momentum. The rate of increase of total momentum resolved in any fixed direction equals the total external force resolved in that direction. If there are no external forces, the total momentum resolved in any fixed direction is invariable and the mass-centre moves with constant velocity along a straight line.

Principle of angular momentum. The rate of increase of angular momentum equals the total moment of the external forces about the axis of reference. If there are no external forces, the total angular momentum is invariable about any fixed axis.

Principle of conservation of energy. The change in kinetic energy of a system, moving under finite forces, which is such that the geometrical relations describing it do not contain time explicitly, is equal to the work done by the forces, i.e.

$$\frac{1}{2}\Sigma m\left[\left(\frac{dx}{dt}\right)^2+\left(\frac{dy}{dt}\right)^2+\left(\frac{dz}{dt}\right)^2\right]=\Sigma\int(Xdx+Ydy+Zdz).$$

If the external forces have a potential (i.e. if the right-hand side of the above equation is a complete differential), the value of the integral depends only upon the final and initial configurations of the system and is independent of the mode of change. Such forces are called *conservative*.

The *potential energy* of a system of particles or a body is defined as the work done by the forces acting on it when moving from a given position to a datum position.

The sum of the kinetic and potential energies of a system of particles or a body subject to the action of conservative forces is constant during the motion.

1.33. Constrained motion of a particle

If a particle is constrained to move on given curve with velocity v,

$$\text{tangential acceleration} = \frac{dv}{dt} = \frac{d^2s}{dt^2} = v\frac{dv}{ds},$$

$$\text{normal acceleration} \quad = v\frac{d\psi}{dt} = \frac{v^2}{\rho},$$

where s is the arc of the curve measured from some fixed point, $\delta\psi$ the angle between neighbouring normals and $\rho = ds/d\psi$, is the radius of curvature.

The dynamic equations are

$$mv\frac{dv}{ds} = \text{component of force in direction of tangent} = T,$$

$$\frac{mv^2}{\rho} = \text{component of force in direction of normal} = N.$$

Circular pendulum. If the angle of swing θ is small ($\sin\theta \simeq \theta$), the period is $2\pi\sqrt{(l/g)}$. For oscillation through a finite angle α on either side of the vertical, the time of swinging through an arc θ is

$$t = \left(\frac{l}{g}\right)^{\frac{1}{2}} \int_0^{\phi} \frac{d\phi}{(1 - \sin^2 \frac{1}{2}\alpha \sin^2 \phi)^{\frac{1}{2}}},$$

where

$$\sin\phi = \sin\tfrac{1}{2}\theta / \sin\tfrac{1}{2}\alpha.$$

The integral is an elliptic integral. Approximately, the period is given by

$$2\pi\sqrt{\frac{l}{g}}\,(1 + \tfrac{1}{4}\sin^2 \tfrac{1}{2}\alpha) \simeq 2\pi\sqrt{\frac{l}{g}}\left(1 + \frac{\alpha^2}{16}\right).$$

Motion in a resisting medium. If a particle falls from rest under gravity (assumed constant) in a medium in which resistance varies as the square of the velocity, the equation of motion is

$$\frac{d^2x}{dt^2} = g - \mu v^2,$$

and

$$v = \sqrt{\left(\frac{g}{\mu}\right)}\tanh\,[t\sqrt{(g\mu)}],$$

where $\sqrt{(g/\mu)}$ is the terminal velocity,

$$x = \frac{1}{\mu}\ln\cosh\,[t\sqrt{(g\mu)}].$$

If the particle is projected vertically upwards in the same medium with the initial velocity v_0, the equation of motion is

$$\frac{d^2x}{dt^2}=-g-\mu v^2.$$

The velocity at height x is given by the equation

$$\ln\frac{\mu v_0^2+g}{\mu v^2+g}=2\mu x,$$

and the velocity at the end of time t by the equation

$$\text{arc tan } v_0\sqrt{(\mu/g)}-\text{arc tan } v\sqrt{(\mu/g)}=t\sqrt{(g\mu)}.$$

Plane ballistics

The *standard ballistic coefficient* C_0 is defined by $C_0=m/d^2$, where m is the mass of the projectile and d its diameter.* The retardation r experienced by the projectile during its flight is given by

$$r=\kappa\rho V^2/C_0,$$

where κ is the drag coefficient, ρ the air density and V the velocity. The equations of motion for a plane trajectory are

$$\frac{du}{dt}=\frac{d^2x}{dt^2}=-r\cos\theta,$$

$$\frac{dv}{dt}=\frac{d^2y}{dt^2}=-g-r\sin\theta,$$

where u and v are component velocities along Ox (horizontal) and Oy (vertical), respectively, and θ is the inclination of the trajectory to the horizontal.

In terms of θ, the equations become

$$\frac{d(V\cos\theta)}{d\theta}=\frac{\kappa\rho V^3}{C_0 g},$$

$$\frac{dx}{d\theta}=-\frac{V^2}{g},$$

$$\frac{dy}{d\theta}=-\frac{V^2}{g}\tan\theta,$$

$$\frac{dt}{d\theta}=-\frac{V}{g\cos\theta}.$$

Siaaci's method of solution for flat trajectories ($\theta\simeq 0$, $\cos\theta\simeq 1$) consists in evaluating θ, x, y, t as functions of velocity.

* In British ballistic practice, empirical coefficients expressing the effect of shape and stability are included in the definition of C_0.

1.34. Motion in three dimensions

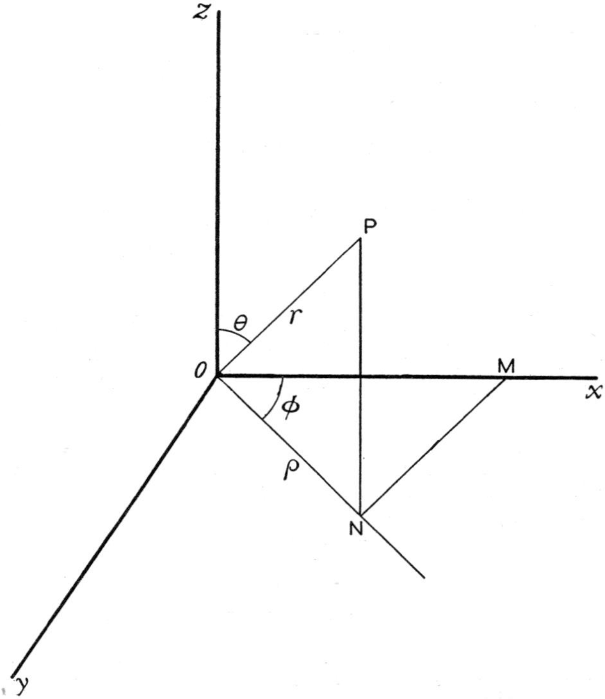

(*a*) Polar co-ordinates r, θ, ϕ:

Acceleration along $OP = \frac{d^2r}{dt^2} - r\left(\frac{d\theta}{dt}\right)^2 - r\sin^2\theta\left(\frac{d\phi}{dt}\right)^2$.

Acceleration perpendicular to OP in plane zPN, θ increasing,

$$= \frac{1}{r}\frac{d}{dt}\left(r^2\frac{d\theta}{dt}\right) - r\sin\theta\cos\theta\left(\frac{d\phi}{dt}\right)^2.$$

Acceleration perpendicular to plane zPN, ϕ increasing,

$$= \frac{1}{r\sin\theta}\frac{d}{dt}\left(r^2\sin^2\theta\frac{d\phi}{dt}\right).$$

(*b*) Cylindrical co-ordinates z, ρ, ϕ:

Acceleration in direction $ON = \frac{d^2\rho}{dt^2} - \rho\left(\frac{d\phi}{dt}\right)^2$.

Acceleration perpendicular to the plane $zPN = \frac{1}{\rho}\frac{d}{dt}\left(\rho^2 \frac{d\phi}{dt}\right)$.

Acceleration parallel to $Oz = \frac{d^2z}{dt^2}$.

1.4. Dynamics of rigid bodies

Moments of inertia. Let r be the distance of an element of mass δm of a body of uniform density from a given line. The moment of inertia of the body about this line (axis) is $\Sigma r^2 \delta m$. If M be the total mass of the body and I the moment of inertia, the *radius of gyration* k is defined by the equation $I = Mk^2$. If the co-ordinates of the element δm be (x, y, z), the quantities $\Sigma xy\delta m$, $\Sigma xz\delta m$ and $\Sigma yz\delta m$ are then called the *products of inertia* with respect to the various pairs of axes.

Parallel axes theorem. If Mk^2 be the moment of inertia of a body about an axis through its centre of mass, its moment of inertia about a parallel axis distant a from the original axis is $M(k^2 + a^2)$.

Perpendicular axes theorem. If the moments of inertia of a lamina about two perpendicular axes meeting in a point O are I_1 and I_2 respectively, its moment of inertia about an axis through O perpendicular to its plane is $I_1 + I_2$.

Special formulae. The radius of gyration of the area between the curve $y = f(x)$, the axis of x and two bounding ordinates, with reference to Ox as axis, is given by

$$k^2 = \tfrac{1}{3}\int y^3\, dx \div \int y\, dx.$$

The corresponding equation for a uniform solid of revolution is

$$k^2 = \tfrac{1}{2}\int y^4\, dx \div \int y^2\, dx.$$

Principal axes of a body. For any body there exists at each point a set of three perpendicular axes, called the *principal axes*, such that the products of inertia of the body about them, taken two at a time, are zero. The principal axes are the three principal diameters of the *momental ellipsoid* at the point.

Routh's mnemonic. The moment of inertia about an axis of symmetry of a body is

mass $\times$ the sum of the squares of the perpendicular semi-axes $\div d$, where $d = 3$, 4 or 5 according as the body is rectangular, elliptical or ellipsoidal in shape.

Simple examples of moments of inertia

Body	*Location of axis*	k^2
Uniform straight rod, length $2a$	Through centre, perp. to length	$\frac{1}{3}a^2$
Arc of circle, radius a, subtending 2θ at centre	Through centre, perp. to plane	a^2
	About diameter bisecting arc	$\left(1-\frac{\sin 2\theta}{2\theta}\right)\frac{a^2}{2}$
Rectangle, sides $2a$, $2b$	Through centre, perp. to plane	$\frac{1}{3}(a^2+b^2)$
Triangle, sides a, b, c	Through mass centre, perp. to plane	$(a^2+b^2+c^2)/36$
Ellipse, semi-axes a, b	Major axis a	$\frac{1}{4}b^2$
	Through centre, perp. to plane	$\frac{1}{4}(a^2+b^2)$
Ellipsoid, semi-axes a, b, c	Axis a	$\frac{1}{5}(b^2+c^2)$
Right solid, sides $2a$, $2b$, $2c$	Through centre, perp. to plane of $b+c$	$\frac{1}{3}(b^2+c^2)$
Thin hollow sphere, radius a	Diameter	$2a^2/3$
Hollow sphere, external and internal radii a and b	Diameter	$2(a^5-b^5)/5(a^3-b^3)$
Uniform solid circular cylinder, length l, radius a	Axis of cylinder	$\frac{1}{2}a^2$
	Diameter of one end	$\frac{1}{4}a^2+\frac{1}{3}l^2$
	Diameter through centre of mass	$\frac{1}{4}a^2+\frac{1}{12}l^2$
Uniform solid circular cone, height h, radius a	Axis of cone	$3a^2/10$
	Diameter of base	$3(\frac{1}{2}a^2+\frac{1}{3}h^2)/10$
Solid anchor ring, radius a, cross-section radius b	Axis of ring	$a^2+\frac{3}{4}b^2$
Regular polygon, radii of circumscribed and inscribed circles, R, r	Through centre, perp. to plane	$\frac{1}{6}(R^2+2r^2)$

Change of axis. Let Ox, Oy be rectangular axes in the plane of a lamina and let A, B, H be the moments and product of inertia about these axes, i.e.

$$A=\iint y^2\,dm,\quad B=\iint x^2\,dm,\quad H=\iint xy\,dm.$$

The moment of inertia of the lamina for an axis inclined at θ to Ox in the positive sense is

$$I = A\cos^2\theta - 2H\cos\theta\sin\theta + B\sin^2\theta.$$

1.41. Kinematics of a rigid body

A rigid body has, in general, 6 degrees of freedom, and its position is determined when 3 points in the body are fixed with reference to an external frame, or when the co-ordinates of a point G in the body are known together with the directions of any two fixed lines in the body relative to the external frame.

Every displacement of a rigid body is equivalent to a motion of translation plus a rotation about an axis passing through a point in the body (Euler's theorem).

Angular velocities. Angular velocity is a vector, and two angular velocities may be compounded by the parallelogram law. If a body possesses an angular velocity ω about an axis, its motion is equivalent to ω about a parallel axis distant h from the original axis plus a linear velocity ωh.

If a point O in a body moves with linear velocities u, v, w parallel to fixed axes Ox, Oy, Oz, and with angular velocities ω_1, ω_2, ω_3 about the same axes, the component velocities of a point $P(x, y, z)$ in the body are

$$u + \omega_2 z - \omega_3 y \text{ parallel to } Ox$$

$$v + \omega_3 x - \omega_1 z \text{ parallel to } Oy$$

$$w + \omega_1 y - \omega_2 x \text{ parallel to } Oz.$$

Angular momenta. Let Ox', Oy' and Oz' be axes *fixed in the body* and let Ox, Oy, Oz be a reference frame in space chosen so that at the instant under consideration it coincides with Ox', Oy', Oz'. A rigid body moving about the fixed point O has angular momenta

$$A\omega_1 - F\omega_2 - E\omega_3 \text{ about } Ox$$

$$B\omega_2 - D\omega_3 - F\omega_1 \text{ about } Oy$$

$$C\omega_3 - E\omega_1 - D\omega_2 \text{ about } Oz,$$

where A, B, C are the moments of inertia, and D, E, F the products of inertia, respectively, about the body axes.

The kinetic energy of the body is

$$\tfrac{1}{2}[A\omega_1^2 + B\omega_2^2 + C\omega_3^2 - 2(D\omega_2\omega_3 + E\omega_3\omega_1 + F\omega_1\omega_2)].$$

If the moving axes be chosen to be the principal axes (see p. 283), the products of inertia D, E, F, are all zero.

1.42. General equations of motion of a rigid body

If X, Y, Z are the components of external forces, parallel to axes Ox, Oy, Oz respectively, acting on a particle of mass m situated at (x, y, z) at time t, the equations of motion of the rigid body, considered as an assembly of particles, are

$$\Sigma m \frac{d^2x}{dt^2} = \Sigma X, \quad \Sigma m \frac{d^2y}{dt^2} = \Sigma Y, \quad \Sigma m \frac{d^2z}{dt^2} = \Sigma Z,$$

and

$$\Sigma m\left(y \frac{d^2z}{dt^2} - z \frac{d^2y}{dt^2}\right) = \Sigma(yZ - zY),$$

$$\Sigma m\left(z \frac{d^2x}{dt^2} - x \frac{d^2z}{dt^2}\right) = \Sigma(zX - xZ),$$

$$\Sigma m\left(x \frac{d^2y}{dt^2} - y \frac{d^2x}{dt^2}\right) = \Sigma(xY - yX).$$

These equations are the analytical expressions of the principles of linear and angular momentum (p. 279).

The centre of mass of a rigid body moves as if all the mass of the body were collected at this point, with the external forces acting in directions parallel to those in which they act on the body.

The motion of a rigid body about its centre of mass is the same as it would be if the centre of mass were fixed and the original forces acted on the body.

Hence the equations of motion express the two principles: (i) the rate of change of total momentum parallel to an axis equals the sum of the external forces parallel to the same axis, and (ii) the rate of change of the total moment of momentum about an axis equals the sum of the moments of the external forces about the same axis.

(The moment of momentum of a body about an axis is frequently called the angular momentum of the body about the axis (see p. 279).)

1.43. Motion in one dimension

Rotation about a fixed axis. The equation of motion is

$$\frac{d}{dt}(I\omega) = N,$$

where I is the moment of inertia of the body about the axis, ω its angular velocity and N the total moment of the external forces about the axis. The kinetic energy of the body is $\frac{1}{2}I\omega^2$; $I\omega$ is the angular momentum.

Compound pendulum. A rigid body swinging under gravity about a fixed horizontal axis behaves like a simple pendulum of length k^2/h for small oscillations, where k is the radius of gyration about the fixed axis and h is the distance between the axis and the centre of gravity of the body.

1.44. Motion in two dimensions

The position of a lamina in a plane is determined if the co-ordinates of a fixed point (usually the centre of mass $(\bar{x}, \bar{y})$) are known, together with the inclination of a line fixed in the body to a line fixed in the plane (θ). The dynamical equations are:

for motion of the centre of mass:

$$M\frac{d^2\bar{x}}{dt^2}=\Sigma X,\ M\frac{d^2\bar{y}}{dt^2}=\Sigma Y,$$

for motion about the centre of mass:

$$\frac{d}{dt}\left(Mk^2\frac{d\theta}{dt}\right)=\Sigma(x'Y-y'X),$$

where (x', y') are co-ordinates relative to the centre of mass and k is the radius of gyration of the lamina about a line through the centre of mass perpendicular to the plane of motion.

The angular momentum of the body about the origin O is $Mvp + Mk^2\dfrac{d\theta}{dt}$, where p is the normal from O to the direction of motion of the centre of mass. An alternative expression is $M\rho^2\dfrac{d\psi}{dt}+Mk^2\dfrac{d\theta}{dt}$, where (ρ, ψ) are the polar co-ordinates of the centre of mass with respect to O.

Bodies rolling without sliding down a rough inclined plane. For a plane inclined at α to the horizontal, the constant accelerations are as follows: solid sphere: $\frac{5}{7}g\sin\alpha$; thin spherical shell, $\frac{3}{5}g\sin\alpha$; uniform solid disc, $\frac{2}{3}g\sin\alpha$; uniform thin ring, $\frac{1}{2}g\sin\alpha$.

1.45. Motion in three dimensions

The general equations of motion of a rigid body referred to axes whose directions are fixed consist of (i) the equations of motion of the mass centre $(\bar{x}, \bar{y}, \bar{z})$, viz.

$$M\frac{d^2\bar{x}}{dt^2}=\Sigma X,\ M\frac{d^2\bar{y}}{dt^2}=\Sigma Y,\ M\frac{d^2\bar{z}}{dt^2}=\Sigma Z,$$

and (ii) the equations of motion about the centre of mass, viz.

$$\frac{d}{dt}[A\omega_1 - F\omega_2 - E\omega_3] = L,$$

$$\frac{d}{dt}(B\omega_2 - D\omega_3 - F\omega_1] = M,$$

$$\frac{d}{dt}(C\omega_3 - E\omega_1 - D\omega_2) = N,$$

where ω_1, ω_2, ω_3 are the angular velocities at any instant about axes through the centre of mass parallel to the axes of co-ordinates, L, M, N are the moments of the external forces about lines parallel to the axes of co-ordinates through the centre of mass, and A, B, C, D, E, F are the moments and products of inertia about the axes.

Euler's dynamical equations. Let ω_1, ω_2, ω_3 be referred to the principal (moving) axes of a body moving about a fixed point. The equations of motion become

$$A\frac{d\omega_1}{dt} - (B - C)\omega_2\omega_3 = L,$$

$$B\frac{d\omega_2}{dt} - (C - A)\omega_3\omega_1 = M,$$

$$C\frac{d\omega_3}{dt} - (A - B)\omega_1\omega_2 = N,$$

with the notation as before.

Kinetic energy of a rigid body. The kinetic energy of a rigid body is equal, at any instant, to the kinetic energy of the whole mass supposed placed at the centre of mass and moving with it, plus the kinetic energy of the whole mass relative to the centre of mass.

Bifilar suspension. If a uniform rod of length $2a$, suspended in a horizontal position by two vertical cords, each of length l, attached to its ends and to fixed points, is given an angular velocity ω about a vertical axis through its centre, it will perform small oscillations of period $2\pi\sqrt{(l/3g)}$ and will rise through a distance $a^2\omega^2/6g$.

Spinning top. Let C, A be the moments of inertia of a top of mass M about the line joining the centre of mass to the toe and about a perpendicular axis (rotating with the top) passing through the centre of mass respectively. Let ω be the rate of spin and let a be the distance from the centre of mass to the toe. The condition for stability when spinning in a vertical position on a smooth surface is

$$\omega > \frac{\sqrt{(4MAga)}}{C}.$$

Gyroscopic resistance. If a body of moment of inertia I spinning about Ox with angular velocity ω is subjected to a torque T about Oy, it will precess about Oz. The gyroscopic resistance offered by the body to the torque T is $I\omega\Omega$, where Ω is the angular velocity of precession.

A free gyroscope can be used to measure angles; a constrained gyroscope can be used to measure angular velocities.

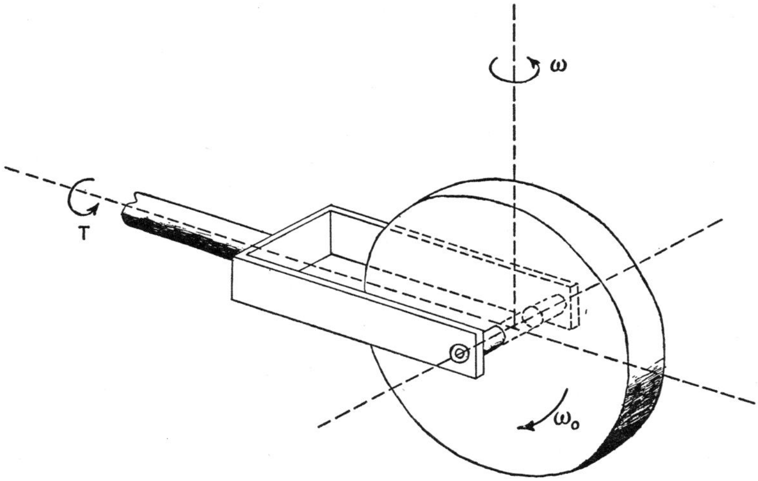

In the "rate-measuring" (constrained) gyroscope, the gyroscopic force is measured by a constraint (spring). Let the flywheel be spun at the constant angular velocity ω_0, and let the system be subjected to an angular velocity ω about the input axis. A torque T, measured by the small displacement of a spring-mass system, develops about the output axis. The angular velocity ω is given by

$$\omega = T/I\omega_0.$$

In some systems the flywheel is replaced by a vibrating mass.

1.46. Lagrange's equations of motion in generalized co-ordinates

Let the rectangular co-ordinates (x, y, z) of any particle of a system be expressed in terms of a certain number of independent variables

$\theta, \phi, \ldots$ Let K be the kinetic energy and T the potential energy of the system. Lagrange's equations are of the type

$$\frac{d}{dt}\left(\frac{\partial K}{\partial \dot{\theta}}\right)=\frac{\partial K}{\partial \theta}-\frac{\partial T}{\partial \theta},$$

where $\dot{\theta}=d\theta/dt$. If $L=K-T$, the Lagrangian function, the equations may be written in the form

$$\frac{d}{dt}\left(\frac{dL}{d\dot{\theta}}\right)=\frac{dL}{d\theta}.$$

1.5. Response of a mechanical system (instrument equation).

A mechanical system, such as an indicating or a recording instrument, is subject to inertia and friction. Let θ_0 (radians) be the movement of the output shaft (or pointer) when an input of θ_i (radians) is applied to the input shaft. The equation of motion is

$$I\frac{d^2\theta_0}{dt^2}+f\frac{d\theta_0}{dt}+k\theta_0=k\theta_i,$$

where f is the coefficient of viscous friction and k expresses the torsional stiffness of the restraints (springs) opposing the motion of the output shaft (or pointer).

The complementary function of this equation determines the transient condition and the particular integral gives the steady state.

The complementary function is given by an expression of the form

$$\theta_0=e^{-ft/2I}\,(A\cos\omega t+iB\sin\omega t),$$

where A and B are constants and $i=\sqrt{-1}$.

The *undamped natural frequency* $\omega_n=\sqrt{(k/I)}$, and the *damping ratio* ζ is defined by $\zeta=f/2\sqrt{(kI)}$.

The following cases may be distinguished:

Damping ratio	*Transient response*
$\zeta=0$	No damping; system oscillates with constant amplitude of frequency $\omega=\omega_n$
$0<\zeta<1$	Damped oscillations of frequency $\omega<\omega_n$
$\zeta=1$	Critical damping; oscillations just cease
$\zeta>1$	Over-damped; no oscillations

The damping ratio is usually found from the relation $\omega=\omega_n\sqrt{(1-\zeta^2)}$, and the equation of motion may be written

$$\frac{d^2\theta_0}{dt^2}+2\zeta\omega_n\frac{d\theta_0}{dt}+\omega_n^2\,\theta_0=\omega_n^2\,\theta_i.$$

The *damping factor* $f/2I = \zeta\omega_n$.

Response to unit step function. If the initial conditions are

$$\theta_i = 0 \text{ for } t < 0; \quad \theta_i = 1 \text{ for } t \geqslant 0,$$

the following solutions hold for the transient state:

(*a*) under damped, $\zeta < 1$,

$$\theta_0 = 1 - e^{-\xi\omega_n t}[\cos \omega_n\sqrt{(1-\zeta^2)}t + \frac{\zeta}{\sqrt{(1-\zeta^2)}} \sin \omega_n\sqrt{(1-\zeta^2)}t];$$

(*b*) critically damped, $\zeta = 1$,

$$\theta_0 = 1 - e^{-\omega_n t}(1 + \omega_n t);$$

(*c*) over damped, $\zeta > 1$,

$$\theta_0 = 1 - e^{-\zeta\omega_n}\left[\cosh \omega_n\sqrt{(\zeta^2-1)}t + \frac{\zeta}{\sqrt{(\zeta^2-1)}} \sinh \omega_n\sqrt{(\zeta^2-1t)}\right].$$

CHAPTER 2

ELASTICITY

2.1. Elasticity is defined as the property of a substance that causes it to regain its original shape after deformation by an applied force. The deformation is measured as *strain*. *Stress*, the force per unit area producing the strain, is usually resolved into a *normal* and a *tangential* stress.

Hooke's law. Strain is proportional to stress. This holds only over a limited range of conditions.

Moduli of elasticity = ratio of stress and strain

$$\text{Young's modulus } E = \frac{\text{applied force per unit area of cross-section}}{\text{increase in length per unit length}}$$

(tensile elasticity).

$$\text{Modulus of rigidity } n = \frac{\text{tangential stress per unit area}}{\text{angular deformation}}$$

(shear elasticity)

$$\text{Bulk modulus } K = \frac{\text{compressive or tensile force per unit area}}{\text{change in volume per unit volume}}$$

(volume elasticity).

$$\text{Poisson's ratio } \sigma = \frac{\text{decrease in width per unit width}}{\text{longitudinal strain}}.$$

For an isotropic solid,

$$n = \frac{E}{2(1+\sigma)}; \quad K = \frac{E}{3(1-2\sigma)}; \quad \sigma = \frac{E}{2n} - 1$$

$$-1 \leqslant \sigma \leqslant \tfrac{1}{2}.$$

Typical values (dynes cm.$^{-2}$):

Substance	E	n	K	σ
Copper	$1{\cdot}2\times10^{12}$	$4{\cdot}6\times10^{11}$	$1{\cdot}3\times10^{12}$	0·34
Steel	$2{\cdot}1\times10^{12}$	$8{\cdot}1\times10^{11}$	$1{\cdot}6\times10^{12}$	0·29
Glass (average values) .	7×10^{11}	3×10^{11}	5×10^{11}	0·25

2.2. Bending of beams

In the following table, $I=bd^3/12$ for beams of rectangular cross-section of width b, thickness d, and $I=\pi a^4/64$ for beams of circular cross-section, diameter d. W=load (concentrated or distributed), l=length of beam.

Load distribution	*Maximum deflection*
Cantilever, uniformly loaded	$Wl^3/8EI$
Cantilever, load at free end	$Wl^3/3EI$
Beam supported at ends, loaded in centre	$Wl^3/48EI$
Beam clamped at ends, loaded in centre	$Wl^3/192EI$
Beam supported at ends, uniformly loaded	$5Wl^3/384EI$
Beam clamped at ends, uniformly loaded	$Wl^3/384EI$

Torsion of a cylindrical rod or wire. A rod of circular cross-section, radius a, requires a couple C given by

$$C=\frac{\pi n a^4\,\theta}{2l}$$

to twist it through an angle θ radians, where l is the length of the wire. If a block of heavy material, having a moment of inertia I, is fastened to the end of the wire, rotated, and allowed to execute vibrations, the periodic time T is given by

$$T=2\pi\sqrt{\left(\frac{2lI}{\pi n a^4}\right)},$$

thus allowing n to be found experimentally by timing the vibrations.

A rod of elliptical cross-section, semi-axes a and b, requires a couple C given by

$$C=\frac{\pi n a^3 b^3 \theta}{(a^2+b^2)l}$$

to twist it through an angle θ.

Spiral spring, nearly horizontal, radius r, applied force f. The extension d is

$$d=\frac{2lfr^2}{\pi n a^4}.$$

Time of oscillation in the vertical for spring fastened at one end, weight M at the free end, is

$$T=2\pi\sqrt{\left(\frac{2lr^2M}{\pi n a^4}\right)},$$

the mass of the spring being neglected.

The energy stored in a spiral spring is equal to half the product of the force it exerts and its elongation.

Extension of a bar. Let T be the tension, ω the cross-sectional area and ξ the displacement of a point originally at x from a fixed reference point. Then

$$T = E\omega \frac{d\xi}{dx}$$

For a bar hanging vertically with a load W at the lower end, the tension and extension are

$$T = W + \rho w(l - x), \qquad \xi = \frac{Wl}{E\omega} + \frac{1}{2}\frac{\rho l^2}{E},$$

where ρ is the density of the material and l the length of the rod.

2.3. General equations for the flexure of a beam

The flexural rigidity of a beam is measured by the quantity $E\omega\kappa^2 = EI$, where $\omega\kappa^2$ is the quadratic moment of the cross-section area ω with respect to the neutral line. If y be the downward deflection of the neutral line and $w(x)$ the load intensity, the following relations hold for the shear stress S and the bending moment M

$$S = -\frac{d}{dx}\left(EI\frac{d^2y}{dx^2}\right), \quad M = EI\frac{d^2y}{dx^2}, \quad \frac{d^2M}{dx^2} = w(x).$$

For a uniform beam these reduce to

$$S = -EI\frac{d^3y}{dx^3}, \quad EI\frac{d^4y}{dx^4} = w.$$

If the uniform beam has no loads except at the ends, the constants of integration are found from the following rules:

(i) at a free end, $\dfrac{d^2y}{dx^2} = \dfrac{d^3y}{dx^3} = 0$,

(ii) at a clamped end, y and $\dfrac{dy}{dx}$ are given,

(iii) at a supported end, y is given and $\dfrac{d^2y}{dx^2} = 0$.

Clapeyron's theorem of three moments. Consider a continuous beam uniformly loaded and supported at A, B, C at the same level. Let $AB = a$, $BC = b$. Then

$$aM_A + 2(a+b)M_B + bM_C = \tfrac{1}{4}w(a^3 + b^3).$$

CHAPTER 3

SURFACE TENSION

3.1. Surface tension T is defined as the tension in dynes exerted across unit length of a line imagined drawn in the surface of a liquid. Surface tension is attributed to intermolecular forces and is measured in dynes cm.$^{-1}$. Some typical values, for liquids in contact with air, are:

water (at 15° C.), $T=74{\cdot}2$; paraffin oil (at 25° C.), $T=26{\cdot}4$.

Eötvos' rule is that T is approximately proportional to the difference between the actual temperature of the liquid and its critical temperature.

3.2. Capillary tube

A capillary tube, placed vertically in a large vessel containing liquid, supports a column of the liquid because of surface tension. If r(cm.) is the radius of the tube and α the angle between the meniscus and the wall of the tube, the upward force is $2\pi rT\cos\alpha$ dynes. If h is the height of the bottom of the meniscus above the external free surface, the surface tension is given by

$$T=\frac{(h+\frac{1}{3}r)r\rho g}{2\cos\alpha},$$

where ρ is the density of the liquid. (Note that for mercury α exceeds a right angle because the meniscus curves upwards.)

Soap bubble. If r is the radius of the bubble and p the amount by which the pressure inside exceeds atmospheric, the surface tension is given by

$$T=\tfrac{1}{4}pr.$$

3.3. Kelvin's vapour pressure equation

The vapour pressure above a liquid surface is related to the surface tension and the radius of curvature of the surface. For a spherical drop of radius r, density ρ', the Kelvin relation is

$$R\theta\ln(e_d/e_p)=\frac{2MT}{\rho' r},$$

where e_d, e_p are the vapour pressures over the drop and a plane surface, respectively, θ is absolute temperature, M is the molecular weight of the liquid and R is the universal gas constant ($=8{\cdot}315$ joules).

If the drop surface carries a charge of ne units, where e is the unit electronic charge, the relation becomes

$$R\theta \ln (e_d/e_p) = \frac{M}{\rho'}\left(\frac{2T}{r} - \frac{n^2e^2}{8\pi r^4}\right).$$

The Kelvin relation is important in meteorology in problems relating to the formation of clouds.

3.4. Ripples

The velocity v of a wave of length λ propagated under the influence of gravity and surface tension in a liquid of density ρ is

$$v = \sqrt{\left\{\frac{\lambda}{2\pi}\left(g + \frac{4\pi^2 T}{\lambda^2 \rho}\right)\right\}}.$$

This is a minimum when

$$\lambda = 2\pi\sqrt{\left(\frac{T}{g\rho}\right)}; \quad v = \sqrt{2}\left(\frac{Tg}{\rho}\right)^{\frac{1}{4}}.$$

(For water, λ is about 1·7 cm. and v is about 23 cm. sec.$^{-1}$.) Waves of length less than that corresponding to the minimum velocity are called "ripples" and are propagated chiefly by surface tension.

When ripples are produced by an electrically maintained tuning fork dipping into the liquid, the surface tension may be found by noting the wavelength λ and the time of vibration $\tau = \lambda/v$ from the relation

$$\frac{T}{\rho} = \frac{\lambda^3}{2\pi\tau^2} - g\left(\frac{\lambda}{2\pi}\right)^2.$$

CHAPTER 4

MECHANICS OF FLUIDS

A *perfect* or *ideal fluid* is one devoid of viscosity, or internal friction. In such a fluid *pressure* is the only internal stress. A fluid, liquid or gas, may be *incompressible* or *compressible.* A homogeneous incompressible fluid is one in which density has the same value at all points; a heterogeneous incompressible fluid is one in which density changes do not arise as a result of motion, i.e. density is not necessarily the same at all points but the density of a fluid element is regarded as invariable during its motion.

4.1. Hydrostatics

(i) Pressure (p) is the same in all directions.

(ii) *Archimedes principle.* The buoyancy (upward force) of an immersed body equals the weight of the fluid displaced and acts vertically through the c. of g. of the displaced fluid.

(iii) *Hydrostatic equation.* In a fluid at rest, subject to gravity,

$$\frac{dp}{dz} = -g\rho,$$

where z is height measured from the bottom of the fluid and ρ is density. (For the derivation of the barometric-height formula see Chapter 14).

(iv) *Centre of pressure.* The c. of p. is the point on a submerged body through which the resultant of the fluid pressures acts.

For a liquid subject to gravity, with the axis of y coinciding with the line in which the plane of the area meets the liquid surface, the co-ordinates of the c. of p. are

$$x_p = \frac{\iint x^2\,dx\,dy}{\iint x\,dx\,dy}, \quad y_p = \frac{\iint xy\,dx\,dy}{\iint x\,dx\,dy}.$$

(Cf. formulae for moments of inertia.)

When Ox is a line of symmetry, $y_p = 0$ and $x_p = k^2/h$, where k is the radius of gyration of the area about the y-axis and h is the distance of the centroid of the area from this line.

Simple examples of c. of p.

(i) Rectangle, one side in surface, other side (a) vertical. $x_p = 2a/3$.

(ii) Semicircular area, diameter $2r$ in surface. $x_p = 3\pi r/16$.

(iii) Circular area, centre distant h from line in which plane meets surface. $x_p = h + r^2/4h$.

(iv) Trapezium $ABCD$, side AB in surface, sides $AD(=a)$ and $BC(=b)$ vertical c. of p. is $(a+b)(a^2+b^2)/2(a^2+ab+b^2)$ below surface.

(v) The c. of p. of a wholly immersed triangle is the same as the mass centre of three particles placed at the mid-points of the sides with masses proportional to their depths.

Equilibrium of a floating body. A submerged body is in stable equilibrium when its weight equals that of the displaced fluid and its c. of g. lies below the c. of g. of the displaced fluid.

Metacentre. When a partially submerged body, having a plane of symmetry, is tilted slightly from its original position, the centre of buoyancy H moves to a new position H'. The limiting position of the point M at which the vertical through H' meets the line joining H to the c. of g. of the body in the tilted position is called the *metacentre*. (It is thus the point at which the body, when suspended, experiences, for small displacements, moments equal to the hydrostatic moments.) The *metacentric height* is the distance between the metacentre and the c. of g.

For static stability the metacentre must be above the c. of g.

Formula for metacentre. If Ox is the line of symmetry and Oy the axis about which the body is turned,

$$HM = Ak^2/V,$$

where A is the area of the surface section, k its radius of gyration about Oy, and V the immersed volume. For a solid of revolution floating with its axis vertical, $HM = Aa^2/4V$, where a is the radius of the circular section of the body made by the surface of the fluid.

4.2. Motion of an incompressible ideal fluid

The acceleration of a fluid particle in the Eulerian system is given by the three expressions of the type

$$\frac{\partial u}{\partial t} + u\frac{\partial u}{\partial x} + v\frac{\partial u}{\partial y} + w\frac{\partial u}{\partial z}\left(\equiv \frac{du}{dt} \text{ or } \frac{Du}{Dt}\right),$$

where u, v, w are the components of velocity along axes Ox, Oy, Oz respectively. Steady flow, defined by $\partial u/\partial t$, etc., $=0$, means that any property of the fluid (e.g. velocity, density), measured at a point, does not change with time. (Note that this does not exclude the possibility of acceleration, e.g. in steady flow in a pipe of variable cross-section.)

The principle of conservation of mass is expressed by the *equation of continuity*

$$\frac{\partial \rho}{\partial t}+\frac{\partial u}{\partial x}+\frac{\partial v}{\partial y}+\frac{\partial w}{\partial z}=0,$$

where ρ is density. In an incompressible fluid $\partial\rho/\partial t=0$ and hence *div* $\mathbf{V}=0$. The principle of conservation of energy is expressed by *Bernoulli's theorem*, viz., if the external forces have a potential P, and there is a functional relation between pressure and density, the sum of the kinetic, potential and pressure energies per unit mass at a point in a field of irrotational flow depends only on the time. If the field is steady, the sum of the energies has the same value at all points in the field.

For steady motion

$$\frac{1}{2}q^2+\int\frac{dp}{\rho}+P=\text{constant},$$

where q is the resultant velocity. If ρ is constant and p is the total pressure at a point, this becomes, in the absence of external forces,

$$\tfrac{1}{2}\rho q^2+p=\text{constant}.$$

If the flow is rotational, the relations hold along a streamline. The constant is called the *total head*.

Torricelli's theorem. The speed of efflux of a liquid of constant density from a small orifice in a large vessel, under gravity, is $\sqrt{2gh}$, where h = height of liquid surface above the orifice.

Venturi meter.
$$q=\sqrt{\left\{\frac{2\Delta p}{\rho(r^2-1)}\right\}},$$

where Δp = difference in pressure between entrance and throat, r = ratio of cross-sections of entrance and throat.

Pitot-static tube. The quantity $p_D=\frac{1}{2}\rho q^2$ is called the dynamic pressure

$$q=\sqrt{\left\{\frac{2}{\rho}\left(p_D-p_S\right)\right\}}$$

where p_S = static pressure.

4.21. Kinematics of two-dimensional incompressible flow

A *streamline* is a curve whose direction coincides with that of the fluid motion at all points. When the motion is steady, the streamline pattern is invariable with time and the paths of the fluid particles are streamlines.

The flux of fluid across any line joining two points in the plane of motion is the same for all curves connecting the two points. The flux is expressed by the *stream function* $\psi(x, y)$ which has the following properties:

(i) the streamline pattern can be plotted by giving C equally spaced values (e.g. 0, 1, 2, . . .) in the equation $\psi=C$;

(ii) the velocity components u, v are given by

$$u=\frac{\partial\psi}{\partial y}, \quad v=-\frac{\partial\psi}{\partial x};$$

(iii) ψ satisfies Laplace's equation

$$\nabla^2\psi=\frac{\partial^2\psi}{\partial x^2}+\frac{\partial^2\psi}{\partial y^2}=0.$$

Since fluid cannot cross a streamline, any streamline may be regarded as the boundary of an impervious surface, and the space on one side of a streamline, or wholly enclosed by it, may be supposed filled with solid matter without disturbing the flow elsewhere. Thus if one streamline were a circle, the remaining streamlines indicate how fluid could move past a long circular cylinder without violating the principle of conservation of mass.

Irrotational motion. The simplest form of fluid motion, called *irrotational,* is one in which the individual fluid elements do not rotate (but may be translated or distorted). In such cases there exists a *velocity potential* $\phi(x, y)$ with the following properties:

(i) the velocity components u, v are given by

$$u=\frac{\partial\phi}{\partial x}, \quad v=\frac{\partial\phi}{\partial y};$$

(ii) $\phi(x, y)$ satisfies Laplace's equation $\nabla^2\phi=0$.

If a velocity potential exists, the motion is irrotational, and vice versa.

Conjugate functions. If the motion is irrotational, the velocity potential ϕ and the stream function ψ are the real and imaginary parts, respectively, of a holomorphic function $w(z)$ (called the complex potential) of the complex variable $z=x+iy$. Conversely, by separating into its real and imaginary parts any holomorphic function of z, there are obtained families of equipotentials and streamlines of a possible two-dimensional irrotational flow.

Examples

(*a*) $w(z)=z^2=(x+iy)^2=x^2-y^2+2ixy$. The equipotentials are the family $x^2-y^2=$constant, and the streamlines $xy=$constant (i.e.

hyperbolae). By taking the axes $x=0$, $y=0$ to be impermeable boundaries, the streamline pattern is that for flow in a right-angled corner.

(*b*) Irrotational flow without circulation past a long circular cylinder

$$w(z)=V\left(z+\frac{a^2}{z}\right), \quad z\neq 0,$$

where V is the velocity at infinity, parallel to the axis of x. The streamline $\psi=0$ consists of the part of the x-axis and the circle $x^2+y^2=a^2$; elsewhere $\psi(x, y)=V\{y-a^2y/(x^2+y^2)\}$.

The components of velocity, in polar co-ordinates, are:

radial $$u_r=\frac{1}{r}\frac{\partial\psi}{\partial\theta}=V\left(1-\frac{a^2}{r^2}\right)\cos\theta,$$

tangential $$u_t=-\frac{\partial\psi}{\partial r}=V\left(1+\frac{a^2}{r^2}\right)\sin\theta.$$

4.22. Flow with rotation

The components of *vorticity*, ξ, η, ζ, or Ω_x, Ω_y, Ω_z, are given by

$$\xi=\frac{1}{2}\left(\frac{\partial w}{\partial y}-\frac{\partial v}{\partial z}\right), \quad \eta=\frac{1}{2}\left(\frac{\partial u}{\partial z}-\frac{\partial w}{\partial x}\right), \quad \zeta=\frac{1}{2}\left(\frac{\partial v}{\partial x}-\frac{\partial u}{\partial y}\right).$$

The *circulation* is defined to be the line integral of the tangential component of the velocity around a closed curve lying in the fluid and is independent of the shape of the curve.

$$\text{Vorticity}=\lim\left\{\frac{\text{circulation around an elementary area}}{\text{elementary area}}\right\}$$

as the area tends to zero.

The strength of a vortex is defined to be the circulation around it, and the circulation on any closed curve equals the sum of the strengths of the vortices contained therein.

Helmholtz's theorem. In the absence of body forces, individual vortices in an inviscid fluid always consist of the same fluid particles, i.e. they move with the fluid. In plane two-dimensional flow of an incompressible ideal fluid, particles retain their vorticity unchanged, and for a perfect gas, vorticity along any streamline is proportional to the pressure.

Kelvin's theorem. In an ideal homogeneous fluid, not subject to body forces, an irrotational flow cannot develop vorticity.

4.3. Forces

Incompressible flow. The force experienced by a body in motion relative to a fluid is usually resolved into two components: *lift,* the component perpendicular to the direction of motion of the body as whole, and *drag,* the component in the direction of motion. For a body (such as an aerofoil) at rest in a stream of fluid, the direction of motion is that of the fluid remote from the body.

D'Alembert's paradox. A body of any shape totally immersed in an incompressible inviscid fluid moving steadily experiences no drag.

Kutta-Joukowski theorem. If a steady irrotational two-dimensional stream, of density ρ and velocity V, surrounds a closed curve on which there is a circulation K, a lift of magnitude ρVK is set up.

The lift set up in irrotational motion past a two-dimensional contour may be found by (i) finding a complex potential such that its imaginary part yields a family of streamlines with straight flow at infinity and a closed curve representing the contour in the finite part of the z-plane; (ii) use of Bernoulli's theorem to determine the pressure on the contour from the velocity distribution; and (iii) integration of the pressure over the contour to determine the force.

Example: Magnus effect. Flow around a long circular cylinder with circulation K.

The complex potential is

$$w(z) = V\left(z + \frac{a^2}{z}\right) + \frac{iK}{2\pi} \ln\left(\frac{z}{a}\right), \quad z \neq 0.$$

The radial component of velocity is the same as in the example of irrotational flow without circulation, but the tangential component has the additional term $K/2\pi r$. The forces experienced by the cylinder are

lift per unit span $= \rho KV$ (Kutta-Joukowski theorem);

drag $= 0$ (D'Alembert's paradox).

Aerofoils. The Joukowski mapping function is of the form $w = z + b^2/z$ and is applied to a circle which includes the origin. The points $z = \pm b$ are called the *singular points* of the transformation. The following are the most important special cases of this transformation:

(i) Circle centred at $z = 0$. In general, the circle on the z-plane transforms into an ellipse on the w-plane. A circle passing through the singular points transforms into part of the real axis on the w-plane.

(ii) Circle centred on real axis of z-plane. The most important case is when the radius of the circle is slightly greater than b, and the circle passes through one singular point, with the other inside the circle. The curve in the w-plane is pear-shaped, symmetrical, with a cusp at one end (rudder or fin shape). The axis of symmetry is the part of the real axis between $\pm 2b$ (this is called the *skeleton*), and the point of maximum thickness is b from the bulbous nose.

(iii) Circle centred on imaginary axis of z-plane. When the original circle passes through the singular points, the curve in the w-plane is a circular arc with the part of the real axis between $\pm 2b$ as chord.

(iv) Circle centred at point not on either axis in z-plane, but passing through one singular point. If the centre of the circle is placed close to the imaginary axis, the typical Joukowski aerofoil profile is obtained in the w-plane.

Joukowski's hypothesis. The circulation around an aerofoil is determined by the condition that the rear separation point coincides with the sharply pointed tail.

The *aerodynamic centre* of the aerofoil is the point about which the moment of the aerodynamic force is independent of the angle of attack (α) and therefore proportional to ρV^2. For a slender profile the aerodynamic centre is $\frac{1}{4}$ chord-length from the leading edge.

The lift coefficient C_L is defined by

$$\text{lift per unit span} = \tfrac{1}{2} C_L \rho V^2$$

where V is the translational velocity of the aerofoil. For a simple Joukowski aerofoil, neglecting wing-tip effects,

$$C_L = 2\pi \sin\alpha \simeq 2\pi\alpha,$$

where α is the angle of attack, assumed small and measured in radians.

4.31. Momentum theorems

The forces exerted by the fluid on a submerged body are usually evaluated by the momentum theorems. A *control surface* is an arbitrary curve which always consists of the same particles and is thus a *material surface*.

Linear momentum theorem for steady flow. In steady motion, the component of external forces (such as weight or fluid thrusts) in any agreed direction, acting on fluid enclosed by an arbitrary closed control surface S, exactly balances the flux of linear momentum in the agreed direction across S.

Angular momentum theorem for steady flow. The sum of the moments of the external forces about an arbitrary axis, acting on fluid bounded by an arbitrary control surface S, exactly balances the flux of angular momentum, about the same axis, across S.

Integral expressions for two-dimensional flow

Net rate of outflow of linear momentum across S

$$=\int_S \rho u V \cos\alpha \, dS = \text{resultant force.}$$

Net rate of outflow of angular momentum across S

$$=\int_S \rho(xv - yu) V \cos\alpha \, dS = \text{resultant torque.}$$

Theorem of Blasius. Let X, Y be the components of resultant force exerted by an inviscid fluid on an infinite cylinder (e.g. aerofoil of infinite aspect ratio) immersed in a fluid whose motion is described by the complex potential $w(z)$. Let M_0 be the moment of the resultant force about an axis through the origin. Then

$$X - iY = \frac{1}{2} i\rho \int_S \left(\frac{dw}{dz}\right)^2 dz.$$

$$M_0 = \text{real part of } \left(-\frac{1}{2}\rho \int_S z\left(\frac{dw}{dz}\right)^2 dz\right).$$

(Thus the problem of evaluating the forces is reduced to finding the residues of the complex functions.)

Additional mass. A totally submerged body moving in an inviscid incompressible fluid behaves with respect to external forces as if it possessed an additional mass equal to the quotient of the momentum passed from the body to the fluid (initially at rest) and the speed of the body.

A long elliptic cylinder moving normally to the major axis a has an apparent additional mass $\frac{1}{4}\pi l a^2 \rho$, where l is the length of the cylinder. For a circular disc of diameter a the additional mass is $\frac{8}{3}\rho a^3$.

4.4. Compressible flow

Bernoulli's equation for compressible flow is

$$\int \frac{dp}{\rho} + \frac{1}{2} q^2 + P = \text{constant},$$

where P is the potential of the external forces. The speed of efflux of gas from a vessel in which pressure is p_1 and density ρ_1 to an atmosphere of pressure p_0, is (neglecting any external forces) given by

$$q^2=\frac{2\gamma}{\gamma-1}\frac{p_1}{\rho_1}\left\{1-\left(\frac{p_0}{p_1}\right)^{(\gamma-1)/\gamma}\right\},$$

where $\gamma=c_p/c_v$ is the ratio of the specific heats, it being assumed that the expansion is adiabatic.

Subsonic and supersonic motions. The Mach number M is defined to be the ratio of the actual speed and that of sound waves in the fluid. Because the velocity of sound is subject to local variations, the Mach number is evaluated with reference to the relative speed of the air-stream remote from the body.

The motion is subsonic if $M<1$ and supersonic if $M>1$. The critical Mach number M_C is defined as the Mach number at which shock effects (e.g. shock stall on an aerofoil) are first detected. The transonic region is somewhat loosely defined as the range of speeds for which $M_C \leqslant M<1$.

Glauert-Prandtl rule. If a wing is not too thick, and its forward speed is well below that corresponding to M_C, the lift coefficient C_L is increased by compressibility effects by the factor $(1-M^2)^{-\frac{1}{2}}$.

Lift and drag of a plane aerofoil of infinite aspect ratio at supersonic speeds. If the aerofoil is inclined at a small angle α to the direction of the airstream at infinity,

$$C_L=\frac{4\pi\alpha}{\sqrt{(M^2-1)}}\;;\;C_D=\frac{4\pi\alpha^2}{\sqrt{(M^2-1)}}\,.$$

(The drag is caused by shock waves and is sometimes referred to as "wave-drag". It has no relation with viscous drag.)

4.5. Equations of motion

Eulerian form, inviscid fluid, cartesian co-ordinates:

$$\frac{du}{dt}\equiv\frac{\partial u}{\partial t}+u\frac{\partial u}{\partial x}+v\frac{\partial u}{\partial y}+w\frac{\partial u}{\partial z}=X-\frac{1}{\rho}\frac{\partial p}{\partial x},$$

$$\frac{dv}{dt}\equiv\frac{\partial v}{\partial t}+u\frac{\partial v}{\partial x}+v\frac{\partial v}{\partial y}+w\frac{\partial v}{\partial z}=Y-\frac{1}{\rho}\frac{\partial p}{\partial y},$$

$$\frac{dw}{dt}\equiv\frac{\partial w}{\partial t}+u\frac{\partial w}{\partial x}+v\frac{\partial w}{\partial y}+w\frac{\partial w}{\partial z}=Z-\frac{1}{\rho}\frac{\partial p}{\partial z},$$

where u, v, w are component velocities along Ox, Oy, Oz respectively, ρ is density, p is pressure and X, Y, Z are the components of external force per unit mass at (x, y, z).

If a velocity potential ϕ and an external force potential P exist, these equations become

$$-d\left(\frac{\partial \phi}{\partial t}\right)+\frac{1}{2}\,dq^2+dP+\frac{1}{\rho}\,dp=0,$$

where $q^2=u^2+v^2+w^2$. If there is a functional relation between p and ρ,

$$\int\frac{dp}{\rho}-\frac{\partial \phi}{\partial t}+\frac{1}{2}q^2+P=\text{constant},$$

which is Bernoulli's equation.

Lagrangian form, inviscid fluid. Let a, b, c be the initial co-ordinates of the representative particle and x, y, z its co-ordinates after time t. Then

$$\frac{\partial^2 x}{\partial t^2}\frac{\partial x}{\partial a}+\frac{\partial^2 y}{\partial t^2}\frac{\partial y}{\partial a}+\frac{\partial^2 z}{\partial t^2}\frac{\partial z}{\partial a}=-\frac{\partial P}{\partial a}-\frac{1}{\rho}\frac{\partial p}{\partial a}, \text{ etc.},$$

where P is the potential of the external forces.

Vectorial forms:

$$\frac{\partial \mathbf{V}}{\partial t}+(\mathbf{V}\,.\,\nabla)\mathbf{V}=\mathbf{F}-\frac{1}{\rho}\,\nabla p,$$

or

$$\frac{\partial \mathbf{V}}{\partial t}+\text{grad}\left(\frac{1}{2}\,u^2\right)-\mathbf{V}\times\text{rot }\mathbf{V}=\mathbf{F}-\frac{1}{\rho}\,\text{grad }p.$$

Writing rot $\mathbf{V}=\Omega$, so that $\Omega_x=\frac{\partial w}{\partial y}-\frac{\partial v}{\partial z}$, etc., we obtain the *vorticity equations*

$$\frac{\partial u}{\partial t}+\frac{\partial}{\partial x}\left(\frac{1}{2}\,u^2\right)-\left(v\Omega_z-w\Omega_y\right)=X-\frac{1}{\rho}\frac{\partial p}{\partial x},$$

with similar equations for v and w.

Helmholtz's equation. If p is a function of ρ,

$$\frac{d\Omega}{dt}-(\Omega\,.\,\nabla)\mathbf{V}+\Omega\,\text{div }\mathbf{V}=0.$$

For an incompressible fluid, div $\mathbf{V}=0$ (equation of continuity), and Helmholtz's equation reduces to

$$\frac{d\Omega}{dt}=(\Omega\,.\,\nabla)\mathbf{V}.$$

Viscous fluids. The Navier-Stokes equations for a compressible viscous fluid consist of three equations of the type

$$\rho\frac{du}{dt}=X-\frac{\partial p}{\partial x}+\frac{\partial}{\partial x}\left[\mu\left(2\frac{\partial u}{\partial x}-\frac{2}{3}\operatorname{div}\mathbf{V}\right)\right]+\frac{\partial}{\partial y}\left[\mu\left(\frac{\partial u}{\partial y}+\frac{\partial v}{\partial x}\right)\right]$$
$$+\frac{\partial}{\partial z}\left[\mu\left(\frac{\partial w}{\partial x}+\frac{\partial u}{\partial z}\right)\right],$$

where μ is the dynamic viscosity (see Chapter 5). If the fluid is incompressible, these equations reduce to three equations of the type

$$\rho\frac{du}{dt}=X-\frac{\partial p}{\partial x}+\mu\nabla^2 u,$$

or

$$\frac{du}{dt}=\frac{X}{\rho}-\frac{1}{\rho}\frac{\partial p}{\partial x}+\nu\nabla^2 u,$$

where ν is the kinematic viscosity. In vector notation,

$$\rho\frac{d\mathbf{V}}{dt}=\mathbf{F}-\operatorname{grad}p+\mu\nabla^2\mathbf{V}.$$

Transformations of Laplace's equation $\nabla^2\phi=0$

(i) In polar co-ordinates (r, θ):

$$\frac{\partial^2\phi}{\partial r^2}+\frac{1}{r^2}\frac{\partial^2\phi}{\partial\theta^2}+\frac{1}{r}\frac{\partial\phi}{\partial r}=0.$$

(ii) In spherical polar co-ordinates (r, θ, ω):

$$\sin\theta\frac{\partial}{\partial r}\left(r^2\frac{\partial\phi}{\partial r}\right)+\frac{\partial}{\partial\theta}\left(\sin\theta\frac{\partial\phi}{\partial\theta}\right)+\frac{1}{\sin\theta}\frac{\partial^2\phi}{\partial\omega^2}=0.$$

$(x=r\cos\theta,\ y=r\sin\theta\cos\omega,\ z=r\sin\theta\sin\omega.)$

Particular solutions of Laplace's equation

(i) Source or sink in 2 dimensions, $\phi=\ln r$; in 3 dimensions, $\phi=1/r$.

(ii) If $f(x, y, z)$ is a solution, so is $\frac{1}{r}f\left(\frac{x}{r^2}, \frac{y}{r^2}, \frac{z}{r^2}\right)$.

CHAPTER 5

VISCOSITY

A FLUID at rest exhibits an internal stress, pressure, which acts perpendicularly to the interface between contiguous surfaces. When the fluid moves (or a solid body moves through the fluid), a tangential stress appears, analogous to friction between solid bodies. Such a stress, attributed to the molecular constitution of the fluid, is called *viscosity*.

If a fluid exhibits a shearing stress τ per unit area, and a shear du/dz, where u is velocity and z is a co-ordinate length across the flow, the *dynamic coefficient* of viscosity μ is defined by the relation

$$\tau = \mu \frac{du}{dz},$$

provided that the motion is not turbulent.

A fluid for which μ is independent of du/dz is called Newtonian. The dimensions of μ are $ML^{-1}T^{-1}$, and in the c.g.s. system μ is measured in g. cm.$^{-1}$ sec.$^{-1}$. In many problems of fluid motion it is more convenient to use the *kinematic coefficient* ν defined by $\nu = \mu/\rho$, where ρ is the density of the fluid. The dimensions of ν are L^2T^{-1} and in the c.g.s. system ν is measured in cm.^{2} sec.$^{-1}$.

Typical values

Substance	μ(g. cm.$^{-1}$ sec.$^{-1}$)	ν(cm.^{2} sec.$^{-1}$)
water at 20° C.	$1{\cdot}01 \times 10^{-2}$	$1{\cdot}01 \times 10^{-2}$
glycerine at 20° C.	8·56	6·80
air at 20° C. and 760 mm. pressure	$1{\cdot}83 \times 10^{-4}$	0·15

For liquids, μ and ν are nearly independent of pressure and decrease with increasing temperature. For gases, μ and ν are not markedly dependent on pressure and increase with increasing temperature. The kinematic viscosity of air is greater than that of water at the same temperature.

5.1. Slow motion (laminar flow)

The following formulae refer to non-turbulent motion (see below):

(*a*) Steady flow through a channel of width $2b$ with parallel flat walls:

$$u(z) = -\frac{1}{2\mu}\frac{dp}{dx}(b^2 - z^2),$$

where $u(z)$ is the velocity profile across the channel, $\frac{dp}{dx}$ is the pressure gradient in the direction of flow (x) and z is measured across stream from one wall.

(*b*) Couette flow (flow between two flat parallel walls, one at rest, the other moving in its own plane with constant velocity U).

$$u(z) = \frac{Uz}{2b},$$

where $2b$ is the distance between planes.

(*c*) Concentric rotating cylinders. Let the inner and outer radii be r_1 and r_2, and the steady angular velocities ω_1 and ω_2 respectively. The velocity profile between the cylinders is

$$u(r) = \frac{1}{r_2^2 - r_1^2}\left\{r(\omega_2 r_2^2 - \omega_1 r_1^2) + \frac{r_1^2 r_2^2}{r}(\omega_1 - \omega_2)\right\}.$$

When the inner cylinder is at rest and the outer cylinder rotates, the torque transmitted to the outer cylinder by the fluid is

$$4\pi\mu h \frac{r_1^2 r_2^2}{r_2^2 - r_1^2}\omega_2,$$

where h is the height of the cylinder.

(*d*) Two discs, one at rest, one rotating steadily. The couple required to keep one disc at rest when the other rotates at a constant angular velocity ω is approximately

$$\frac{\pi\mu\omega a^4}{2l},$$

where a = radius of discs, l = separation. Edge effects are neglected.

(*e*) Stokes' law. A non-rotating sphere of radius r moving slowly and steadily through a fluid at speed u experiences a resistance $6\mu\pi r u$.

The terminal velocity of a small sphere of density ρ' falling through a fluid of density ρ is thus $\frac{2}{9}\frac{r^2}{\mu}(\rho' - \rho)$.

(*f*) Poiseiulle formula for slow steady flow through a pipe of circular cross-section.

$$Q = \frac{\pi r^4}{8\mu}\left(\frac{p_1 - p_2}{l}\right)$$

where Q = quantity flowing through a section in unit time and $(p_1 - p_2)/l$ is the pressure gradient over the length l of the pipe.

5.2. Laminar and turbulent flow. Reynold's number

The formulae given above apply only when the motion is laminar (or non-turbulent). Turbulence cannot be defined in exact mathematical terms, but is understood to imply a state in which the velocity at any point exhibits finite irregular oscillations, so that only statistical functions (means, correlations, etc.) of the properties can be embodied in mathematical formulae. The state of the motion depends upon the magnitude of the dimensionless Reynolds' number $R = ul/\nu$, where u is a characteristic velocity, l a characteristic length and ν is the kinematic viscosity. The Reynold's number also indicates the relative importance of the inertia and friction forces in the motion; where R is small, friction forces dominate. This condition holds, for example, in the motion contemplated in Stokes' law, which is valid only for $R < 1$. Pipe flow remains laminar for $R < 2 \times 10^3$, the reference length (l) being the pipe diameter.

5.3. Boundary layers

When a fluid of small viscosity (e.g. air) moves relative to a solid surface, frictional effects are important only in a shallow boundary layer adjacent to the surface. Elsewhere, the fluid moves as if it were inviscid. The motion in the boundary layer may be laminar or turbulent, and this has a marked effect on the resistance. For a flat plate the flow remains laminar if $R < 3{\cdot}5 \times 10^5$ (approx.), where the reference velocity is that of the undisturbed stream and the reference length is distance measured from the leading edge of the plate. The depth of the boundary layer, defined as the distance normal to the plate at which the disturbed velocity (u) along the plate differs by 1 per cent. from the undisturbed (free stream) velocity is $5(\nu x/u)^{\frac{1}{2}}$ (x being measured from the leading edge) in laminar flow. The skin friction of the plate in laminar flow is given approximately by $1{\cdot}33 S\rho u^2/(2\sqrt{xu/\nu})$, where S = wetted area of plate. When the boundary layer becomes turbulent the corresponding expressions are:

$$\text{depth of boundary layer} \simeq 0{\cdot}37x(ux/\nu)^{-1/5},$$

$$\text{skin friction} \simeq 0{\cdot}036 S\rho u^2 (ux/\nu)^{-1/5},$$

where u is now to be interpreted as the mean velocity of the turbulent flow and $10^6 < R < 10^7$.

5.4. Drag coefficients

It is customary to express the drag, or component of fluid resistance in the direction of motion, by a non-dimensional drag coefficient C_D, defined by

$$\text{drag} = \tfrac{1}{2} C_D \rho u^2 S,$$

where S is the wetted area. In general, C_D is determined experimentally Stokes' law implies that the drag coefficient of a sphere is $24R^{-1}$, provided that $R < 1$.

CHAPTER 6

WAVE MOTION AND SOUND

6·1. If x be a distance, t time and c a velocity, any function of the form $f(x+ct)$ represents a wave motion in which the curve $y=f(x)$ moves along the x-axis with velocity c. Such functions satisfy the one-dimensional equation of wave motion, viz.,

$$\frac{\partial^2 u}{\partial t^2}=c^2\frac{\partial^2 u}{\partial x^2},$$

of which $u=f(x+ct)+f(x-ct)$ is the general solution.

A simple harmonic progressive wave is defined by one or other of the equations

$$y=a\sin(mx-nt+\phi)=a\sin\frac{2\pi}{\lambda}(x-ct+\phi')=a\sin 2\pi\left(\frac{x}{\lambda}-\frac{\tau}{t}+\phi'\right).$$

Here $\lambda=2\pi/m$ is the wavelength, $\tau=\lambda/c=2\pi/n$ is the period, $c=n/m$ is the velocity of propagation and ϕ (or ϕ') is the phase. The reciprocal of the period is the frequency (ν) and the reciprocal of the wavelength is the wave-number (k). The phase of the wave depends upon the instant selected as the zero of time and is thus arbitrary.

Two s.h. progressive waves of the same amplitude and frequency travelling in opposite directions produce a disturbance given by $y=a\{\sin(mx-nt)+\sin(mx+nt)\}=2a\sin mx\cos nt$, called a standing wave. The curve intersects the x-axis at fixed points called nodes.

Two s.h. waves of equal amplitude and slightly different wave-lengths travelling together produce a wave group. If the waves are dispersive (velocity of propagation varying with wavelength) the group velocity c_g is given by

$$c_g=c-\lambda\frac{dc}{d\lambda}.$$

6.2. Waves in fluids

The main results are:

(i) surface waves under the action of gravity, deep fluid,

$$c=\sqrt{(g\lambda/2\pi)};$$

(ii) capillary waves

$$c=\sqrt{(2\pi T/\rho\lambda)}$$

T=surface tension, ρ=density;

(iii) combined gravity and capillary effects

$$c=\sqrt{\left(\frac{g\lambda}{2\pi}+\frac{2\pi T}{\rho\lambda}\right)};$$

(iv) shallow fluid, depth h, long waves under gravity

$$c=\sqrt{(gh)}.$$

The energy of a train of s.h. progressive waves is half potential and half kinetic. For such waves at the surface of water, under gravity, the total energy per wavelength is $\frac{1}{2}g\rho a^2\lambda$, where a is the amplitude, and this is transmitted at a rate equal to the group velocity.

6.3. Long waves (Rossby type) in the atmosphere

A zonal current of steady uniform velocity V, when perturbed, can generate long waves as a consequence of the variation of relative vorticity with latitude (caused by the change of the Coriolis force with latitude). For stationary waves the length is given by Rossby's formula

$$\text{wave-length} = 2\pi\sqrt{\frac{V}{\beta}},$$

where $\beta = \dfrac{2\Omega \cos\phi}{R}$, R = radius of earth, Ω = angular velocity of earth about its axis, ϕ = latitude. In latitude 45°, the wavelength lies between 3000 and 8000 km. when V lies between 5 and 25 m. sec.$^{-1}$.

6.4. Sound waves

The velocity of sound depends on the absolute temperature of the fluid, and is given by

$$c^2 = \frac{dp}{d\rho} = \gamma p/\rho = \gamma RT \text{ for a perfect gas } (\gamma = \text{ratio of specific heats}).$$

Typical values for c are:

dry air at 0° C.	$3{\cdot}31 \times 10^4$ cm. sec.$^{-1}$
hydrogen at 0° C.	$13{\cdot}0 \times 10^4$,, ,,
water at 20° C.	$14{\cdot}1 \times 10^4$,, ,,

An approximate formula for gases is $c = c_0(1 + \frac{1}{2}at)$cm. sec.$^{-1}$, where $a \simeq 3{\cdot}7 \times 10^{-3}$, t in °C.

The intensity of a sound wave is defined as the rate at which energy is transmitted across unit area of a plane parallel to the wave front. For a pure note (sinusoidal variation) of amplitude A this is $\frac{1}{2}\rho c(2\pi/\lambda)^2 A^2$, where λ is the wavelength. Beats are formed when two notes of nearly the same frequency are sounded together.

Musical scales. The ratios of frequencies are:

note . . .	C	D	E	F	G	A	B	C'
sol-fa names .	Doh	ray	me	fah	soh	lah	te	doh
ratio of frequencies	1·000	1·125	1·250	1·333	1·500	1·667	1·875	2·000
equi-tempered scale	1·000	1·122	1·260	1·335	1·498	1·682	1·888	2·000

The frequency of middle C is 256 cycles sec.$^{-1}$. Concert pitch is based on $A = 440$ cycles sec.$^{-1}$.

CHAPTER 7

LIGHT

(a) GEOMETRICAL OPTICS

7.1. Geometrical and physical optics

Light is regarded as a form of energy propagated by wave motion, and as such is defined primarily in terms of its speed (c), frequency (ν) and wavelength (λ). In all cases

$$\lambda\nu = c.$$

The wave properties of light are emphasized in *physical optics*, but for many purposes it is possible to effect a considerable simplification by concentrating attention on the direction in which the energy travels. A line depicting this direction is called a *ray*. The basis of *geometrical optics* is that rays passing through homogeneous isotropic media are straight lines.

Propagation. Light energy passes through a vacuum in straight rays at a constant speed $c = 2{\cdot}99793 \times 10^{10}$ cm. sec.$^{-1} \simeq 3 \times 10^{10}$ cm. sec.$^{-1}$ for all frequencies.

Refraction. When light traverses a material medium, its speed is reduced and becomes dependent on colour. The ray is then said to be *refracted*, and except at normal incidence, is bent. The frequency ν of monochromatic light is unaffected by such passage, but the wavelength λ is changed in accordance with the relation $\lambda = c/\nu$.

The *index of refraction* μ is defined by

$$\mu = \frac{c}{c'} = \frac{\lambda\nu}{c'} = \frac{\lambda}{\lambda'},$$

where c' and λ' are the speed and wavelength, respectively, of light in the material medium. For light of the mean sodium D-line ($\lambda = 5893 \times 10^{-8}$ cm.) the value of μ_D for air is $1{\cdot}000292$. For most laboratory experiments this may be considered as unity without appreciable error.

Values of μ for material media are usually quoted for the sodium D-line with respect to air at 15° C. Approximate values are

$$\text{water: } \mu_D = 4/3; \quad \text{crown glass: } \mu_D = 3/2.$$

7.2. Laws of refraction

(i) The incident and the refracted rays, and the normal to the surface at the point of incidence, are coplanar.

(ii) *Snell's law.* If i is angle of incidence and r the angle of refraction,

$$\frac{\sin i}{\sin r}=\frac{\mu'}{\mu}\simeq\frac{1}{\mu} \text{ for surfaces in air.}$$

Total internal reflection occurs when $\sin r>\mu/\mu'$ and $\mu'/\mu>1$. When light passes through a medium bounded by parallel planes, the incident and emergent rays are parallel.

Triangular prisms. A triangular prism of apex angle A deviates a ray incident at i_1 and emergent at i_2 by the amount $D=i_1+i_2-A\simeq A(\mu-1)$ for thin prisms (small A) in air. The condition for minimum deviation D' is

$$\sin \tfrac{1}{2}(A+D')=\mu \sin \tfrac{1}{2}A.$$

7.21. Refraction at curved surfaces

In considering refraction or reflection at curved surfaces it is necessary to adopt a *sign convention.* That used here is the "real is positive" convention, in which distances from real objects and images are reckoned positive, and to virtual objects and images negative. If the object distance is u and the image distance v, a ray refracted at a spherical surface of radius r separating a medium of refractive index μ from a denser medium of refractive index μ' satisfies in all cases the equation

$$\frac{\mu}{u}+\frac{\mu'}{v}=\frac{\mu'\sim\mu}{r}=\text{"power" of the surface,}$$

provided that all angles are small. The power of a surface is reckoned positive when the surface is convex to the less-dense medium.

Lagrange's law. If α_1, α_2 are the (small) inclinations of the rays to the axis, y_1 and y_2 the object and image heights respectively, then for a spherical surface,

$$\mu y_1\alpha_1=\mu' y_2\alpha_2.$$

7.22. Reflection

The angles of incidence and reflection, measured with respect to the tangent to the surface at the point of incidence, are equal.

Spherical mirrors. The basic equation is

$$\frac{1}{v}+\frac{1}{u}=\frac{1}{f}=\frac{2}{r},$$

where u is the object distance, v the image distance, r the radius of curvature and f the focal length. This equation holds for both convex and concave mirrors with a sign convention (e.g. the "real is positive" convention; see above). In the "real is positive" convention the focal length of a concave mirror (real focus) is positive and that of a concave mirror (virtual focus), negative.

Formation of images in spherical mirrors

Mirror	*Position of object*	*Image*
Concave	Beyond centre of curvature	Real, inverted, diminished
Concave	Between centre of curvature and principal focus	Real, inverted, magnified
Concave	At centre of curvature	Real, inverted, unchanged in size
Concave	Inside principal focus	Virtual, erect, magnified
Convex	All positions	Virtual, erect, diminished

The *transverse linear magnification* is defined as the ratio of the height of the image and the height of the object (positive when erect, negative when inverted).

$$\text{Magnification} = -\frac{v}{u} = -\frac{f}{u-f} = -\frac{v-f}{f}.$$

Longitudinal linear magnification (small objects) $= \dfrac{-v^2}{u^2}$.

Superficial magnification $= \dfrac{v^2}{u^2}$.

Newton's formula. If x and x' are object and image distances respectively, measured from the focus of the mirror,

$$xx' = f^2.$$

7.3. Thin lenses

The basic equation connecting the object distance, image distance and focal length of a thin lens is identical with that for a mirror, and the "real is positive" convention applies as before. A concave lens has a virtual focus and a concave lens a real focus. The focal length of a convex lens is thus reckoned to be positive and that of a concave lens negative. Newton's formula holds unaltered, as do the expressions for the magnification.

Formation of images in lenses

Lens	*Position of object*	*Image*
Convex	At a great distance ($>2f$) from lens	Real, inverted, diminished
Convex	$2f$ from lens	Real, inverted, unchanged in size
Convex	Between f and $2f$	Real, inverted, magnified
Convex	Inside focus	Virtual, erect, magnified
Concave	All positions	Virtual, erect, diminished

The *power* F of a lens is defined to be the reciprocal of the focal length in metres, and a lens is said to have a power of one *dioptre* when its focal length is one metre. The power of a finite number of thin lenses in contact is the sum of the powers of the individual lenses, it being understood that the adjective "thin" means "of thickness small compared with the focal length".

Power (*or focal length*) *of a thin lens.* For a lens made of material of refractive index μ, having bounding surfaces of radii of curvature r_1, r_2 respectively, the basic relation is

$$F=\frac{1}{f}=\left(\mu-1\right)\left(\frac{1}{r_1}+\frac{1}{r_2}\right),$$

with the sign convention that r is positive for a convex surface and negative for a concave surface.

Thick lens. If t is the thickness of the central portion of the lens, a first approximation is given by

$$F=\frac{1}{f}=\left(\mu-1\right)\left(\frac{1}{r_1}+\frac{1}{r_2}\right)+\frac{(\mu-1)^2}{\mu}\frac{t}{r_1r_2}.$$

7.31. Defects of images

Spherical aberration. A mirror or a lens gives a blurred image because different rays from any point on the object make different angles with the line joining the point to the optical centre and hence come to a focus at slightly different positions. This defect is measured in terms of the longitudinal and lateral aberrations. For a ray incident at angle i from a point source on the axis of a concave mirror of radius r,

$$\text{longitudinal spherical aberration}=\tfrac{1}{2}r(\sec i-1)\simeq\tfrac{1}{4}ri^2,$$

$$\text{lateral spherical aberration}=\tfrac{1}{2}r(\sec i-1)\tan 2i\simeq\tfrac{1}{2}ri^3,$$

where the approximations are valid for small values of i (in radians).

In terms of the peripheral radius h of the mirror these approximations become $h^2/4r$ and $h^3/2r^2$ respectively.

Chromatic aberration produces an image with coloured fringes because of the different amounts of refraction suffered by the component colours. The dispersive power of a lens is defined by

$$\omega = \frac{\mu_F - \mu_C}{\mu_D - 1},$$

where μ_C, μ_D and μ_F are the refractive indices corresponding to the red H-line ($\lambda = 6563 \times 10^{-8}$ cm.), the yellow Na-line ($\lambda = 5893 \times 10^{-8}$ cm.) and the green-blue H-line ($\lambda = 4862 \times 10^{-8}$ cm.). Values of ω usually lie in the range 0·02 to 0·05. The reciprocal of ω, called the *constringence* and denoted by ν, is also used.

7.32. Simple optical instruments

Optical instruments of the simple types dealt with here are characterized by (*a*) magnification, (*b*) resolving power, (*c*) field.

Magnification $= M$

$$= \frac{\text{apparent size of object seen through the instrument}}{\text{apparent size of object viewed by the unassisted eye}}.$$

Single convex lens (hand magnifier)

Normal position: $M = \dfrac{D}{f}$, where $D \simeq 25$ cm., is the least distance of distinct vision.

Lens held to eye: $M = 1 + \dfrac{D}{f}$.

Compound microscope (objective plus eyepiece)

If g = optical tube length = distance between second principal focus of the objective and the first principal focus of the eyepiece, and f_o, f_e are the focal lengths of the objective and eyepiece respectively, the magnification achieved in the normal position (final image at infinity) is

$$M = \frac{Dg}{f_o f_e}$$

= (linear magnification due to objective)
× (magnifying power of eyepiece).

The resolving power is given by

$$h = \frac{\lambda}{2\mu \sin i},$$

where i is the semi-angle which the objective aperture subtends at the object, λ is the wavelength of the light and μ is the refractive index of the medium (e.g. oil). The quantity $\mu \sin i$ is the *numerical aperture* of the microscope.

Astronomical telescope (objective plus eyepiece; inverted image)

$$\text{Magnification} = \frac{f_o}{f_e} = \frac{\text{diameter of entrance pupil}}{\text{diameter of exit pupil}},$$

$$\text{Resolving power} = \frac{1{\cdot}22\lambda}{d},$$

where d is the diameter of the objective.

Terrestrial telescope (objective plus erector plus eyepiece; image erect)

$$\text{Magnification} = \frac{vf_o}{uf_e},$$

where u and v are object and image distances, respectively, for the erector lens.

The *apparent field of view* of a telescope is defined to be the product of the total field and the magnification. It is the angle subtended at the eye by the image of the actual field, and in practice rarely exceeds 50°. For hand binoculars for general purposes the optimum magnification appears to lie between 6 and 8. For night use the exit pupil should be 7 mm. in diameter, but smaller values are adequate for use by day.

Camera

$$\text{Stop number } S = \frac{\text{focal length of lens}}{\text{diameter of stop aperture}} = \frac{f}{D},$$

$$\text{Intensity of illumination on sensitive plate} = \frac{\pi}{4} k \frac{B}{S^2},$$

where B is the brightness of the object (candles per unit area) and k represents the fraction of the light lost by reflection and absorption by the lens.

(*b*) Physical Optics

7.4. Photometry

The fundamental unit is that of *luminous intensity*, measured either by *candle power* (*international candle*) or the *candela*. The candela is defined by the relation that a black body (q.v.) radiates 60 candela cm.$^{-2}$ at the temperature of solidification of platinum.

The unit of *luminous flux* is the *lumen* = flux emitted by a source of 1 candle power within the unit solid angle. Hence a source of 1 c.p. emits 4π lumens $\simeq 12{\cdot}57$ lumens.

The least mechanical equivalent of light

$$= \frac{\text{radiant flux (watts)}}{\text{luminous flux (lumens)}} = 1{\cdot}6 \times 10^{-3} \text{ watts lumen}^{-1}.$$

Inverse square law. A point source of C c.p., distant r cm. from a surface and such that the axis of the pencil of rays makes an angle α with the normal to the surface, produces an illumination of the surface of $C \cos \alpha / r^2$ lumens cm.$^{-2}$.

Illumination of surface = luminous flux received per unit area.

Metric unit of illumination = 1 lumen m.$^{-2}$ = metre-candle or lux,

British unit of illumination = 1 lumen ft.$^{-2}$ = foot-candle,

1 foot-candle = 10·76 metre-candles or lux.

Lambert's law. The brightness of a diffuse surface is proportional to the cosine of the angle formed by the normal to the surface and the direction of view.

Brightness of a surface = luminous intensity projected in a specified direction.

Units: candles cm.$^{-2}$, candles in.$^{-2}$ or millilamberts.

1 lambert = brightness of a perfectly diffusing surface emitting 1 lumen cm.$^{-2}$.

1 lambert $= \frac{1}{\pi}$ candles cm.$^{-2} \simeq 0{\cdot}318$ candles cm.$^{-2}$.

1 candle in.$^{-2}$ = 487 millilamberts.

A perfectly diffusing surface is one which looks equally bright from all directions.

Orders of magnitude. The zenith sun gives an illumination of a horizontal surface of the order of 10^4 foot-candles in clear days in summer. At the end of twilight the illumination is of the order of $\frac{1}{2}$ foot-candle and a full moon in the zenith gives about 0·02 foot-candle. Indoors on a bright day the illumination is of the order of 20 foot-candles and at least 3 foot-candles is needed for reading normal print.

7.5. Interference

Young's experiment. If d is the separation of the secondary sources and D the distance from the sources to the screen, the positions of the bands are given by:

$$\left.\begin{array}{ll}\text{dark bands:} & (n+\frac{1}{2})\lambda D/d \\ \text{bright bands:} & n\lambda D/d\end{array}\right\} n \text{ integral}$$

and the separation is $\lambda D/d$.

Fresnel's biprism

$$\text{Separation} = \frac{(b+d)\lambda}{2b(\mu-1)\alpha},$$

b = distance from slit to prism, d = distance from prism to observer, α = angle of prism.

Fresnel mirrors

$$\text{Separation} = \frac{(b+d)\lambda}{2b\alpha},$$

α = angle between mirrors.

Thin films. If a thin film of thickness d is illuminated by a parallel beam and r is the angle of refraction, the conditions for brightness and darkness are:

$$\left.\begin{array}{ll}\text{darkness:} & 2\mu d \cos r = n\lambda \\ \text{brightness:} & 2\mu d \cos r = (n+\frac{1}{2})\lambda\end{array}\right\} n \text{ integral.}$$

Newton's rings. If R is the radius of curvature of a convex lens in contact with a plane reflecting surface, the radii are:

$$\left.\begin{array}{ll}\text{for bright rings:} & \sqrt{\{(n+\frac{1}{2})R\lambda\}} \\ \text{for dark rings:} & \sqrt{(nR\lambda)}\end{array}\right\} n \text{ integral.}$$

If r_n is the radius of a dark ring of rank n, the wavelength of the light is

$$\lambda = r_n^2/Rn.$$

7.6. Diffraction

When light passes near the edge of an obstacle, or through a thin slit or small orifice, diffraction patterns of light and dark bands are seen on a screen.

Fraunhofer diffraction. Let d = width of slit, θ = angle of diffraction. Intensity, single slit $I = I_0 \dfrac{\sin^2 \beta}{\beta}$, $\beta = \dfrac{\pi d \sin \theta}{\lambda}$ for normal incidence.

Zeros of intensity are at $\beta = n\pi$ (n integral), maxima at $\tan \beta = \beta$, 1st zero at $\sin \theta_1 = \lambda/d$.

$$\text{Circular orifice, first minimum:} \quad \sin \theta = 1{\cdot}22\lambda/d,$$

$$\text{Multiple parallel slits:} \quad \sin \theta = n\lambda/(a+b),$$

where a = width of slit, b = distance between slits, n integral. (This also applies to a diffraction grating.)

Fresnel half-period zones. For a circular aperture and a spherical wave-front the radius r_n of the nth ring is

$$r_n = \sqrt{\left(\frac{n\lambda}{\frac{1}{p}+\frac{1}{q}}\right)},$$

where p = distance from aperture to screen, q = distance from aperture to source. For a plane wave let $q \rightarrow \infty$, when $r_n = \sqrt{(pn\lambda)}$.

The points on the axis at which the illumination is a maximum are given by

$$\frac{1}{p}+\frac{1}{q}=\frac{2n\lambda}{\rho^2},$$

where ρ = radius of aperture, n is integral.

X-ray diffraction by crystals. Bragg's law:

$$\sin\theta = \frac{n\lambda}{2d}, \quad n \text{ integral},$$

d = separation of lattice planes.

Doppler effect. Change of frequency is given by

$$\nu' = \frac{\nu_0\sqrt{(1-v^2/c^2)}}{1-(v/c)\cos\theta} \simeq \nu_0 \frac{c}{c-v\cos\theta},$$

where v = speed of source, θ = angle between line of sight and direction of motion.

7.7. Polarization

All light is regarded as consisting of electric (E) and magnetic (H) vibrations. The vibrations are normal to the direction of the rays (light is a transverse wave motion). In unpolarized light the E and H vibrations are in all planes, with the associated E and H vibrations normal to each other. In *plane polarized* light the E vibrations are confined to a *plane of vibration* and the H vibrations to a *plane of polarization,* normal to the plane of the E vibrations.

Brewster's law. Complete plane polarization occurs at a surface when the reflected and refracted rays are normal to each other.

The Brewster angle is defined by $\tan^{-1}\mu$ (about 57° for glass in air).

Polariscope. The optical activity of a solution is defined in terms of the specific rotary power given by θ/cl, where θ is the angle through which the vibration direction is rotated, c is the concentration of the active substance (g cm.$^{-3}$) and l is the length of the column in decimeters. The rotation is called *dextro* if the plane of polarization is rotated anti-clockwise when looking through the liquid away from the source of light, otherwise *laevo*. The magnetic rotation of polarized light is measured per cm. per unit magnetic field by Verdet's number θ/Hl, where H(gauss) is the field strength, l is the length of the light path parallel to the lines of force and θ is measured in minutes. Light passing through an isotropic medium has a spherical wavefront; that passing through an anisotropic medium has an ellipsoidal wavefront. Certain substances, such as calcite (Iceland spar) or the synthetic material polaroid, have the property of *double refraction*, i.e. of producing two refracted rays, called "ordinary" and "extraordinary" respectively. The ordinary beam has a spherical, and the extra-ordinary beam an ellipsoidal, wavefront. A Nichol prism is a polished crystal of calcite cut so that when illuminated by unpolarized light in a specific direction, only the extraordinary beam passes. This beam is polarized. Parallel Nichols give a bright field, crossed Nichols a dark field.

7.8. Beer's law

If a beam of light of intensity I_0 is reduced to one of intensity I_0q after passing through unit thickness of a medium, the intensity after transmission through a similar layer m units thick is

$$I = I_0 q^m.$$

The quantity q is called the *transmission coefficient*. The *extinction coefficient a* is defined by

$$a = -\ln q$$

and Beer's law becomes

$$I = I_0 e^{-am},$$

where e is the base of natural logarithms.

Scattering of light caused by molecules or very small spheres is given by *Rayleigh's inverse fourth-power law*:

$$\text{Scattering power} = \text{extinction coefficient due to scattering} = \frac{32\pi^3(\mu-1)^2}{3N_L\lambda^4},$$

where N_L is the Loschmidt number, μ the refractive index and λ the wavelength. The relative intensity of unpolarized light scattered at angle θ by a sphere of volume V distant d from the observer is

$$\frac{g\pi^2}{2d^2}\left(\frac{\mu^2-1}{\mu^2+2}\right)^2 \frac{V^2}{\lambda^4}(1+\cos^2\theta),$$

provided that the radius of the sphere is small. (See also Chapter 9.)

7.9. Fresnel formulae

Let I_0 = intensity of the incident beam, I_r that of the reflected beam, i and r the angles of incidence and refraction respectively.

For unpolarized light

$$\frac{I_r}{I_0}=\frac{1}{2}\left\{\frac{\sin^2(i-r)}{\sin^2(i+r)}+\frac{\tan^2(i-r)}{\tan^2(i+r)}\right\}.$$

If the light is polarized in the plane of incidence,

$$\frac{I_r}{I_0}=\frac{\sin^2(i-r)}{\sin^2(i+r)},$$

and if polarized perpendicular to the plane of incidence,

$$\frac{I_r}{I_0}=\frac{\tan^2(i-r)}{\tan^2(i+r)}.$$

At normal incidence, for polarized or unpolarized light,

$$\frac{I_r}{I_0}=\left(\frac{\mu-1}{\mu+1}\right)^2.$$

(This formula is a useful approximation for unpolarized light for all except large deviations from the normal.)

If unpolarized light is incident at Brewster's angle $\tan^{-1}\mu$,

$$\frac{I_r}{I_0}=\frac{1}{2}\left(\frac{\mu^2-1}{\mu^2+1}\right)^2,$$

and if the light is completely polarized at Brewster's angle,

$$\frac{I_r}{I_0}=\left(\frac{\mu^2-1}{\mu^2+1}\right)^2.$$

If I' is the intensity of the refracted beam, for light polarized in the plane of incidence

$$\frac{I'}{I_0}=\frac{4\sin^2 i\sin^2 r}{\sin^2(i+r)},$$

and polarized perpendicular to the plane of incidence

$$\frac{I'}{I_0}=\frac{4\sin^2 r\cos^2 i}{\sin^2(i+r)\cos^2(i-r)}$$

CHAPTER 8

RADIATION AND SPECTROSCOPY

THE term *radiation* is usually applied to the transference of energy by electromagnetic waves. Such waves are defined in terms of wavelength or frequency or wave number. The wavelength is usually expressed in *Ångstrom units* (Å), i.e. as multiples of 10^{-8} cm., but the *micron* $\mu = 10^{-4}$ cm. is also used, especially in dealing with visible radiation (light). Frequency, expressed in kilocycles (10^3) or megacycles (10^6) per second, is used mainly for radio, television and radar waves, the relation between wavelength and frequency being the universal wave equation

$$\text{wavelength} \times \text{frequency} = \text{velocity} \simeq 3 \times 10^{10} \text{ cm. sec.}^{-1}.$$

The wave number is the reciprocal of the wavelength.

8.1. General

The electromagnetic spectrum extends from cosmic rays (λ about 5×10^{-4}Å) to the longest radio waves (λ in thousands of metres). The various parts of the spectrum, arranged in order of increasing wavelength (decreasing frequency), are: cosmic rays, gamma rays, X-rays, ultra-violet light, visible light, infra-red rays, radar and television waves, radio waves.

The visible rays are comprised between $\lambda = 3930$Å (violet) and $\lambda = 7594$Å (red).

The solar spectrum is almost entirely contained between $\lambda = 3000$Å and $\lambda = 20{,}000$Å, the absence of radiation below 3000Å being attributed to absorption by ozone in the upper layers of the Earth's atmosphere. Over 40 per cent. of the energy received from the sun lies in the infra-red ($\lambda > 7594$Å).

The maximum wavelength for X-rays is about 12Å, and the minimum wavelength for gamma-radiation is about 0·07Å.

8.2. Fundamental laws

The *intensity of radiation* is defined in terms of the amount of energy received on a unit surface, normal to the beam, in unit time. The units are: erg cm.$^{-2}$ sec.$^{-1}$, g. cal cm.$^{-2}$ sec.$^{-1}$ or watts cm.$^{-2}$.

In meteorology, the unit is usually the gramme calorie per square centimetre per minute, and the relations are

$$1 \text{g. cal. cm.}^{-2} \text{min.}^{-1} = 4{\cdot}19 \times 10^7 \text{erg cm.}^{-2} \text{min.}^{-1} = 6{\cdot}97 \times 10^{-2} \text{watt cm.}^{-2}.$$

8.3. Thermal radiation

Prévost's law of exchanges. A body receives and emits radiation simultaneously. In equilibrium, and provided no process other than radiation is involved, the rates of loss and gain of heat by radiation are equal.

Definition of a black body (full radiator). The intensity of the radiation emitted by a hot body depends on the area of the surface, its absolute temperature and the wavelength of the radiation. For a given area, temperature and wavelength the intensity has an upper bound. A body which emits the maximum intensity for all wavelengths is termed a black body or full radiator. (The word "black" has no reference to the colour of the body.)

Kirchhoff's law. The ratio

$$\frac{\text{intensity of radiation emitted}}{\text{fraction of radiation absorbed}}=\frac{\text{emissive power}}{\text{absorptivity}}=\frac{e_\lambda}{a_\lambda}$$

depends only on the absolute temperature of the body and the wavelength λ.

Every body absorbs radiation of wavelength equal to that which it emits at the same temperature, and the wavelengths and intensity of the radiation emitted by a black body depend only upon its absolute temperature.

Stefan's law. A black body at absolute temperature T_1 when placed in a black enclosure at temperature T_2, gains or loses energy at the rate $\sigma(T_1^4-T_2^4)$, where $\sigma=5{\cdot}67\times10^{-5}$ erg cm.$^{-2}$ sec.$^{-1}$.

Planck's formula. The radiant energy $E(\lambda, T)\delta\lambda$, of wavelengths lying between λ and $\lambda+\delta\lambda$, from unit surface area of a black body at absolute temperature T is

$$\frac{c_1\delta\lambda}{\lambda^5(e^{c_2/\lambda T}-1)}\text{ erg sec.}^{-1},$$

where $c_1=8\pi hc$, h being Planck's constant$=6{\cdot}63\times10^{-27}$ erg sec. and c=velocity of light; $c_2=hc/k$, where k is Boltzmann's constant$=1{\cdot}38\times10^{-16}$ erg deg.$^{-1}$ (See Chapter 15 for numerical values).

Wien's displacement law. The wavelength of maximum emissive power of a black body is given by

$$\lambda_{max}=\frac{0{\cdot}2898}{T},$$

when λ is measured in cm. and T is the absolute temperature.

8.4. Spectroscopy

A *continuous spectrum* contains light of all wavelengths, between certain limits.

A *line spectrum* contains only light of certain wavelengths. Solid bodies, when heated, produce continuous spectra. Monatomic gases give line spectra; polyatomic gases (such as water vapour) give *band spectra*.

An *emission spectrum* is produced when the rays do not pass through an absorbing medium. Otherwise, an *absorption spectrum* is obtained. Hot gases and vapours absorb the radiation which they emit (Kirchhoff's law).

Solar spectrum. The distribution of energy in the solar spectrum in clear air is as follows (average for whole year):

Colour	*UV*	*V*	*B-G*	*Y*	*O-R*	*Infra-red*
Wave-length (μ)	0·3-0·4	0·4-0·47	0·47-0·56	0·56-0·63	0·63-0·76	>0·76
Per cent .	0·5	10·0	15·8	11·7	17·4	44·6

(The solar constant = intensity of radiation from the sun at the mean distance of the earth = intensity of sunbeams at the outer limit of the atmosphere, is not yet precisely determined, but may be taken to be 2g. cal. cm.$^{-2}$ min.$^{-1}$ = 139·4 m.watts cm.$^{-2}$ with very little error.)

In spectroscopy, the wavelength is often replaced by its reciprocal, the *wave number* $\bar{\nu}$. (The product of the wave number and the velocity of light gives the frequency.)

Balmer series for hydrogen. The wave numbers of the lines in the hydrogen spectrum are given by

$$\bar{\nu}=R\left(\frac{1}{2^2}-\frac{1}{n^2}\right), \quad n=3, 4, 5, \ldots .$$

R = Rydberg's constant = 109677·6 cm.$^{-1}$.

The general expression for the wave number derived from the simple Bohr model of the atom is

$$\bar{\nu}=\frac{2\pi^2 mZ^2e^4}{h^3c}\left(\frac{1}{n''^2}-\frac{1}{n'^2}\right),$$

where Ze = (positive) nuclear charge, e = electron charge, m = mass of electron, h = Planck's constant. The various hydrogen series are obtained from this expression as follows:

Lyman series: $n''=1$, $n'=2, 3, 4, \ldots$

Balmer series: $n''=2$, $n'=3, 4, 5, \ldots$

Paschen series: $n''=3$, $n'=4, 5, 6, \ldots$.

The *Zeeman effect* is the effect of a strong magnetic field on spectral lines, resulting in each being broken up into several components. The deviations of the wavelengths of the new lines from the old are given by

$$\delta\lambda = \pm \frac{H}{4\pi c} \frac{e}{m} \lambda^2,$$

where H is the magnetic field strength, c is the velocity of light and e/m is the specific charge of an electron (ratio of charge to mass).

The *Stark effect* is the splitting of spectral lines by the action of an intense electric field. The separations are multiples of $3hF/8\pi^2 mZ$, where F is the electric field strength (volt-cm.)

Raman effect. The spectrum of monochromatic light which has suffered scattering by passing through a medium contains not only light of the original wavelength but certain weaker lines differing from the original lines by constant amounts. These are the Raman lines. (See also Chapter 13.)

CHAPTER 9

ELECTRICITY AND MAGNETISM

9.1. Fundamental laws

(i) *Coulomb's law.* The force F between electric charges Q_1 and Q_2, separated by distance d, is given by

$$F \propto \frac{Q_1 Q_2}{\epsilon d^2},$$

where ϵ is a constant, depending on the medium, called the *permittivity* or *dielectric constant.*

(ii) The force F between two magnetic poles of strength m_1 and m_2, separated by distance d, is given by

$$F \propto \frac{m_1 m_2}{\mu d^2},$$

where μ is a constant, depending on the medium, called the *permeability*.

Units.

The *absolute electrostatic system* (e.s.u.) is based on the c.g.s. system.

Unit *charge* is defined as that charge which repels a like charge *in vacuo* with a force of 1 dyne.

Unit *field strength* is defined as that in which unit charge experiences unit force.

The permittivity ϵ is unity for a vacuum and approximately unity for air.

The *absolute electromagnetic system* (e.m.u.) is based on the c.g.s. system with $\mu = 1$ for a vacuum.

Unit magnetic pole is defined as that pole which placed at unit distance from a like pole of equal strength repels it with a force of 1 dyne.

Unit *current* is defined as that current, when flowing in a circular arc of length 1 cm., radius 1 cm., exerts unit force on a unit pole at the centre of the arc.

Dimensions of Electrical and Magnetic Quantities

Quantity	Dimensions: electrostatic system	Dimensions: electromagnetic system	Number of e.s. units in 1 e.m. unit
Force	LMT^{-2}		1
Energy or work	L^2MT^{-2}		1
Power	L^2MT^{-3}		1
Charge	$\epsilon_0^{\frac{1}{2}}L^{\frac{3}{2}}M^{\frac{1}{2}}T^{-1}$	$\mu_0^{-\frac{1}{2}}L^{\frac{1}{2}}M^{\frac{1}{2}}$	3×10^{10}
Current	$\epsilon_0^{\frac{1}{2}}L^{\frac{3}{2}}M^{\frac{1}{2}}T^{-2}$	$\mu_0^{-\frac{1}{2}}L^{\frac{1}{2}}M^{\frac{1}{2}}T^{-1}$	3×10^{10}
E.m.f., p.d. or potential	$\epsilon_0^{-\frac{1}{2}}L^{\frac{1}{2}}M^{\frac{1}{2}}T^{-1}$	$\mu_0^{\frac{1}{2}}L^{\frac{3}{2}}M^{\frac{1}{2}}T^{-2}$	$\frac{1}{3 \times 10^{10}}$
Resistance	$\epsilon_0^{-1}L^{-1}T$	μ_0LT^{-1}	$\frac{1}{9 \times 10^{20}}$
Inductance	$\epsilon_0^{-1}L^{-1}T^2$	μ_0L	$\frac{1}{9 \times 10^{20}}$
Capacitance	ϵ_0L	$\mu_0^{-1}L^{-1}T^2$	9×10^{20}
Magnetic flux	$\epsilon_0^{-\frac{1}{2}}L^{\frac{1}{2}}M^{\frac{1}{2}}$	$\mu_0^{\frac{1}{2}}L^{\frac{3}{2}}M^{\frac{1}{2}}T^{-1}$	$\frac{1}{3 \times 10^{10}}$
Magnetic flux density	$\epsilon_0^{-\frac{1}{2}}L^{-\frac{3}{2}}M^{\frac{1}{2}}$	$\mu_0^{\frac{1}{2}}L^{-\frac{1}{2}}M^{\frac{1}{2}}T^{-1}$	$\frac{1}{3 \times 10^{10}}$
Magnetic intensity	$\epsilon_0^{\frac{1}{2}}L^{\frac{1}{2}}M^{\frac{1}{2}}T^{-2}$	$\mu_0^{-\frac{1}{2}}L^{-\frac{1}{2}}M^{\frac{1}{2}}T^{-1}$	3×10^{10}
M.m.f.	$\epsilon_0^{\frac{1}{2}}L^{\frac{3}{2}}M^{\frac{1}{2}}T^{-2}$	$\mu_0^{-\frac{1}{2}}L^{\frac{1}{2}}M^{\frac{1}{2}}T^{-1}$	3×10^{10}
Pole Strength	$\epsilon_0^{-\frac{1}{2}}L^{\frac{1}{2}}M^{\frac{1}{2}}$	$\mu_0^{\frac{1}{2}}L^{\frac{3}{2}}M^{\frac{1}{2}}T^{-1}$	$\frac{1}{3 \times 10^{10}}$
Reluctance	ϵ_0LT^{-2}	$\mu_0^{-1}L^{-1}$	9×10^{20}

Practical units. These are chiefly the ampere, ohm, volt, coulomb, henry, farad, watt and joule. The system coming into general use today is the *rationalized metre-kilogram-second* (*m.k.s.*) *system.* The relations between this and the e.s.u. and e.m.u. systems are given below.

Rationalized m.k.s. units and the absolute systems.

Quantity	Name of Rationalised m.k.s. unit	Name of unit in absolute c.g.s. system	Number of c.g.s. e.m.u. in 1 m.k.s. unit	Number of c.g.s. e.s.u. in 1 m.k.s. unit	Notes
Length	metre	centimetre	100		These are commonly used multiples of the centimetre and the gram.
Mass	kilogram	gram	1,000		
Time	second	second	1		
Force	newton or joule/metre	dyne	10^5		A force of 1 newton is equivalent to rather less than $\frac{1}{4}$ lb wt.
Torque	newton at 1 metre	dyne-centimetre	10^7		
Energy	joule	erg	10^7		
Power	watt	erg/second	10^7		
Charge	coulomb		10^{-1}		
Current	ampere		10^{-1}		
E.m.f. or p.d. or potential	volt	erg (e.s. system)	10^8	$\frac{1}{300}$	
Resistance	ohm		10^9		
Inductance	henry	centimetre (e.m. system)	10^9		
Capacitance	farad	centimetre (e.s. system)		9×10^{11}	

Electric flux	coulomb			$3 \times 10^9 \times 4\pi$	In the rationalised m.k.s. system the total electric flux across a closed surface is numerically equal to the charge enclosed. (The corresponding definition in the e.s.c.g.s. system is here taken as $4\pi \times$ the charge enclosed)
Electric flux density	coulomb/metre^2			$3 \times 10^5 \times 4\pi$	
Electric intensity or electric force or electric field strength	volt/metre			$\frac{1}{3} \times 10^{-4}$	
Magnetic flux	weber	maxwell (e.m. system)	10^8		
Magnetic flux density	weber/metre^2	gauss (e.m. system)	10		
Pole strength	weber				In the rationalised m.k.s. system the magnetic pole strength is numerically equal to the flux from the pole.
Magnetic intensity or magnetic force	ampere/metre	oersted (e.m. system)	$\frac{4\pi}{1{,}000}$		An alternative name for the m.k.s. unit is the ampere-turn/metre.
M.m.f.	ampere	gilbert (e.m. system)	$\frac{4\pi}{10}$		
Reluctance	ampere-turn/weber		$\frac{4\pi}{10^9}$		
Permeance	henry or weber/ ampere-turn		$\frac{10^9}{4\pi}$		Permeance is the reciprocal of reluctance.

Permeability of vacuum $\mu_0 = 4\pi \times 10^{-7}$ henry/metre in the rationalised m.k.s. system (by definition)
Permittivity of vacuum $\varepsilon_0 = 8{\cdot}85 \times 10^{-12}$ farad/metre in the rationalised m.k.s. system (by measurement)

9.11. Definitions in the m.k.s. system and laboratory standards*

The International Committee on Weights and Measures defines the *ampere* as the steady current which, flowing through two parallel straight long thin conductors placed *in vacuo* 1 metre apart produces between these conductors a force of 2×10^{-7} newtons (1 newton = 1 kg. m. sec.$^{-2}$) per metre of length. Alternatively, 1 ampere is a flow of electricity of 1 coulomb sec.$^{-1}$, a coulomb being defined as the charge that deposits $1{\cdot}118\times10^{-3}$ gram of silver (or liberates $1{\cdot}04\times10^{-5}$ gram of hydrogen) in its passage through a silver (or water) voltameter under specified conditions.

Potential difference (p.d.) is measured in *volts* (V), the quotient of the energy (W) expended between two points in a current, and the quantity of electricity flowing (Q)

$$V=W/Q \text{ or } W=VQ \quad (\text{joules}=\text{volts}\times\text{coulombs})$$

Absolute potential at a point is the p.d. between that point and some specified zero, such as the Earth.

Alternatively, in terms of power (P) and current (I)

$$P=VI \quad (\text{watts}=\text{volts}\times\text{amps})$$

Electromotive force (e.m.f.), also measured in volts, is the total p.d. available for circulating electricity in a current. *Back e.m.f.* is defined as the ratio

$$\frac{\text{rate of conversion of energy into a particular form}}{\text{current flowing}}.$$

Resistance (R) is measured in *ohms* (Ω). If Ohm's law holds,

$$R=V/I$$

The laboratory standard for the ohm is the resistance at 0° C. of a column of mercury, constant cross-section, length 106·3 cm., mass 14·4521 g.

Resistivity (ρ) is measured in ohm-metres (Ωm) and defined by

$$\rho=RA/l,$$

where A is the cross-section and l is the length of the specimen.

Magnetic flux (ϕ) is measured in volt-seconds or *webers* (Wb). The definition depends on Faraday's law, that for a circuit in a varying magnetic field, the product of the induced voltage and the time taken for a specified change is independent of the rate of change. The magnetic flux is $\int V\,dt$, and since an increasing flux is associated with

* Based upon *The Teaching of Electricity*, Science Masters Association, 1954.

an induced e.m.f. that opposes the increase, the negative sign is introduced,

i.e. $$\phi = -\int V\,dt \text{ or } V = -d\phi/dt.$$

Magnetic flux density or magnetic induction (B), measured in volt-sec. m.$^{-2}$ (Wb m.$^{-2}$), is defined by

$$B = \frac{d\phi}{dA} \text{ or } \phi = \int B dA,$$

where dA is the area of an imaginary small surface surrounding the point.

Magnetizing force (H) is measured in amp turns per metre, the current flowing around unit length of a long solenoid or the surface density of the current.

$$H = NI/l,$$

e.g. the value of H at the centre of a circular coil of N turns of radius r is $NI/2r$, where I is the current flowing.

Permeability (μ) is measured in volt-sec. (amp m.)$^{-1}$ or henry per metre (H m.$^{-1}$) and defined by

$$\mu = B/H.$$

The permeability of a vacuum is μ_0 (see below). *Relative permeability* is the ratio of the permeability of the medium and that of a vacuum and is thus a pure number.

Inductance (L = self inductance, M = mutual inductance) is measured in henries.

$$L = V \div \left(\frac{dI}{dt}\right); \; 1 \text{ henry} = \frac{1 \text{ volt}}{1 \text{ amp-sec.}^{-1}} = 1 \text{ volt-sec. amp}^{-1},$$

i.e. the e.m.f. induced in a secondary circuit by unit rate of change of current in the primary circuit.

Electric field intensity (E) is measured in volts m.$^{-1}$ and defined by

$$E = -dV/dx$$

where x is the direction of the field and V is the potential function.

Electric displacement density (D) is measured in coulomb m.$^{-2}$ and defined as the vector of magnitude equal to the limiting value of the ratio

$$\frac{\text{charge displaced across an imaginary small surface perpendicular to the surface}}{\text{area of the surface}}$$

Its direction is that of the field.

Permittivity (ϵ), measured in farad m.$^{-1}$, is defined by $\epsilon = D/E$. The permittivity of a vacuum is ϵ_0. Relative permittivity, a pure number, is defined as the ratio of the permittivity of a vacuum and that of a medium (see below).

Capacitance (C) is measured in farads (practically in microfarads, μF, and in picofarads (pF) = micromicrofarads), defined by the relation

$$C = Q/V \text{ or } 1 \text{ farad} = 1 \text{ coulomb volt}^{-1}.$$

Magnetic dipole moment (M) is measured in weber-metres. A coil in which a current is flowing exhibits a torque in a magnetic field (e.g. the ordinary galvanometer).

$$M = \text{torque}/H.$$

Pole strength (m), measured in webers, is defined by the ratio

$$m = \frac{\text{magnetic dipole moment}}{\text{distance between poles}} = \frac{M}{l}.$$

Intensity of magnetization (J) is measured in webers (metres)$^{-2}$ and defined by the ratio

$$J = \frac{\text{magnetic moment}}{\text{volume}}.$$

Magnetic area moment, measured in (ampere turns) (metre)^2, is the quotient

$$(\text{maximum torque}) \div B.$$

Numerical relations

1 joule $= 10^7$ erg $= 0{\cdot}2389$ g. cal; 1 watt $= 1$ joule sec.$^{-1}$; 1 horse-power $= 746$ watts; 1 kilowatt-hour = energy supplied when volts $\times$ amps $\times$ hours $= 1000$.

Notes on the relations between the c.g.s. and m.k.s. system

(i) The main difficulty in using the m.k.s. system after becoming accustomed to the c.g.s. system lies in the values chosen for the permeability (μ_0) and the permittivity (ϵ_0) of empty space. In the c.g.s. system $\mu_0 = 1$, in m.k.s. $\mu_0 = 4\pi \times 10^{-7}$ newtons amp^{-2}. Also newtons amp^{-2} = joules amp^{-2} m.$^{-1}$ = watt-sec. amp^{-2} m.$^{-1}$ = (volt-sec. m.$^{-2}$) $\div$ (amp m.$^{-1}$), the units of B/H. In the c.g.s. system $\epsilon_0 = 1$ in e.s.u. and $\epsilon_0 = c^{-2}$ (c = velocity of light) in e.m.u. In m.k.s. the value is $\epsilon_0 = 4\pi \times 10^{-7}$ volt-sec. (amp m.)$^{-1} \simeq 10^{-9}/(36\pi)$ farad m.$^{-1} = 8{\cdot}854 \times 10^{-12}$ farad m.$^{-1}$.

(ii) To change from the c.g.s. to the rationalized m.k.s. system, the rule is: write the formula with the permeability and permittivity included (these are often omitted because their values are unity) and replace μ by $\mu/4\pi$ and ϵ by $4\pi\epsilon$.

Examples

(*a*) Electric field intensity from a point charge Q in a medium of permittivity ϵ:

c.g.s. expression $Q/\epsilon r^2$

m.k.s. expression $Q/4\pi\epsilon r^2$.

(*b*) Magnetizing force inside a long solenoid of N turns, current I. The c.g.s. expression is often written as $H=4\pi NI$, but the rationalized m.k.s. expression is $H=NI$, according to the above rules.

(iii) In the rationalized m.k.s. system, a useful mnemonic for the appearance of π in the formulae is as follows: π does not appear in "plane" formulae, $1/(2\pi)$ appears in "cylindrical" formulae, $1/(4\pi)$ appears in "spherical" formulae.

Example

The field above an infinite plane of surface charge density Q is given by $E=Q/\epsilon$ m.k.s.; that near a long line, linear density of charge Q is $E=Q/(2\pi\epsilon r)$ m.k.s. and that surrounding a point charge Q is $E=Q/(4\pi\epsilon r^2)$ m.k.s.

9.2. Elementary formulae of electrical circuits

It is assumed that the elements of the circuit can be "lumped" i.e. a circuit consists of a resistance R, a capitance C and an inductance L. The dimensions of the circuit must be small compared with the ratio c/ω, where c is the velocity of light and ω is the frequency of the alternating current.

The impedance Z between two points is defined by

$$\text{impedance}=\frac{\text{voltage drop}}{\text{current}}=\frac{\delta V}{I}.$$

Ohm's law. In constant physical conditions, the ratio $\delta V/I$ is constant for any particular conductor, i.e. depends only on the form, dimensions and physical condition of the conductor. The constant value is called the *resistance*. Metals and electrolytes obey Ohm's law.

Circuit elements in series: $Z=Z_1+Z_2$.

Circuit elements in parallel: $1/Z=1/Z_1+1/Z_2$.

Capacitors (condensers). A capacitor is defined as the combination of two insulated separated conductors bearing an equal and opposite charge. The capacitance of a single conductor is the limiting value obtained as the separation becomes infinite.

Connected in parallel: $C=C_1+C_2$.

Connected in series: $1/C=1/C_1+1/C_2$.

Kirchhoff's rules. (i) At a junction, the algebraic sum of the currents flowing towards the junction equals the sum of the currents flowing away from it. (ii) In any closed current, the algebraic sum of the voltage drops across the elements is zero.

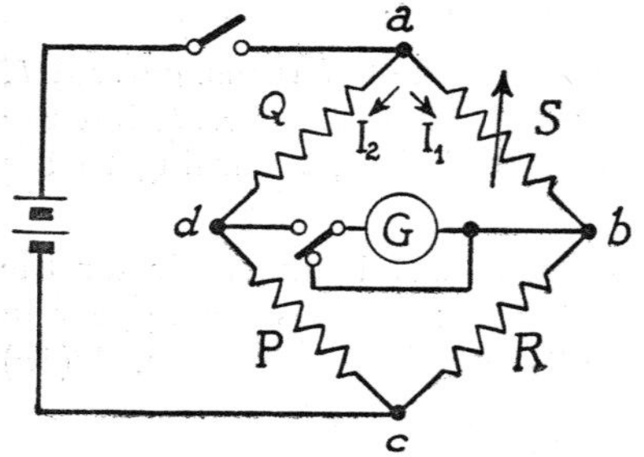

Wheatstone Bridge

Wheatstone bridge. S=standard resistance; R=unknown resistance; P and Q the ratio arms.

$$R=SP/Q.$$

Carey Foster bridge. P and Q nominally equal; l_1 and l_2 the positions of the slider for successive tests with R and S interchanged.

$$S-R=(l_1-l_2)r$$

where r is the resistance per unit length of the slide wire.

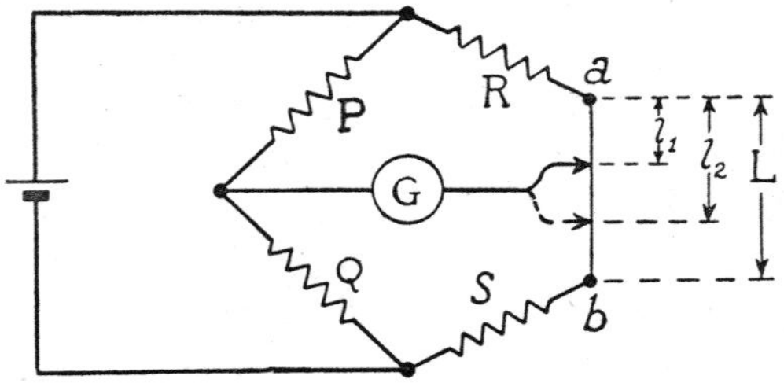

Carey Foster Slide-wire Bridge

9.21. Alternating currents

Inductance. Inductance (L) is proportional to the e.m.f. divided by the rate of change of current (dI/dt) (Faraday's law). The direction of the induced e.m.f. is such that the induced current produces a force opposing the motion (Lenz's law).

Inductances in series: $L=L_1+L_2$.

Inductances in parallel: $1/L=1/L_1+1/L_2$.

Root-mean-square (r.m.s.) values. If $I=I_D+I_0\sin\omega t$, the r.m.s. value of $I(\bar{I})$ is $\sqrt{(I_D{}^2+\frac{1}{2}I_0{}^2)}$. If $I_D=0$, i.e. current is a pure sine wave, without d.c. component, $\bar{I}\simeq 0{\cdot}707I_0$. The average value of the current per half-cycle is approximately $0{\cdot}637I_0$.

Circuit containing resistance, capacitance and inductance in series. Consider the alternating e.m.f. $E_0 \cos \omega t$ as the real part of the vector $E_0 e^{i\omega t}$ where $i=\sqrt{-1}$.

The e.m.f. equation is

$$L\frac{dI}{dt}+RI+\frac{1}{C}\int I dt=E_0 e^{i\omega t},$$

which yields a transient and a steady state solution.

The steady current is given by

$$I=\frac{E_0 \cos(\omega t-\theta)}{\sqrt{\left\{\left(L\omega-\frac{1}{C\omega}\right)^2+R^2\right\}}},$$

where $\tan\theta=\left(L\omega-\frac{1}{C\omega}\right)\Big/R$. The impedance Z of the circuit is

$$Z=\sqrt{\left\{\left(L\omega-\frac{1}{C\omega}\right)^2+R^2\right\}}.$$

The resonant frequency is $\omega=1/\sqrt{(CL)}$, when $I=(E_0/R)\cos\omega t$, and the circuit behaves as if resistance alone enters. The fraction $L\omega/R$ is usually denoted by Q, and in radio practice is used as a measure of the "selectivity" of the circuit.

Capacity and resistance in parallel

$$I=\frac{E_0 \cos(\omega t+\theta)}{\sqrt{(\omega^2C^2+R^{-2})}}, \quad \tan\theta=\omega CR.$$

Resistance and inductance in parallel

$$I=\frac{E_0 \cos(\omega t+\theta)}{\sqrt{\{R^{-2}+(\omega L)^{-2}\}}}, \quad \tan\theta=R/L\omega.$$

Electrostatics

9.3. Electric field

The electric condition at a place may be defined either in terms of electric intensity E or of potential V.

Gauss' theorem

$$\int_S E\cos\theta\, ds=4\pi\Sigma Q,$$

where E is the electric intensity at any point on the closed surface S, θ is the angle between the direction of E and the normal to the surface, dS is an element of area and ΣQ represents the total charge within the surface.

Poisson's equation. If ρ is the volume density of charge in the space considered, and x, y, z are rectangular co-ordinates, since $E=-\nabla V$, it follows that

$$\nabla^2 V=\frac{\partial^2 V}{\partial x^2}+\frac{\partial^2 V}{\partial y^2}+\frac{\partial^2 V}{\partial z^2}=-\frac{\rho}{\epsilon}\text{ m.k.s.}=-\frac{4\pi\rho}{\epsilon}\text{ e.s.u.}$$

In polar co-ordinates, r, θ, ϕ, Poisson's equation is

$$\frac{1}{r^2}\left\{r\frac{\partial^2(Vr)}{\partial r^2}+\frac{1}{\sin\theta}\frac{\partial}{\partial\theta}\left(\frac{\partial V}{\partial\theta}\sin\theta\right)+\frac{1}{\sin^2\theta}\frac{\partial^2 V}{\partial\phi^2}\right\}=-\frac{\rho}{\epsilon}\text{ m.k.s.}$$
$$=-\frac{4\pi\rho}{\epsilon}\text{ e.s.u.}$$

In cylindrical co-ordinates r, θ, z, the equation becomes

$$\frac{1}{r}\frac{\partial}{\partial r}\left(r\frac{\partial V}{\partial r}\right)+\frac{1}{r^2}\frac{\partial^2 V}{\partial\theta^2}+\frac{\partial^2 V}{\partial z^2}=-\frac{\rho}{\epsilon}\text{ m.k.s.}=-\frac{4\pi\rho}{\epsilon}\text{ e.s.u.}$$

9.4. Fields of simple charge distributions

(i) For a point distant r from a positive charge Q, Coulomb's law gives

$$E=\frac{Q}{4\pi\epsilon r^2}\text{ m.k.s.}=\frac{Q}{\epsilon r^2}\text{ e.s.u.}$$

$$V=\frac{Q}{4\pi\epsilon r}\text{ m.k.s.}=\frac{Q}{\epsilon r}\text{ e.s.u.}$$

(ii) Long line, linear density of charge Q.

$$E=\frac{Q}{2\pi\epsilon r}\text{ m.k.s.}\quad=\frac{2Q}{\epsilon r}\text{ e.s.u.}$$

$$V=\frac{Q\ln r}{2\pi\epsilon}\text{ m.k.s.}=\frac{2Q\ln r}{\epsilon}\text{ e.s.u.}$$

(iii) Infinite plane, surface charge density Q.

$$E=\frac{Q}{\epsilon}\text{ m.k.s.}\quad=\frac{4\pi Q}{\epsilon}\text{ e.s.u.}$$

$$V=\frac{Qr}{\epsilon}\text{ m.k.s.}=\frac{4\pi Qr}{\epsilon}\text{ e.s.u.}$$

(iv) Sphere, total charge Q, radius a.

$$E=\frac{Q}{4\pi\epsilon r^2}\ (r\geqslant a)\text{ and }\frac{Q}{4\pi\epsilon a^2}\ (r\leqslant a)\text{ m.k.s.}$$

$$=\frac{Q}{\epsilon r^2}\quad(r\geqslant a)\text{ and }\frac{Q}{\epsilon a^2}\quad(r\leqslant a)\text{ e.s.u.}$$

$$V = \frac{Q}{4\pi\epsilon r} \quad (r \geqslant a) \text{ and } \frac{Q}{4\pi\epsilon a} \quad (r \leqslant a) \text{ m.k.s.}$$

$$= \frac{Q}{\epsilon r} \quad (r \geqslant a) \text{ and } \frac{Q}{\epsilon a} \quad (r \leqslant a) \text{ e.s.u.}$$

The force on a charge Q in a field of intensity E is QE m.k.s. The force exerted by one point charge Q_1 on another Q_2, distant r away is given by

$$F = \frac{Q_1 Q_2}{4\pi\epsilon r^2} \text{ m.k.s.} = \frac{Q_1 Q_2}{\epsilon r^2} \text{ e.s.u.}$$

Electric doublet of strength μ. The potential V is

$$V = \frac{\mu x}{4\pi(x^2+y^2+z^2)^{3/2}} = \frac{\mu \cos\theta}{4\pi r^2} \text{ m.k.s.}$$

$$= \frac{\mu x}{(x^2+y^2+z^2)^{3/2}} = \frac{\mu \cos\theta}{r^2} \text{ e.s.u.}$$

where (x, y, z) are rectangular co-ordinates and (r, θ) polar co-ordinates.

9.41. Capacitors (condensers)

If δV is the p.d. between insulated conductors bearing equal and opposite charges Q, the capacitance C is given by $C = Q/\delta V$.

Simple capacitors

(i) Parallel plate, area A, separation d, $A > d^2$.

$$C = \frac{A\epsilon}{d} \text{ m.k.s.} = \frac{A\epsilon}{4\pi d} \text{ e.s.u.}$$

(ii) Concentric circular cylinders, length l, radii r_1, r_2, $l > r_2 - r_1$.

$$C = \frac{2\pi l\epsilon}{\ln(r_1/r_2)} \text{ m.k.s.} = \frac{l\epsilon}{2\ln(r_1/r_2)} \text{ e.s.u.}$$

(iii) Concentric spheres, radii r_1 and r_2.

$$C = \frac{4\pi\epsilon r_1 r_2}{r_2 - r_1} \text{ m.k.s.} = \frac{\epsilon r_1 r_2}{r_2 - r_1} \text{ e.s.u.}$$

(iv) Sphere remote from other conductors, radius r.

$$C = 4\pi\epsilon r \text{ m.k.s.} = \epsilon r \text{ e.s.u.}$$

(v) Circular disc, radius r.

$$C = \frac{r}{2\pi^2\epsilon} \text{ m.k.s.} = \frac{2r}{\pi\epsilon} \text{ e.s.u.}$$

(vi) Parallel circular cylinders, radii r_1, r_2, length l, separation $d<l$.

$$C=\frac{l}{8\pi\epsilon}\Big/\left\{\cosh^{-1}\left[\pm\frac{d^2-r_1^2-r_2^2}{2r_1r_2}\right]\right\} \text{ m.k.s.}$$

$$=\frac{l}{2\epsilon}\Big/\left\{\cosh^{-1}\left[\pm\frac{d^2-r_1^2-r_2^2}{2r_1r_2}\right]\right\} \text{ e.s.u.}$$

The work done in charging a condenser is $W=Q^2/2C$.

9.5. Magnetic effects of currents

Ampères law. If an element δl of a conductor carries a current I, the magnetic force at a distance r in a medium of permeability μ is

$$\delta H=\frac{\mu I \sin\theta}{4\pi r^2}\,\delta l \text{ m.k.s.}=\frac{\mu I \sin\theta}{r^2}\,\delta l \text{ e.m.u.}$$

where θ is the angle between the element δl and the radius r. This expression is to be integrated around a complete circuit to give H.

In vector notation

$$\delta\mathbf{H}=\frac{\mu I}{4\pi}\frac{\delta\mathbf{s}\times\mathbf{r}}{\mathbf{r}^3} \text{ m.k.s.}=\mu I\,\frac{\delta\mathbf{s}\times\mathbf{r}}{\mathbf{r}^3} \text{ e.m.u.}$$

Special cases

(i) Long straight conductor.

$$H=\frac{I}{2\pi r} \text{ m.k.s.}=\frac{2I}{r} \text{ e.m.u.}$$

(ii) At centre of ellipse, circumference L, area A.

$$H=\frac{IL}{4A} \text{ m.k.s.}=\frac{\pi IL}{A} \text{ e.m.u.}$$

(iii) At centre of circular coil of N turns of radius r.

$$H=\frac{IN}{2r} \text{ m.k.s.}=\frac{2\pi IN}{r} \text{ e.m.u.}$$

(iv) At point on axis of circular coil of N turns, distant x from centre.

$$H=\frac{NI\,r^2}{2(x^2+r^2)^{3/2}} \text{ m.k.s.}=\frac{2\pi NI\,r^2}{(x^2+r^2)^{3/2}} \text{ e.m.u.}$$

(v) On the axis of a solenoid of N turns.

$$H=\tfrac{1}{2}NI(\cos\theta_1-\cos\theta_2) \text{ m.k.s.}=2\pi NI(\cos\theta_1-\cos\theta_2) \text{ e.m.u.}$$

where θ_1, θ_2 are the angles between the axis and the lines joining the point to the ends of the solenoid. For a "long" solenoid, $\theta_1\simeq 0°$ and $\theta_2\simeq 180°$, when

$$H=NI \text{ m.k.s.}=4\pi NI \text{ e.m.u.}$$

Faraday's law. An e.m.f. is induced in a circuit by variations in the magnetic field threading the circuit. The induced voltage integrated over the time for a specified change of field is independent of the rate of change.

Inductance. Expressions for the self-inductance of practical arrangements are usually complicated and semi-empirical. Accurate expressions, for use in laboratory work, can be found in standard works of reference.* The expressions given below are theoretical.

(i) Circular loop, radius b, of cylinder of radius a and permeability μ' in a medium of permeability μ.

$$L = b\left[\mu\left(\ln\frac{8b}{a} - 2\right) + \frac{1}{4}\mu'\right] \text{ m.k.s.}$$

$$= 4\pi b\left[\mu\left(\ln\frac{8b}{a} - 2\right) + \frac{1}{4}\mu'\right] \text{ e.m.u.}$$

(ii) Solenoid, area A, length l, N turns per unit length.

$$L = A\mu N^2 l \text{ m.k.s.} = 4\pi A\mu N^2 l \text{ e.m.u.}$$

(This also holds approximately for a toroidal coil of circular cross-section small compared with the length of the ring.)

(iii) Parallel cylinders, radius a, separation b.

$$L = \frac{\mu}{4\pi}\left(1 + 2\ln\frac{b^2}{a^2}\right) \text{ m.k.s.} = \mu\left(1 + 2\ln\frac{b^2}{a^2}\right) \text{ e.m.u.}$$

(iv) Coaxial cable, inner radius a, outer radius b, length l.

$$L = 2l\mu \ln(b/a) \text{ m.k.s.} = 8\pi l\mu \ln(b/a) \text{ e.m.u.}$$

Mutual inductance. The maximum value produced by coupling is $\sqrt{(L_1L_2)}$. The ratio $M/\sqrt{(L_1L_2)}$ is called the *coupling factor* and is usually expressed as a percentage.

For two closely wound coils on a ring of radius a, cross-section b, of material of permeability μ,

$$M = \mu N_1 N_2[a - \sqrt{(a^2 - b^2)}] \text{ m.k.s.} = 4\pi\mu N_1 N_2[a - \sqrt{(a^2 - b^2)}] \text{ e.m.u.}$$

where N_1, N_2 are the number of turns in the two coils.

The work done in building up a current I through an inductance L is $\frac{1}{2}LI^2$.

Forces. A long straight conductor of length l carrying a current I placed at right angles to a magnetic induction B experiences a force of BlI newtons. The torque on a coil of N turns, area A, in the plane

* E.g. *Radio Engineers Handbook* by F. E. Terman, New York, 1943.

of an induction B is $BANI$. Hence in a moving-coil galvanometer the deflection θ is

$$\theta=\frac{\mu}{\tau} BANI \text{ m.k.s.}=\frac{4\pi\mu}{\tau} BANI \text{ e.m.u.}$$

where τ is the torque per radian of the suspension.

Two long straight parallel conductors carrying currents I_1 and I_2, distance d apart, exert a force on each other of $\mu I_1 I_2/2\pi d$ m.k.s.$=$ $2\mu I_1 I_2/d$ e.m.u. per unit length on each other. (This is the basis of the *ICWM* definition of the ampere quoted on p. 332.)

9.6. Electromagnetic theory

Electric displacement **D**. In a conductor, an electric field produces a flow of electrons; in an insulator, the electrons are displaced. The magnitude of the electric displacement depends on the magnitude of the field and the medium. In general,

$$\mathbf{D}=\epsilon\mathbf{E},$$

where **E** is the charge intensity and ϵ is the permittivity. In magnetism,

$$\mathbf{B}=\mu\mathbf{H},$$

where **B** is the magnetic induction, **H** the magnetic field intensity and μ the permeability. For empty space the values assigned to ϵ and μ are

$$\epsilon_0=8{\cdot}85\times10^{-12} \text{ farad (metre)}^{-1} \text{ m.k.s.}=1 \text{ c.g.s.}$$

$$\mu_0=4\pi\times10^{-7} \text{ henry (metre)}^{-1} \text{ m.k.s.}=1 \text{ c.g.s.}$$

Maxwell's equations of the electromagnetic field may be written in various equivalent forms. Let $\mathbf{I}$=electric current density, ρ=charge density, then

$$\text{curl } \mathbf{E}=-\frac{\partial\mathbf{B}}{\partial t} \text{ m.k.s.}=-\frac{1}{c}\frac{\partial\mathbf{B}}{\partial t} \text{ c.g.s.}$$

$$\text{curl } \mathbf{H}=\mathbf{I}+\frac{\partial\mathbf{D}}{\partial t} \text{ m.k.s.}=\frac{4\pi\mathbf{I}}{c}+\frac{1}{c}\frac{\partial\mathbf{D}}{\partial t} \text{ c.g.s.}$$

$$\text{div } \mathbf{D}=\rho \text{ m.k.s.}=4\pi\rho \text{ c.g.s.}$$

$$\text{div } \mathbf{B}=0.$$

These equations, together with the equation of conservation of charge

$$\text{div } \mathbf{I}+\frac{\partial\rho}{\partial t}=0,$$

determine (with suitable boundary conditions) the electrical and magnetic fields.

Poynting's theorem. The flux of electromagnetic energy is given by

$$\mathbf{E}\times\mathbf{H} \text{ m.k.s.} = \frac{c}{4\pi}(\mathbf{E}\times\mathbf{H}) \text{ c.g.s.}$$

evaluated across unit area normal to the direction of flow.

The electromagnetic wave is transverse, with the electric and magnetic vectors normal to the direction of propagation. The usual convention is to take Oy to be the direction of the electric vector $\mathbf{E}$, so that $\mathbf{E}$ and $\mathbf{H}$ are both in the plane of the wave and normal to each other.

For a sinusoidal wave form,

$$E_y = E_0 \sin 2\pi \left(\frac{x}{\lambda} - \frac{t}{\tau}\right),$$

$$H_z = H_0 \sin 2\pi \left(\frac{x}{\lambda} - \frac{t}{\tau}\right),$$

where E_0, H_0 are the amplitudes, λ is wavelength and τ is the periodic time. The energy of the wave is

$$\frac{E_0 H_0}{2c} \text{ m.k.s.} = \frac{E_0 H_0}{4\pi c} \text{ c.g.s. per unit volume}$$

= pressure exerted on unit area of an absorbing surface ("pressure of light"). For details of the fields produced by various arrangements of transmitting antenna (aerials) reference should be made to specialized reference works.*

9.7. Magnetization

J is measured by

$$J = B - \mu_0 H \text{ m.k.s.} = \frac{1}{4\pi}(B - \mu_0 H) \text{ c.g.s.}$$

and *magnetic susceptibility* κ by

$$\mu_0 \kappa = J/H \text{ m.k.s. and c.g.s.}$$

Ferromagnetic substances (iron, cobalt, nickel and certain alloys) are easily magnetized and have high values of μ. Other substances are paramagnetic ($\kappa > 0$) or diamagnetic ($\kappa < 0$).

Paramagnetism. The Langevin formula for the magnetic moment M per unit volume is

$$M = \mu N L\left(\frac{\mu H}{kT}\right),$$

* E.g. *Radio Engineers Handbook* by F. E. Terman, New York, 1943.

where N=number of atoms or molecules per unit volume, L is Langevin's function $L(x)=\coth x-x^{-1}$, T is absolute temperature and μ is the magnetic dipole moment.

If $\mu H/kT \ll 1$ (weak fields), the susceptibility is given by

$$\kappa=N\mu^2/3kT.$$

This is Curie's law, that paramagnetic susceptibility varies inversely as the absolute temperature. The quantity $N\mu^2/3k$ is called the *Curie constant.*

Ferromagnetism. If the total effective field is

$$H'=H+\beta M$$

because of the molecular field (proportional to the intensity of magnetization), the *Curie temperature* T_c, below which spontaneous magnetization (with $H=0$) is possible is $N\beta\mu^2/3k$. For $T>T_c$ the susceptibility is given by

$$\kappa=\frac{N\mu^2}{3k(T-T_c)}\,.$$

9.8. Thermoelectricity

Seebeck effect. When a circuit is made of two different metals, with the junctions maintained at different temperatures, a current flows.

Peltier effect. When a current flows across the junction of two different metals, a quantity of heat, proportional to the total charge crossing the junction, is evolved or absorbed.

$$\text{Heat evolved}=I^2R+\pi I,$$

where π is the *Peltier coefficient.*

The *Thomson effect* associates temperature gradient with potential gradient. If two points differ in absolute temperature by δT, the e.m.f. is $\sigma\delta T$, where σ is the *Thomson coefficient.*

In a complete circuit the e.m.f. is

$$\int\left\{\frac{d\pi}{dT}-(\sigma_1-\sigma_2)\right\}dT.$$

Thermoelectric power is defined to be dE/dT, where E=e.m.f. The following relations hold:

$$\pi=T\frac{dE}{dT}\,.$$

$$\sigma_1-\sigma_2=T\frac{d^2E}{dT^2}\,.$$

9.9. Electrolysis

Faraday's laws

(i) The mass of a given substance liberated at an electrode is proportional to the quantity of electricity (current × time) passing through the electrode.

(ii) The masses of different elements liberated by the same quantity of electricity are proportional to their chemical equivalents.

Note.

The *chemical equivalent* is the number of grams of the element which will combine with or replace 8 grams of oxygen or 1·008 grams of hydrogen. Chemical equivalent = atomic weight ÷ valency.

The *electrochemical equivalent* is the weight of the element liberated or deposited by 1 coulomb of electricity.

The *faraday* is the amount of electricity carried by the atoms in the gram-equivalent (equivalent expressed in grams) of a univalent element, and equals 96493·7 coulombs.

Ionic mobilities. The ions in an electrolyte move with speeds of the order of 10^{-4} cm. sec.$^{-1}$ per unit p.d. If v = speed of positive ions and u = speed of negative ions in a given electric field, the ratio $v/(u+v)$ is called the *transport ratio.*

The *equivalent conductivity* λ is defined to be conductivity ÷ concentration.

The *degree of dissociation* γ is defined as

$$\gamma = \frac{\text{number of dissociated molecules}}{\text{total number of molecules}}.$$

Arrennius theory is that $\gamma = \lambda_c/\lambda_\infty$, where λ_∞ is the limiting equivalent conductivity at infinite dilution (complete dissociation).

Reversible cells. Let T = absolute temperature of the cell, E the e.m.f., H the work equivalent of the chemical reaction when unit charge passes through the cell. Helmholtz's equation is

$$E = H + T\frac{dE}{dT}.$$

Ostwald's law for weak electrolytes. At concentration c,

$$c\lambda_c^2 = \text{constant} \times \lambda_\infty(\lambda_\infty - \lambda_c).$$

The *hydrogen-ion concentration,* a measure of the acidity of a solution, is defined to be the number of grams of hydrogen ions per litre of solution. The numerical measure is $p_H = \log_{10}(1/H^\bullet)$, where $H^\bullet$ is the hydrogen-ion concentration.

CHAPTER 10

ELECTRONICS

THE term *electronics* usually comprises the science of circuits incorporating electronic valves (or tubes), which in turn depend for their action on the control of electrons emitted from suitable sources, usually heated metal. The electron is the atom of electricity, having a (rest) mass of about 9×10^{-28} grams and a negative charge of $4{\cdot}8 \times 10^{-10}$ e.s.u. $= 1{\cdot}6 \times 10^{-19}$ coulomb. The unit of energy is the *electron-volt* (e.v.), defined as the increase of energy by, or the work done on, an electron when moving through a p.d. of 1 volt.

$$1 \text{ e.v.} = 1{\cdot}6 \times 10^{-12} \text{ erg} = 1{\cdot}6 \times 10^{-19} \text{ joule.}$$

10.1. Electronic emission

Electrons are usually emitted from metals. The *net work function* ϕ is the energy that an electron must have to liberate itself from the parent metal. Typical values are:

Metal	ϕ *(e.v.)*
caesium	1·75
copper	4·2
thorium	3·4
tungsten	4·55
platinum	6·15

Electron emission may be brought about by (*a*) heat, (*b*) absorption of electromagnetic energy (photo-electric effect), (*c*) bombardment of metal by electrons or ions (secondary emission), (*d*) action of an external electric field (auto-electronic or field emission).

10.2. Mass-energy relation

As a consequence of the theory of relativity, the total energy of a mass m moving at speed v is divided into rest energy plus kinetic energy. The mass m is given by

$$m = \frac{m_0}{\sqrt{(1 - v^2/c^2)}},$$

where m_0 is the rest mass and c is the speed of light. Approximately,

$$mc^2 = m_0c^2 + \tfrac{1}{2}m_0v^2$$

$$\text{total energy} = \text{rest energy} + \text{kinetic energy.}$$

(The ratio m/m_0 increases as v increases, but differs inappreciably from unity unless v exceeds $0{\cdot}01c$, and is only about $1{\cdot}15$ when $v = \frac{1}{2}c$.) The correction is sometimes necessary when dealing with accelerated electrons.

10.3. Energy distribution

In a perfect gas, the Maxwellian law states that of the total number of molecules N, the number δN having energies between W and $W+\delta W$, is

$$\delta N = \frac{2N}{\pi^{1/2}(kT)^{3/2}} W^{1/2} e^{-W/kT} \delta W,$$

where T is absolute temperature and k is Boltzmann's constant $= 1{\cdot}38 \times 10^{-23}$ joule °K.$^{-1}$.

The Fermi-Dirac distribution (obtained by the application of quantum mechanics to electrons in a metal) is

$$\delta N = \frac{3N}{2W_0^{3/2}} \cdot \frac{W^{1/2}}{e^{(W-W_0)/kT}+1} \delta W,$$

where

$$W_0 = \frac{h^2}{2m}\left[\frac{3N}{8\pi}\right]^{2/3}$$

and h is Planck's constant $= 6{\cdot}63 \times 10^{-34}$ joule cycle^{-1} and m is the mass of an electron. N, measured in electrons m^{-3}, varies slowly with temperature, and for practical purposes may be regarded as the (constant) density of atoms in the metal. The Maxwell and Fermi-Dirac formulae give the same distribution for high energy electrons, but differ in the total fraction of electrons involved.

10.4. Thermionic current

The Richardson-Dushmann equation for the electronic current produced by unit area of a metal at T° K. is

$$I = 1{\cdot}204 \times 10^6\, T^2 \exp(-1{\cdot}6 \times 10^4 \phi/T) \text{ amp m}^{-2},$$

Typical practical values, in terms of a given heat power input, are

pure tungsten wire:	5	ma cm.$^{-2}$ watt^{-1}
thoriated tungsten wire:	50	,,
directly-heated oxide-coated wire:	500	,,
indirectly-heated oxide-coated wire:	100	,,

Shot noise. A resistance at T° K. produces a noise power $P = kTB$, where k is Boltzmann's constant and B is the range of frequencies (band width) involved. This noise acts as a limiting factor in the use of thermionic devices for measurements.

10.5. Thermionic valves (or tubes)

A thermionic valve consists essentially of a system of electrodes operating in a high vacuum or, more rarely, in gas at low pressure. The essential electrodes are: (*a*) the cathode, or source of electrons; (*b*) one or more control electrodes or "grids"; and (*c*) the anode, or "plate", kept at a high positive potential with respect to the cathode. The cathode may be either directly or indirectly heated by an electric current derived from the low-tension source. The anode is connected to the high-tension source.

Langmuir-Child law. In a simple parallel-plate *diode* (cathode+ anode, no grid), the current flowing in the anode current is

$$I_a = 2{\cdot}34 \times 10^{-6}\, V^{3/2} d^{-2} \text{ amp (area)}^{-1},$$

where V is the p.d. between anode and cathode, d = distance between anode and cathode. For the practical arrangement of a thin heated wire (cathode) inside a cylinder of diameter a (anode), the relation is

$$I_a = 1{\cdot}508 \times 10^{-5}\, V^{3/2} a^{-1} \text{ amp (unit length)}^{-1}.$$

For a *triode* (cathode, control grid, anode) the current is given by a relation of the type

$$I_a = \text{constant } (V_g + V_a/\mu)^{3/2},$$

where V_g = grid potential, V_a = anode potential, μ = amplification factor of the valve, defined by

$$\mu = \frac{\text{rate of change of anode current with grid voltage}}{\text{rate of change of anode current with anode voltage}}.$$

The *mutual conductance* g_m is defined by

$$g_m = \frac{\delta I_a}{\delta V_g} = \frac{\text{change in anode current}}{\text{change in grid voltage}} \text{ for } V_a = \text{constant}.$$

The mutual conductance is specified for a given value of I_a.

Anode (or dynamic) resistance. r_a is defined as $\delta V_a/\delta I_a$ for V_g = constant. Thus

$$g_m = \frac{\delta I_a}{\delta V_g}, \quad \mu = +\frac{\delta V_a}{\delta V_g}, \quad r_a = +\frac{\delta V_a}{\delta I_a}$$

$$\mu = r_a g_m.$$

The *voltage amplification* in a circuit containing a load resistance R between the anode and the high-tension supply is given, for small changes in V_g, by

$$a = \frac{\mu}{1 + r_a/R},$$

i.e. the valve behaves like a generator of resistance r_a and e.m.f. $\mu\delta V_g$. If C_{kg} and C_{ka} are the inter-electrode capacities, cathode-grid and anode-cathode, respectively

$$\mu = C_{kg}/C_{ka}.$$

10.51. Harmonic distortion

Suppose a signal $A \sin 2\pi ft$, where A is the (small) amplitude of the signal and f its frequency, is applied to the grid of a valve biased (i.e. given a fixed base potential) V_{GB} volts. Further, let the *characteristic curve* (plot of I_a versus V_g) be given by the polynomial

$$I_a = a + bV_g + cV_g^2 + dV_g^3,$$

where a, b, c and d are constants. The anode current is then given by:

$I_a = a + bV_{GB} + cV^2_{GB} + dV^3_{GB} + \frac{1}{2}cA^2 + \frac{3}{4}dA^2V_{GB}$ (d.c. component)

$+A \sin 2\pi ft(b + 2cV_{GB} + 3dV^2_{GB} + \frac{3}{4}dA^2)$ (undistorted amplified signal)

$-\frac{1}{2}A^2 \cos 4\pi ft(c + 3dV_{GB})$ (2nd harmonic distortion)

$-\frac{1}{4}dA^3 \sin 6\pi ft$ (3rd harmonic distortion)

10.52. Multi-grid valves

In a multi-grid valve, such as a pentode, the cathode electronic current depends upon the voltage V_{g_1} impressed on the first (control) grid if the potential of the screen-grid is maintained at a constant value. Only a portion of this current reaches the anode, the fraction depending upon the potential V_{g_3} of the suppressor grid. The anode current I_a is then given approximately by an equation of the form

$$I_a = (a + bV_{g_1})(a' + b'V_{g_3}),$$

where the a's and b's are constants. The equation can be generalized to allow for curvature in the characteristic curves.

10.6. Cathode-ray tubes consist essentially of an electron "gun" (a device for producing and focusing a beam of electrons), horizontal and vertical deflecting plates (electrostatic or electromagnetic) and a fluorescent screen, all enclosed in a highly evacuated tube. The electrostatic deflection is given, for small deflections, approximately by

$$d \simeq \frac{1}{2}\frac{El}{V_a}\left(L + \frac{1}{2}l\right),$$

where E is the electrical intensity (volts m.$^{-1}$) between the plates (i.e. p.d. divided by the separation), l = length of plates in the axial direction,

L = distance from the deflecting field to the screen and V_a is the anode-cathode p.d. The electromagnetic deflection is given, for small deflections, approximately by

$$d \simeq \sqrt{\frac{e}{2m}} \cdot \frac{Bl}{V_a^{1/2}}\left(L+\frac{1}{2}l\right),$$

where B is the flux-density of the magnetic field. The numerical value of $\sqrt{(e/2m)}$ is about 3×10^5.

10.7. Decibel notation

Two powers P_1 and P_2 are said to differ by N bels when

$$\frac{P_1}{P_2}=10^N \text{ or } N=\log_{10}\frac{P_1}{P_2}.$$

In practice, the *decibel*, defined as one-tenth of a bel, is used. Usually, powers are compared by observing the current through a given impedance or the voltage difference across it. For an amplifier in which the input and output impedance are equal

$$P_1/P_2=(V_1/V_2)^2=(I_1/I_2)^2$$

$$N=20 \log_{10} (V_1/V_2)=20 \log_{10} (I_1/I_2) \text{ db.}$$

(*Example.* A gain of 1 db. implies a power ratio of 1·259 or a voltage ratio of 1·122.)

Taking the threshold of audibility at 1000 cycles sec.^{-1} as the zero or datum level, ordinary conversation is about 50 db. above this and the "threshold of pain" is about 120 to 130 db. above the threshold of audibility.

CHAPTER 11

HEAT

11.1. Thermometry

Relations between scales:

$$1^\circ \text{ C.} = 1{\cdot}8^\circ \text{ F.}; \quad 0^\circ \text{ C.} = 32^\circ \text{ F.}; \quad 100^\circ \text{ C.} = 212^\circ \text{ F.}$$

The fixed points are determined by the melting of ice and the boiling of pure water at 760mm. pressure.

Ice point on the absolute scale = 273·16° K.

11.2. Calorimetry

The unit of heat in the c.g.s. system is the *gram calorie* = quantity of heat required to raise 1 g. of water 1° C. The units in use are: the 15° C., 20° C., 4° C. and the mean calorie.

The *British Thermal Unit* (B.Th.U.) is the amount of heat required to raise 1 lb. of water 1° F.

$$1 \text{ B.Th.U.} = 252 \text{ cal}; \quad (15^\circ) \text{ cal} \equiv 4{\cdot}185 \text{ joules.}$$

The *specific heat* of a substance is defined to be the heat required to raise unit mass of a substance by 1 degree (sp.ht. = cal $g.^{-1}$ $deg.^{-1}$).

The *thermal capacity* of a body = mass × specific heat.

Method of mixtures. If a body of mass m and temperature θ_3 is introduced into a calorimeter of thermal capacity C to produce a temperature rise from θ_1 to a maximum of θ_2, the specific heat s of the body is

$$s = \frac{C(\theta_2 - \theta_1) + h}{m(\theta_3 - \theta_2)},$$

where h is the heat lost in the experiment.

Mechanical equivalent of heat: $J = 4{\cdot}185$ joule $\text{cal}^{-1} = 778$ ft. lb. $(\text{B.Th.U.})^{-1}$.

The *latent heats* of a substance are the quantities of heat required to bring about a change of state in 1 g. without change of temperature.

The *heat of formation* of a compound is the quantity of heat liberated or absorbed when 1 g.-molecule of the compound is formed from its elements. Hess' law is that if the reaction occurs in stages, the algebraic sum of the amounts of heat liberated or absorbed in the different stages equals the total amount of heat liberated or absorbed when the reaction is direct.

The *heat of neutralization* is the quantity of heat liberated or absorbed when 1 g.-equivalent of an acid or alkali is neutralized. For strong acids and alkalis the heat of neutralization is approximately $1 \cdot 37 \times 10^4$ cal.

11.3. Thermodynamics

The variables concerned are: pressure (p), absolute temperature (T), volume (v), energy (E), work done by system (dW), heat absorbed by system (dQ), total heat or enthalpy ($H=E+pv$), entropy (ϕ).

The specific heats of a gas are therefore

$$c_p=\left(\frac{\partial Q}{\partial T}\right)_p, \quad c_v=\left(\frac{\partial Q}{\partial T}\right)_v,$$

where the subscript denotes the variable which is maintained constant.

First law of thermodynamics:

$$dE=dQ+dW.$$

Relation between specific heats:

$$c_p-c_v=R/JM,$$

where $R/J=1 \cdot 987$ cal (deg.)$^{-1}$ and M is the molecular weight.

Isothermal expansion from volume v_1 to volume v_2:

$$\text{heat supply (thermal units)}=\frac{m}{M}\frac{R}{J}T \ln (v_2/v_1),$$

where m = mass of gas.

Adiabatic change:

$$pv^\gamma=\text{constant or } Tv^{\gamma-1}=\text{constant or } p^{\gamma-1}T^{-\gamma}=\text{constant},$$

where $\gamma=c_p/c_v$.

Equations of state:

Ideal gas: $pv=RT$.

Van der Waal's gas: $(p+av^{-2})(v-b)=RT$.

Joule-Thomson effect (porous plug experiment). The enthalpy H remains constant.

$$Jc_p\frac{\delta T}{\delta P}\simeq\frac{2a}{RT}-b.$$

The *inversion point* at which the cooling and heating effects balance is $2a/bR$. More accurately,

$$\text{Joule-Thomson coefficient}=\left(\frac{\partial T}{\partial p}\right)_H=\frac{1}{Jc_p}\left[T\left(\frac{\partial v}{\partial T}\right)_p-v\right].$$

Second law of thermodynamics

A self-acting machine cannot transfer heat continuously from a colder to a hotter body and produce no external effect.

The *efficiency* of a heat engine is defined as $\eta = W/Q_1$ = fraction of original heat converted to mechanical work.

Carnot's theorem. The maximum efficiency of any engine working between a source and a receiver at given temperatures is that of a thermodynamically-reversible engine

In the Carnot cycle the ratio (heat rejected)/(heat entry) depends on temperatures of receivers and source only. Hence the *Kelvin scale* of temperature in which the ratio of any two temperatures = (heat absorbed at 1st temp.)/(heat rejected at 2nd temp.) in a Carnot cycle. A Carnot engine with its receiver at absolute zero converts all its heat intake into useful work.

11.31. Entropy

Change in entropy is defined for a reversible process as the ratio of the quantity of heat taken up and the absolute temperature at which it is absorbed.

$$\phi_B - \phi_A = \int_A^B \frac{aQ}{T},$$

evaluated for any reversible process that brings the system from state A to state B. (The second law is equivalent to the statement that in the equation $d\phi = dQ/T$, for any reversible absorption of heat T is an integrating factor such that $d\phi$ is a perfect differential.)

Examples

(i) A body of thermal capacity W thermal units rises in temperature from T_1 to T_2

$$\Delta\phi = JW \ln (T_1/T_2).$$

(ii) Two bodies, initially at $T_0 - \theta$ and $T_0 + \theta$, placed in contact reach a common temperature T_0. The increase of entropy of the whole system is

$$\Delta\phi = JW \ln \left(\frac{T_0^2}{T_0^2 - \theta^2}\right).$$

Maxwell's equations

$$\left(\frac{\partial T}{\partial v}\right)_\phi = -\left(\frac{\partial p}{\partial \phi}\right)_v; \quad \left(\frac{\partial T}{\partial p}\right)_\phi = \left(\frac{\partial v}{\partial \phi}\right)_p;$$

$$\left(\frac{\partial p}{\partial T}\right)_v = \left(\frac{\partial \phi}{\partial v}\right)_T; \quad \left(\frac{\partial v}{\partial T}\right)_p = -\left(\frac{\partial \phi}{\partial p}\right)_T.$$

Clausius-Clapeyron equation

$$\frac{dp}{dT}=\frac{JL}{T(v_2-v_1)},$$

where v_1, v_2 are the specific volumes and L is the latent heat.

Specific heats equation. If s_1, s_2 are the specific heats in the two phases,

$$s_2-s_1=T\frac{d}{dT}\left(\frac{L}{T}\right).$$

Adiabatic stretching of a wire. If δf=increase in stress, α=coefficient of linear expansion at constant load,

$$\delta T/T=-\alpha\delta f/c_pJ.$$

11.4. Transfer of heat

Heat is transferred in three ways: (i) *conduction* (or diffusion of heat) arises from the elastic impact of molecules, without net transfer of matter; (ii) *convection* arises from the mixing of relatively large volumes of fluid, because of motion of the fluid; and (iii) *radiation* is the transference of energy by electromagnetic waves.

Conduction in a solid body

The fundamental law is that the rate of flow of heat from one place to another is proportional to the cross-sectional area perpendicular to the direction of flow and to the temperature gradient. If q be the flux of heat per unit area (cal cm.$^{-2}$ sec.$^{-1}$) and x the direction of the temperature gradient,

$$q=-k\frac{\partial T}{\partial x}.$$

The quantity k is called the *thermal conductivity*. The *thermometric conductivity* κ is defined by $\kappa=k/c\rho$, where c is the specific heat and ρ the density of the solid.

The equation of conduction is

$$\frac{\partial T}{\partial t}=\kappa\nabla^2T=\kappa\left(\frac{\partial^2T}{\partial x^2}+\frac{\partial^2T}{\partial y^2}+\frac{\partial^2T}{\partial z^2}\right)$$

in cartesian co-ordinates. In spherical polar co-ordinates r, θ, ϕ,

$$\frac{\partial T}{\partial t}=\frac{\kappa}{r^2}\left[\frac{\partial}{\partial r}\left(r^2\frac{\partial T}{\partial r}\right)+\frac{1}{\sin\theta}\frac{\partial}{\partial\theta}\left(\sin\theta\frac{\partial T}{\partial\theta}\right)+\frac{1}{\sin^2\theta}\frac{\partial^2T}{\partial\phi^2}\right)\right].$$

In cylindrical co-ordinates r, θ, z,

$$\frac{\partial T}{\partial t}=\kappa\left[\frac{\partial^2T}{\partial r^2}+\frac{1}{r}\frac{\partial T}{\partial r}+\frac{1}{r^2}\frac{\partial^2T}{\partial\theta^2}+\frac{\partial^2T}{\partial z^2}\right].$$

Simple solutions of the equation of conduction

(i) Infinite solid, initial temperature $f(x)$:

$$T=\frac{1}{2\sqrt{(\pi\kappa t)}}\int_{-\infty}^{\infty} f(\theta)\exp\left\{-\frac{(x-\theta)^2}{4\kappa t}\right\}d\theta.$$

(ii) Semi-infinite solid, initial temperature $f(x)$, zero temperature on $x=0$:

$$T=\frac{1}{2\sqrt{(\pi\kappa t)}}\int_{0}^{\infty} f(\theta)\left[\exp\left\{-\frac{(x-\theta)^2}{4\kappa t}\right\}-\exp\left\{-\frac{(x+\theta)^2}{4\kappa t}\right\}d\theta\right].$$

When $f(x)=T_0=$constant, this reduces to

$$T=T_0 \operatorname{erf}\left\{\frac{x}{2\sqrt{(\kappa t)}}\right\},$$

where erf x is the *error function* defined by

$$\operatorname{erf} x=\frac{2}{\sqrt{\pi}}\int_0^x e^{-\theta^2}\,d\theta.$$

(iii) Semi-infinite solid, surface temperature varying sinusoidally with time, $T=T_0\cos(\omega t-\phi)$:

The non-transient part of the solution is

$$T=T_0\exp\{-x\sqrt{(\omega/2\kappa)}\}\cos\{\omega t-\phi-x\sqrt{(\omega/2\kappa)}\}.$$

The amplitude of the oscillations decreases as $\exp\{-x\sqrt{(\omega/2\kappa)}\}$ and the phase lag increases as $x\sqrt{(\omega/2\kappa)}$.

(iv) Semi-infinite solid, constant flux F_0 across $x=0$:

$$T=\frac{2F_0}{k}\left[\sqrt{(\kappa t/\pi)}\exp\left(-\frac{x^2}{4\kappa t}\right)-\frac{x}{2}\left\{1-\operatorname{erf}\left(\frac{x}{2\sqrt{(\kappa t)}}\right)\right\}\right].$$

(v) Instantaneous point source of strength Q at (x', y', z')

$$T=\frac{Q}{8(\pi\kappa t)^{3/2}}\exp\left\{-\frac{(x-x')^2+(y-y')^2+(z-z')^2}{4\kappa t}\right\}.$$

(vi) Continuous point source of constant strength Q per second at (x', y', z') from $t=0$ onwards:

$$T=\frac{Q}{4\pi\kappa r}\left\{1-\operatorname{erf}\frac{r}{\sqrt{(4\kappa t)}}\right\},$$

where $r^2=(x-x')^2+(y-y')^2+(z-z')^2$. As $t\to\infty$,

$$T=\frac{Q}{4\pi\kappa r},$$

corresponding to a source which is maintained indefinitely.

11.5. Convection

Free or *natural convection* implies that the motion of the fluid in the gravitational field, which causes mixing, is maintained solely by differences in density caused by local temperature inequalities. If ΔT is the local elevation in temperature, the acceleration experienced by a particle is $g\Delta T/T_0$, where T_0 is the absolute temperature of the bulk of the fluid. If α is the coefficient of expansion, for a perfect gas $\alpha = 1/T_0$ and the acceleration is $g\alpha$.

If h is the coefficient of heat transfer by natural convection, l a characteristic length, ν the kinematic viscosity, dimensional analysis gives the relation

$$\frac{hl}{k} = \text{constant} \times \left(\frac{gl^3}{\nu^2}\frac{\Delta T}{T}\right)^n \left(\frac{\nu}{\kappa}\right)^m,$$

where n and m are undetermined indices. The equation is usually written as

$$Nu = \text{constant} \times (Gr)^n \sigma^m,$$

where $Nu = \dfrac{hl}{k}$ is the Nusselt number, $Gr = gl^3\Delta T/\nu^2 T$ is the Grashof number, $\sigma = \nu/\kappa$ is the Prandtl number.

A useful empirical formula for the rate of loss of heat per unit area (q) from a horizontal surface in air is

$$q = 6 \times 10^{-5}\Delta T^{5/4} \text{ cal cm.}^{-2} \text{ sec.}^{-1},$$

where $\Delta T°$ C. is the difference between the temperature of the hot surface and that of the air remote from the surface.

For a vertical plate, Pohlhausen's formula is

$$Nu = 0{\cdot}359(Gr)^{1/4}.$$

A continuous point source of heat in still air produces a plume in which the mean temperature excess decreases, approximately, as $z^{-3/2}$ and the vertical velocity as $z^{-1/3}$, where z is height above the source. More exact expressions have been found, but are complicated.* For a continuous line source of infinite length the excess temperature falls off as $1/z$ and the upward velocity is constant.

11.7. Forced convection implies that the motion of the fluid arises from an applied pressure gradient and that the influence of buoyancy

* See O. G. Sutton, *Micrometeorology* (1953), pp. 295-303, and W. R. Railston, *Proc. Phys. Soc. B.*, 67 (1954).

is negligible. With certain restrictions (no dissipation of energy by viscosity) the equation of conduction is

$$\frac{\partial T}{\partial t}+u\frac{\partial T}{\partial x}+v\frac{\partial T}{\partial y}+w\frac{\partial T}{\partial z}=\kappa\nabla^2 T,$$

where u, v, w are the components of fluid motion along Ox, Oy, Oz, respectively. When fluid moves slowly over a hot surface, a laminar thermal boundary layer, similar to the dynamic boundary layer (see Chapter 5), is formed. If δ is the thickness of the thermal boundary layer, l the length of the surface downstream and V the speed of the stream parallel to the surface outside the boundary layer,

$$\frac{\delta}{l}=\text{constant}\sqrt{\frac{\kappa}{lV}}.$$

The quantity Vl/κ is called the Péclet number.

If the flow is turbulent, Latzko's expression for the local rate of heat loss by forced convection from a surface extending infinitely across wind, at a distance x from the leading edge, is

$$q(x)=0{\cdot}0285\rho\, c_p\, VT_0\left(\frac{\nu}{Vx}\right)^{1/5},$$

where V and T_0 are the velocity and temperature, respectively, of the air before it meets the plane surface $x\geqslant 0$.

11.71. Lag of a thermometer

The lag coefficient λ is defined by the equation

$$\frac{dT}{dt}=-\frac{1}{\lambda}(T-T_1),$$

where T is the temperature of the thermometer when surrounded by a medium at temperature T_1. The value of λ varies with the ventilation and empirically $\lambda=K/(\rho v)^n$, where ρ is density, v is the speed of the fluid past the thermometer and K and n are constants. For a mercury-in-glass thermometer ventilated in air by a current of 15 ft. sec.$^{-1}$, λ is about 50 seconds and n is about $\frac{1}{2}$. For an electrical resistance coiled element λ is about 8 seconds and $n\simeq 0{\cdot}7$, with the same ventilation.

CHAPTER 12

KINETIC THEORY OF GASES

12.1. In its simplest form, the kinetic theory of gases assumes that molecules behave like rigid elastic spheres, radius σ, mass m, moving with average speed c.

Density $\rho = Nm/V$, where N is the number of molecules in volume V, hydrostatic pressure $p = \frac{1}{3}\rho c^2$, temperature $T = \frac{1}{3}(m/k)c^2$, where k is Boltzmann's constant $= 1{\cdot}38 \times 10^{-16}$ erg (°C.)$^{-1}$.

The equation of state for a perfect gas is

$$pV = RT = k(M/m)T,$$

where M is the mass of gas occupying volume V.

1 cm.^{3} of gas at S.T.P. (0° C., 760 mm. Hg or 1013 mb.) contains $N_A = 2{\cdot}69 \times 10^{19}$ molecules, where N_A is *Avogadro's number.*

The *molecular weight* of a gas, W, is the ratio m/m_0, where m is the mass of a molecule and $m_0 = 1{\cdot}66 \times 10^{-24}$ g. is 1/16 of the mass of the oxygen molecule (O^{16}), also called the *unit atomic mass.* W g. of a gas is called the *gram-molecule* or *mole.* This mass of gas contains $N_L = 6{\cdot}02 \times 10^{23}$ molecules, where N_L is *Loschmidt's number.*

12.2. Maxwell's velocity distribution

The number dN of molecules having speeds between c and $c+dc$ is given by

$$N\left(\frac{2m^3}{\pi k^3 T^3}\right)^{\frac{1}{2}} c^2 e^{-m^2c^2/2kT}\, dc.$$

12.3. Collisions and free paths

For a mixture of gases, with molecules of diameter σ_1, σ_2, the numbers of collisions in unit time are:

between like molecules: $$2N_1^2\sigma_1^2\left(\frac{\pi kT}{m_1}\right)^{\frac{1}{2}}$$

between unlike molecules: $$2N_1N_2\bar{\sigma}^2\left(\frac{2\pi m_0 kT}{m_1 m_2}\right)^{\frac{1}{2}},$$

where $\bar{\sigma} = \frac{1}{2}(\sigma_1 + \sigma_2)$, $m_0 = m_1 + m_2$.

Mean free path l. For a simple gas

$$l = 1/(\sqrt{2}\pi N\sigma^2).$$

For a mixture of 2 kinds of molecules

$$\frac{1}{l}=\pi\left[\sqrt{2}N_1\sigma_1^2+\left(\frac{1+m_1}{m_2}\right)^{\frac{1}{2}}N_z\bar{\sigma}^2\right]$$

Average speed $=\left(\dfrac{8kT}{\pi m}\right)^{\frac{1}{2}}$; root-mean-square speed $\left(\dfrac{3kT}{m}\right)^{\frac{1}{2}}$.

Typical values (at 0° C. and 760 mm. Hg.)

Gas	*Density*	*Molecular speed*	*Mean free path*	*Collisions per sec.*
	g. cm.$^{-3}$	cm. sec.$^{-1}$	cm.	
air . . .	$1{\cdot}29\times10^{-3}$	$4{\cdot}5\times10^{4}$	$9{\cdot}6\times10^{-6}$	$4{\cdot}7\times10^{9}$
hydrogen . .	$8{\cdot}99\times10^{-5}$	$1{\cdot}8\times10^{5}$	$1{\cdot}8\times10^{-5}$	$1{\cdot}0\times10^{10}$

12.4. Van der Waal's equation of state

$$(p+a\rho^2)(1-b\rho)=kNT.$$

For a model of rigid attracting elastic spheres exerting a force $F(r)$ at distance r

$$a=\frac{2\pi}{3m^2}\int r^3\,F(r)\,dr;\; b=\frac{2\pi\sigma^3}{3m}.$$

12.5. Diffusive properties

Viscosity (diffusion of momentum):

simplest model $\mu=\dfrac{1}{3}\,\rho cl=\dfrac{2}{3\sigma^2}\left(\dfrac{kmT}{\pi^2}\right)^{\frac{1}{2}}$; more accurately:

$$\mu=0{\cdot}179\left(\frac{kmT}{\pi}\right)^{\frac{1}{2}}.$$

Conductivity (diffusion of heat): $\lambda=2{\cdot}525c_v\mu$.

Diffusion of matter: $D=\dfrac{3}{8N\bar{\sigma}^2}\left(\dfrac{kT(m_1+m_2)}{2\pi m_1m_2}\right)^{\frac{1}{2}}$.

CHAPTER 13

ATOMIC PHYSICS

13.1. Elementary particles

Particle	*Charge*	*Rest mass*	*Spin* (units of $h/2\pi$)
electron . .	$-e$	m_0	$\frac{1}{2}$
positron . .	$+e$	m_0	$\frac{1}{2}$
proton . .	$+e$	$1836m_0$	$\frac{1}{2}$
neutron . .	0	$1839m_0$	$\frac{1}{2}$
neutrino . .	0	?	$\frac{1}{2}$
photon . .	0	0	?
μ—meson . .	$\pm e$	$207m_0$	$\frac{1}{2}$
π^+, π^--meson .	$\pm e$	$273m_0$	?
π°-meson . .	0	$262m_0$	0

where

$$e=4{\cdot}8\times10^{-10} \text{ e.s.u.}$$

$$m_0=9\times10^{-28} \text{ gm.}$$

$$h/2\pi=1\times10^{-27} \text{ erg sec.}^{-2} \quad (h=\text{Planck's constant of action}).$$

13.2. Einstein's photoelectric equation

$$\tfrac{1}{2}m\, v_m{}^2=h\nu-W,$$

where v_m = maximum speed of emission of electrons under influence of monochromatic light of frequency ν; W = work function.

13.3. Bohr model of the atom

Quantization condition: $amv=nh/2\pi$ ($n=1, 2, 3, \ldots$ = quantum number) where a = radius of orbit, m = mass of electron, v = speed in orbit.

$$\text{Radius of orbit}=\frac{n^2}{mZe^2}\left(\frac{h}{2\pi}\right)^2, \quad Ze=\text{charge on nucleus.}$$

$$\text{Radius of 1st orbit}\simeq5\times10^{-9} \text{ cm.}$$

$$\text{Speed in orbit}=2\pi Ze^2/nh.$$

Change in energy when atom passes between stationary states with quantum numbers n_1 and n_2 is characterized by

$$\bar{\nu}=\frac{2\pi^2 m^2 Z^2 e^4}{h^3 c}\left(\frac{1}{n_1^2}-\frac{1}{n_2^2}\right),$$

where $\bar{\nu}$ is the wave number ν/c.

Sommerfeld's model. Values of angular momentum are restricted to $kh/2\pi$, where k is the azimuthal quantum number, and values of average radial momentum to $n_r h$, n_r = radial quantum number.

The approximate expression for the energy states is

$$\frac{E}{hc}=\frac{RZ^2}{n^2(1+m/M)}+\frac{R\alpha^2 Z^4}{n^3(1+m/M)}\left(\frac{3}{4n}-\frac{1}{j+\frac{1}{2}}\right)$$

where $\alpha=2\pi e^2/hc$ is the fine structure constant, M = mass of nucleus, $R=2\pi^2 me^4/h^3c$ is the Rydberg constant, j is the total angular momentum of each electron in units of $h/2\pi$ and n is integral.

Electron spin. A spinning electron behaves like a tiny magnet and is therefore equivalent to a system of electrical currents. The angular momentum takes the value

$$\sqrt{\{|s|(|s|+1)\}}h/2\pi,$$

where s is the *spin quantum number.* The component of angular momentum perpendicular to the plane of the orbit is $sh/2\pi$, where $s=\pm\frac{1}{2}$. The natural unit of magnetic moment is the *Bohr magneton*

$$\mu_e=(h/2\pi)(e/2m_0c)=9{\cdot}25\times 10^{-21} \text{ erg oersted}^{-1}.$$

The *nuclear magneton* is $(h/2\pi)(e/2m_pc)$, where m_p = proton mass = 18·36 m_0.

13.4. Moseley's law

$$\sqrt{\bar{\nu}}=a(Z-b),$$

a and b constants.

13.5. Compton effect

Change in wavelength of the scattered ray is

$$\Delta\lambda=\frac{h}{m_0c}(1-\cos\phi),$$

m_0 = rest mass, ϕ = angle of scattering.

13.6. De Broglie waves

The wavelengths of "matter waves" are given by $\lambda=h/mv$, where m is mass of particle and v its speed; their speed is c^2/v.

Examples of de Broglie wavelengths

Body	*Rest mass* (gm.)	*Speed* (cm.$^{-1}$ sec.$^{-1}$)	*Wavelength* (cm.)
100-v. electron . . .	9×10^{-28}	6×10^{6}	10^{-8}
100-v. α-particle . .	6×10^{-24}	7×10^{6}	10^{-10}
cricket ball, fast bowler .	154	3×10^{3}(?)	10^{-32}!

The circumferences of the orbits in Bohr's model are integral multiples of the associated de Broglie wavelengths.

13.7. Schrödinger's wave equation

The amplitude ψ of matter waves satisfies

$$ih\frac{\partial\psi}{\partial t}=\frac{h^2}{2m}\nabla^2\psi+V\psi,$$

or

$$\nabla^2\psi+\frac{8\pi^2 m}{h^2}(E-V)\psi=0$$

where E is the total energy and V is the potential energy of a particle of mass m. Bohr's interpretation is that $|\psi|^2$ measures the probability of finding a particle in unit volume around the given point.

Heisenberg's uncertainty principle. A co-ordinate x and its associated momentum p cannot both be measured precisely. The minimum errors δx, δp are related by $\delta x\delta p\simeq h$.

Pauli's exclusion principle. No two electrons in the same atom can have the same set of quantum numbers.

13.8. Radioactivity

Naturally radioactive substances may emit: α-particles (helium nuclei), β-particles (fast electrons) and γ-rays (high-energy photons, $\lambda\leqslant 0{\cdot}1$Å).

Decay law. $N=N_0e^{-kt}$, $k=$decay coefficient.

1 gm. radium produces $3{\cdot}71\times10^{10}$ disintegrations per second, and this is said to be a source of 1 *curie.*

Displacement law. In α-disintegration 2 units of positive charge and 4 units of atomic mass are lost; the nucleus moves down 2 places in the periodic table. In β-disintegration, 1 electron is lost, the mass is almost unchanged and the nucleus moves up one place in the table.

1. *The Uranium Series*

Active Isotope	*Symbol*	*Element*	*Radiation*	*Half-Life*
Uranium I	U^{238}	Uranium	α	$4{\cdot}5 \times 10^{10}$ years
Uranium X_1	Th^{234}	Thorium	β	24·1 days
Uranium X_2	Pa^{234}	Protoactinium	β	1·14 minutes
Uranium II	U^{234}	Uranium	α	$2{\cdot}35 \times 10^5$ years
Ionium	Th^{230}	Thorium	α	8×10^4 years
Radium	Ra^{226}	Radium	α	$1{\cdot}62 \times 10^3$ years
Radium Emanation	Rn^{222}	Radon	α	3·82 days
Radium A	Po^{218}	Polonium	α & β	3·05 minutes
Radium B (99·96%)	Pb^{214}	Lead	β	26·8 minutes
↳ Astatine (0·04%)	At^{218}	Astatine	α	2 seconds
Radium *C*	Bi^{214}	Bismuth	β & α	19·7 minutes
Radium *C′* (99·96%)	Po^{214}	Polonium	α	$1{\cdot}5 \times 10^{-4}$ seconds
↳ Radium *C″* (0·04%)	Tl^{210}	Thallium	β	1·32 minutes
Radium *D*	Pb^{210}	Lead	β	22 years
Radium *E*	Bi^{210}	Bismuth	β & α	5·0 days
Radium *F* ($\sim$100%)	Po^{210}	Polonium	α	140 days
↳ Thallium ($\sim 10^{-5}$ %)	Tl^{206}	Thallium	β	4·33 minutes
Radium *G*	Pb^{206}	Lead	Stable	

2. *The Thorium Series*

Active Isotope	*Symbol*	*Element*	*Radiation*	*Half-Life*
Thorium	Th^{232}	Thorium	α	$1{\cdot}39 \times 10^{10}$ years
Mesothorium I	Ra^{228}	Radium	β	6·7 years
Mesothorium II	Ac^{228}	Actinium	β	6·13 hours
Radiothorium	Th^{228}	Thorium	α	1·90 years
Thorium *X*	Ra^{224}	Radium	α	3·64 days
Thorium Emanation	Rn^{220}	Radon	α	54·5 seconds
Thorium A	Po^{216}	Polonium	β & α	0·16 seconds
Thorium *B* (~100%)	Pb^{212}	Lead	β	10·6 hours
Astatine (0·014%)	At^{216}	Astatine	α	3×10^{-4} seconds
Thorium *C*	Bi^{212}	Bismuth	β & α	60·5 minutes
Thorium *C′* (66·3%)	Po^{212}	Polonium	α	3×10^{-7} seconds
Thorium *C″* (33·7%)	Tl^{208}	Thallium	β	3·1 minutes
Thorium *D*	Pb^{208}	Lead	Stable	

3. *The Actinium Series*

Active Isotope	*Symbol*	*Element*	*Radiation*	*Half-Life*
Actino-uranium	U^{235}	Uranium	α	$7{\cdot}07 \times 10^{8}$ years
Uranium *Y*	Th^{231}	Thorium	β	24·6 hours
Protoactinium	Pa^{231}	Protoactinium	α	$3{\cdot}2 \times 10^{4}$ years
Actinium	Ac^{227}	Actinium	β & α	21·7 years
Radioactinium (98·8%)	Th^{227}	Thorium	α	18·9 days
Actinium *K* (1·2%)	Fr^{223}	Francium	β	21 minutes
Actinium *X*	Ra^{223}	Radium	α	11·2 days
Actinium Emanation	Rn^{219}	Radon	α	3·92 seconds
Actinium *A*	Po^{215}	Polonium	α & β	$1{\cdot}83 \times 10^{-3}$ seconds
Actinium *B* (~100%)	Pb^{211}	Lead	β	3·61 minutes
Astatine ($\sim 5 \times 10^{-4}$ %)	At^{215}	Astatine	α	$\sim 10^{-4}$ seconds
Actinium *C*	Bi^{211}	Bismuth	β & α	2·16 minutes
Actinium *C′* (99·68%)	Po^{211}	Polonium	α	5×10^{-3} seconds
Actinium *C″* (0·32%)	Tl^{207}	Thallium	β	4·76 minutes
Actinium *D*	Pb^{207}	Lead	Stable	

4. *The Neptunium Series**

Active Isotope	*Symbol*	*Element*	*Radiation*	*Half-Life*
Plutonium ↓	Pu^{241}	Plutonium	β	~10 years
Americium ↓	Am^{241}	Americium	α	500 years
Neptunium ↓	Np^{237}	Neptunium	α	$2{\cdot}20\times10^{6}$ years
Protoactinium ↓	Pa^{233}	Protoactinium	β	27·4 days
Uranium ↓	U^{233}	Uranium	α	$1{\cdot}62\times10^{5}$ years
Thorium ↓	Th^{229}	Thorium	α	7×10^{3} years
Radium ↓	Ra^{225}	Radium	β	14·8 days
Actinium ↓	Ac^{225}	Actinium	α	10 days
Francium ↓	Fr^{221}	Francium	α	4·8 minutes
Astatine ↓	At^{217}	Astatine	α	$1{\cdot}8\times10^{-2}$ seconds
Bismuth ↓	Bi^{213}	Bismuth	β & α	47 minutes
Polonium (96%) ↓	Po^{213}	Polonium	α	$4{\cdot}2\times10^{-6}$ seconds
Thallium (4%) ↓	Tl^{209}	Thallium	β	2·2 minutes
Lead ↓	Pb^{209}	Lead	β	3·3 hours
Bismuth	Bi^{209}	Bismuth	Stable	

Cross-section. The cross-section for a process (e.g. transmutation) is defined as follows. Let n_1=number of bombarding particles, n_2= number of targets, n_3=number of processes that occur per cm.². The cross-section S is defined by the relation $S=n_3/n_1n_2$.

For a target of density ρ, atomic weight A, thickness t:

for process involving an electron as target: $S=\dfrac{n_3}{n_1Z(\rho/A)N_Lt}$,

for process involving a nucleus: $S=\dfrac{n_3}{n_1(\rho/A)N_Lt}$,

where N_L is Loschmidt's number, 6×10^{23}.

13.9. Fission

The process of splitting a nucleus by bombardment with suitable particles (e.g. fast neutrons) is called fission. It is believed that the impact of a fast neutron with a suitable heavy nucleus causes violent

* This series is not found in nature but has been produced artificially.

oscillations and the formation of a "neck". Coulomb repulsive forces then cause the nucleus to break, the parts separating violently, boiling off neutrons. The product nuclei usually are unstable.

Fission is relatively easily produced in U 235, which is present in the naturally found U 238 in the amount of about 0·7 per cent. The cross-section of U 235 for slow (thermal) neutrons is estimated to be about 420×10^{-24} cm.^{2}.

The average number of neutrons per fission for uranium and plutonium is stated to be

U 235	2·5 neutrons per fission
Pu 239	3 neutrons per fission

and as a rough measure of the energy release, the fission of 1 lb. of U 235 is equivalent to 3×10^{13} B.Th.U., which is the energy produced by burning 10^6 tons of coal.*

* Data quoted from *An Outline of Atomic Physics* by O. H. Blackwood, T. H. Osgood and A. E. Ruark, New York, 1955.

CHAPTER 14

METEOROLOGY

14.1. The atmosphere consists of a mechanical mixture of gases, water and pollutants. The main constituents of *clean dry air* are:

nitrogen . . .	78·08 per cent. of volume
oxygen . . .	20·95 ,, ,, ,, ,,
argon . . .	0·93 ,, ,, ,, ,,
carbon dioxide . .	0·03 ,, ,, ,, ,,

Atmospheric pressure (p) is measured in *millibars* (mb.), a bar (1000 mb.) being defined as 10^6 dynes cm.$^{-2}$.

1000 mb. = 750·076 mm. of Hg = 29·53 inches of Hg at 273° K. in lat. 45°. The main physical properties of clean dry air are:

density (ρ) at 273° K. and 1000 mb. .	$1{\cdot}276\times10^{-3}$ g. cm.$^{-3}$
specific heat at constant pressure (c_p) .	0·24
specific heat at constant volume (c_v) .	0·17
ratio of specific heats (γ) . . .	1·405
mean molecular weight M . . .	28·9

14.2. Water vapour, perhaps the most significant constituent of the atmosphere for the meteorologist, is measured in various ways. The density of water vapour (ρ_w), is called the absolute humidity. If e is the partial pressure of water vapour, e_s the saturation value of e, R the universal gas constant and T the absolute temperature, the following relations hold between the various measures:

$$\text{relative humidity } f = 100e/e_s = \frac{100(p-e)x}{0{\cdot}622e_s},$$

$$\text{humidity mixing ratio } x = \frac{0{\cdot}622e}{p-e} \simeq 0{\cdot}622\frac{e}{p}, \text{ since } e \ll p,$$

$$\text{absolute humidity } \rho_w = \frac{(p-e)x}{RT},$$

$$\text{specific humidity } q = \frac{0{\cdot}622e}{p-0{\cdot}37e} \simeq x.$$

14.3. Atmosphere at rest

The basic relation is the hydrostatic equation

$$\frac{dp}{dz}=-g\rho,$$

where z is height and g is the acceleration due to gravity.

If T_m is the mean temperature of the atmosphere up to height z, this equation can be integrated to give the simplest form of the *barometric-height equation,* viz.:

$$p=p_0 \exp\left(-\frac{gz}{RT_m}\right)\simeq p_0 \exp\left(-\frac{3{\cdot}4\times10^{-4}z}{T_m}\right),$$

where p_0 is the surface pressure, z is measured in cm. and T_m in degrees centigrade.

Temperature, on the average, falls with height up to the tropopause, the lower boundary of the stratosphere, but may also increase with height in intermediate layers. The rate of fall of temperature with height is called the *lapse-rate.* A condition in which temperature increases with height (e.g. in the air layers near the ground on a clear calm night) is called an *inversion.*

If the lapse rate in the atmosphere is such a volume of air, on being given a small vertical displacement, changes its temperature adiabatically because of the reduction of pressure but remains in thermal equilibrium with its surroundings, the atmosphere is said to be in statically neutral equilibrium. The value of the lapse rate for which this occurs, the so-called *dry adiabatic lapse rate* Γ is given by

$$\Gamma=-\frac{g}{R}\left(\frac{\gamma-1}{\gamma}\right)\simeq-9{\cdot}86\times10^{-5}\ ^\circ\text{C. cm.}^{-1}.$$

If the lapse rate is less than this value, or is positive, the atmosphere is said to be statically stable. Lapse rates greater (negative) than Γ are called superadiabatic and the atmosphere is then said to be statically unstable. Superadiabatic lapse rates occur regularly near the ground on a hot windless day. The *potential temperature* (θ) of dry air is defined to be the temperature that a volume of air would acquire if it were brought to a standard pressure in adiabatic conditions. If P be the standard pressure,

$$\theta=T\left(\frac{P}{p}\right)^{(\gamma-1)/\gamma}\simeq T\left(\frac{P}{p}\right)^{0{\cdot}29},$$

and

$$\frac{1}{\theta}\frac{d\theta}{dz}=\frac{1}{T}\left(\frac{dT}{dz}+\Gamma\right).$$

The relation between potential temperature and entropy (ϕ) is

$$\phi = c_p \ln \theta + \text{constant}.$$

14.4. Atmosphere in motion

The invariable rule for non-equatorial regions is *Buys Ballot's law*, viz., that an observer standing with his back to the wind has low pressure on his left in the northern hemisphere and high pressure on his left in the southern hemisphere. Thus in the northern hemisphere the direction of the winds around a depression (region of low pressure) is anticlockwise.

The simplest relation between the pressure field and the wind is that given by the *geostrophic balance*. The *geostrophic wind* is defined by

$$\text{geostrophic wind} = \text{pressure gradient} \div 2\omega \sin \phi \,.\, \rho,$$

where $2\omega \sin \phi$ is the Coriolis parameter (ω = angular velocity of the Earth about its axis, ϕ = latitude). This hypothetical wind blows along the isobars and is a good approximation to the observed wind at about 2000 feet above a level surface.

Near a level surface (say, up to 50 metres height) the wind increases regularly with height, but the rate of increase varies with the lapse rate. An approximate relation is

$$u_z = u_1 (z/z_1)^m,$$

where u_z is the mean wind at height z and u_1 is the mean wind at a reference height z_1. The value of m varies with the roughness of the surface and the lapse rate. A typical value is $m = \frac{1}{4}$.

14.5. Radiation

The distribution of energy in the short-wave radiation received from the sum is given on p. 326. The *albedo* of the Earth, i.e. the ratio of the incident radiation to that which is diffusely reflected, is about 0·4, much of which is to be attributed to clouds.

It is generally accepted that natural surfaces, such as grassland, ploughed fields, etc., radiate as black bodies (q.v.). The long-wave radiation from the surface is selectively absorbed and re-emitted by water vapour in the atmosphere. The relationship between absorption and wavelength is complicated, but it is generally accepted that there is a region of transparency centred about 10μ.

14.6. Atmospheric electricity

In fine weather the potential gradient near the ground is of the order of 150 volts $m.^{-1}$, with marked diurnal changes. In fog the gradient may be ten times as large and in thunderstorms may reach values as high as 10,000 volts $m.^{-1}$. The gradient usually decreases with height. A positive gradient (potential increasing with height) implies a negative charge on the ground, about 1 coulomb per 1000 square kilometres. The average air-earth current is of the order of 2 microamps per square kilometre.

Raindrops are usually electrified, especially in thundery weather.

A lightning stroke is a complex phenomenon. The p.d. immediately before the discharge may be of the order of hundreds or thousands of millions of volts and the current in the stroke as high as 20,000 amps. The quantity of electricity involved is small, of the order of 20 coulombs.

14.7. Clouds are classified into three main groups, as follows:

high: cirrus, cirrostratus, cirrocumulus,

medium: altocumulus, altostratus,

low: stratocumulus, nimbostratus, cumulus, cumulonimbus, stratus.

For precise definitions and illustrations, reference should be made to the International Cloud Atlas. The water content of clouds is very variable, ranging roughly from 0·1 to 5 $g.m.^{-3}$.

14.8. Rainfall is measured in inches or millimetres and is so variable over the British Isles that no single representative figure can be quoted. 1 inch of rain is equivalent to about 100 tons of water per acre.

CHAPTER 15

BASIC PHYSICAL CONSTANTS AND DATA

THE values collected here for ease of reference are sufficiently accurate for laboratory exercises and for most calculations performed by the student. For the latest and most accurate values, reference should be made to the standard tables.

CONSTANTS

Loschmidt's number	$N_L = 6{\cdot}02 \times 10^{23}$ per gram molecule.
Avogadro's number	$N_A = 2{\cdot}69 \times 10^{19}$ per cm.^{3} at S.T.P.
Gas constant	$R = 8{\cdot}31 \times 10^7$ ergs (°C. mole)$^{-1}$.
	$= 1{\cdot}99$ cal (°C. mole)$^{-1}$.
Unit atomic mass	$m_0 = 1{\cdot}66 \times 10^{-24}$ g.
Standard volume of a perfect gas	$V_0 = 2{\cdot}24 \times 10^4$ cm.^{3}.
Speed of light *in vacuo*	$c = 2{\cdot}99793 \times 10^{10} \simeq 3 \times 10^{10}$ cm. sec.$^{-1}$.
Rydberg wave number (infinite mass)	$R_\infty = 1{\cdot}09737 \times 10^5$ cm.$^{-1}$.
Gravitational constant	$G = 6{\cdot}67 \times 10^{-8}$ dyne cm.^{2} g.$^{-2}$.
Boltzmann's constant	$k = 1{\cdot}38 \times 10^{-16}$ erg (°C.)$^{-1}$.
Planck's constant	$h = 6{\cdot}63 \times 10^{-27}$ erg sec.
	$h/2\pi = 1{\cdot}05 \times 10^{-27}$ erg sec.
Charge/mass ratio of electron	$e/m = 5{\cdot}27 \times 10^{17}$ e.s.u. g.$^{-1}$.
Energy conversion factor	1 $ev = 1{\cdot}60 \times 10^{-12}$ erg.
permitivity *in vacuo*	$\epsilon_0 = 1$ c.g.s. $= 8{\cdot}85 \times 10^{-12}$ farad m.$^{-1}$ m.k.s.
permeability *in vacuo*	$\mu_0 = 1$ c.g.s. $= 4\pi \times 10^{-7}$ henry m.$^{-1}$ m.k.s.
Stefan's constant	$\sigma = 5{\cdot}67 \times 10^{-5}$ erg cm.$^{-2}$ sec.$^{-1}$ (°C.)$^{-4}$.
Black-body radiation constants (Planck)	$c_1 = 8\pi hc = 4{\cdot}99 \times 10^{-15}$ erg cm; $c_2 = hc/k = 1{\cdot}44$ cm. (°C.)

DATA

Mean radius of Earth	$=6371$ km. $=3959$ miles.
Mean distance Earth-Sun	$=1{\cdot}497\times10^{8}$ km. $\simeq 93$ million miles.
Mass of Earth	$=5{\cdot}98\times10^{27}$ g.
Light year	$=9{\cdot}46\times10^{12}$ km.
Acceleration of gravity	$g=980{\cdot}62$ cm. sec.$^{-2}=32{\cdot}17$ ft. sec.$^{-2}$ in latitude 45°.
Length of seconds pendulum	$=99{\cdot}4$ cm. at London.

CONVERSIONS

To convert	*Multiply by*	*Logarithm*
inches to centimetres	2·54	0·4048
feet to metres	0·3048	$\bar{1}{\cdot}4840$
miles to kilometres	1·609	0·2065
sq. ins. to sq. cm.	6·451	0·8096
cu. ins. to cu. cm.	16·39	1·2145
ounces to grams	28·35	1·4526
pounds to grams	$4{\cdot}536\times10^{2}$	2·6567
tons to kilograms	$1{\cdot}016\times10^{3}$	3·0069
poundals to dynes	$1{\cdot}383\times10^{4}$	4·1407
lb. m.$^{-2}$ to g. cm.$^{-2}$	70·31	1·8470
lb. ft.$^{-3}$ to g. cm.$^{-3}$	$1{\cdot}6\times10^{-2}$	$\bar{2}{\cdot}2047$
ft. lb. to joules	1·356	0·1324
h.p. to ft. lb. sec.$^{-2}$	$5{\cdot}50\times10^{2}$	2·7404
h.p. to watts	$7{\cdot}46\times10^{2}$	2·8727
g. cal to joules	4·184	0·6216
mi. hr.$^{-1}$ to m. sec.$^{-1}$	0·447	$\bar{1}{\cdot}6503$
knots to m. sec.$^{-1}$	0·515	$\bar{1}{\cdot}7118$
ft. sec.$^{-1}$ to km. hr.$^{-1}$	1·097	0·0403

INDEX TO PURE MATHEMATICS

INDEX TO PHYSICS